CPO Focus on Earth Science

An Integrated Middle School Series

cpo science

W9-CYG-915

CPO Focus on Earth Science

First Edition

Copyright © 2007 Delta Education LLC, a member of the School Specialty Family

ISBN-10: 1-58892-247-2

ISBN-13: 978-1-58892-247-2

1 2 3 4 5 6 7 8 9 - QWE- 11 10 09 08 07

CPO Science

80 Northwest Boulevard

Nashua, New Hampshire 03063

(866)588-6951

http://www.cposcience.com

Printed and Bound in the United States of America

Credits

Writers

Mary Beth Abel Hughes - Author
B.S., Marine Biology, College of Charleston; M.S., Biological Sciences, University of Rhode Island

Mary Beth has been a principal writer with CPO Science since 2000. She has taught a range of science and math courses at an innovative high school and at the college level. She has expertise in scientific research, inquiry-based teaching methods, and curriculum development.

James Sammons - Author
B.S., Chemistry and Biology, University of Rhode Island

Has taught middle school science for 30 years. Formerly a research biologist with the National Marine Fisheries Service. Recognized by the Soil Conservation Service, the Department of Energy Residence in Science and Technology program, the National Association of Science Teachers, WGBH's Nova science program, and the National Association of Geoscience Teachers. Jim is a member of the Geological Society of America and the American Geophysical Union.

Patsy Eldridge - Author
B.S., Biology, Grove City College; M.Ed., Tufts University

Experienced high school physical science teacher and national hands-on science trainer and presenter. As an adjunct professor for Endicott College in Beverly, MA, and the College of Charleston, developed content-intensive physical science courses for pre- and in-service educators. Technical background in the medical device field. Patsy has developed curriculum and training materials with CPO Science for six years.

Daniel P. Murray, Ph.D. - Content review
A.B., Dartmouth College; M.S., Brown University; Ph.D., Brown University

Chairman, Department of Geosciences, University of Rhode Island

Senior Editor

Lynda Pennell – Executive Vice President
B.A., English; M.Ed., Administration, Reading Disabilities, Northeastern University; CAGS Media, University of Massachusetts, Boston

Nationally known for high school restructuring and integrating academic and career education. Served as director at an urban school for five years and has 17 years teaching/administrative experience in Boston public schools. Lynda has led development at CPO Science for six years.

Editorial Consultants

Christine Golden
B.A., Psychology, Gordon College; M.B.A., Rivier College

Project manager at *Imperial Communications* since 1999. With 22 years in publishing, now owner and managing editor of *Big Dog Publishing* services. Christine's work centers on editing K-12 textbook material.

Contributing Writers

Laine Ives
B.A., Gordon College; graduate coursework at Cornell University's Shoals Marine Laboratory and Wheelock College

Taught high school English overseas and environmental education at a middle school in New England.

Melissa N. G. Vela
B.A., Earth and Environmental Science, Lehigh University; M.S., Agricultural and Biological Engineering, Cornell University; M.Ed., Curriculum/Instruction, Boston College

Melissa has taught six years of 9th grade earth and space science at Lexington High School (Lexington, MA). She also taught 6th grade physical science and 8th grade algebra at Weston Middle School (Weston, MA).

Jill Elenbaas
B.A., Biology and Environmental Studies, Bowdoin College

Jill is an 8th grade science teacher at Wayland Middle School (Wayland, MA).

Denise Rock
A.S., Applied Marine Biology and Oceanography, Southern Maine Technical College; B.A., General Biology, University of Southern Maine

NASA educator astronaut teacher, Elm Street Middle School (Nashua, NH).

Art and Illustration

Jesse Van Valkenburgh - Design and Illustration
B.F.A., Illustration, Rochester Institute of Technology

Has worked in prepress film production and design. Jesse has worked at PC Connection in Merrimack, N.H., as a graphic designer doing catalog and direct mailing design, logo design, and illustration.

Polly Crisman – Design and Illustration
B.F.A., University of New Hampshire.

Graphic artist with expertise in advertising and marketing design, freelance illustrating, and caricature art. Polly is the CPO primary book illustrator and manages all files.

Bruce Holloway – Cover Design and Illustration
Pratt Institute, N.Y.; Boston Museum School of Fine Arts

Created all CPO Science book covers and many of the CPO specific designs. Expertise in product design, advertising, and three-dimensional exhibit design. Commissioned for the New Hampshire Duck Stamp for 1999 and 2003.

Connections

Catherine C. Reed
B.S., Secondary Education, Akron University; M.Ed., Administration and Curriculum, Baldwin-Wallace College

Taught middle school science and has worked as a middle school specialist for 20 years. Catherine's work has included curriculum development and professional development in the area of inquiry learning.

Sharon O. Faulkner is an educational freelance writer who lives in Andover, Mass.

John K. Manos is an educational freelance writer who lives in Evanston, Ill.

Laura J. Tierney is a freelance writer living in Chelmsford, Mass.

Beverly Vissoe teaches sixth-grade reading at Readington Middle School, Readington, N.J.

Assessment

Mary Ann Erickson
B.S, Naval Architecture and Marine Engineering, Massachusetts Institute of Technology

Ran a technical writing consulting business, writing process control manuals for water treatment plants, software design documentation for simulation software, and operator manuals for mining equipment.

Kelly A. Story
B.S., Chemistry, Gordon College; M.S., Chemistry, University of Massachusetts, Lowell

Taught chemistry and maintains a position as lab instructor at Gordon College, Wenham, Mass.

Equipment Design

Thomas Narro – Senior Vice President
B.S., Mechanical Engineering, Rensselaer Polytechnic Institute

Accomplished design and manufacturing engineer; experienced consultant in corporate re-engineering and industrial-environmental acoustics.

Danielle Dzurik
Bachelor of Industrial Design, Auburn University

At CPO Science, Danielle focuses on product development, new product design, and improving older designs.

Material Support

Michael Grady – Tech services coordinator
A.A., Arranging and Performing, Berklee College of Music; Medical Technician Diploma, Middlesex Community College

Professional musician for more than 20 years, with 10 years experience in customer service fields.

Kathryn Gavin – Quality Control and Purchasing Manager

Responsible for quality control and purchasing and works with product engineering on all new development. Kathryn has been assuring total quality of CPO Science equipment for ten years.

Lisa LaChance – Senior materials specialist
A.S., Accounting

Lisa evaluates samples to ensure that materials meet project requirements, developing and managing the release of specifications. She also evaluates changes to current products to enhance them and/or reduce manufacturing costs.

Technical Support

Tracy Morrow – Framemaker specialist, technical editor and trainer
B.A., English, Texas A&M University; M.A., English, Sam Houston State University

Taught middle school in Klein, Texas, a suburban region outside Houston, for nine years; at Tomball College in Tomball, Texas, for five years; and worked as a technical writer in the oil and gas, airlines, and real estate industries. Tracy offers consulting services and technical training; her expertise is in the editing program Framemaker.

Reviewers

Nancy Joplin
English-language arts department chairwoman
Ray Wiltsey Middle School, Ontario, Calif.

Jodye Selco, Ph.D.
Professor, Center for Education and Equity in Math, Science, and Technology
California State Polytechnic University, Pomona, Calif.

Brian E. Goodrow
Physical science teacher
Apple Valley Middle School, Apple Valley, Calif.

Philip L. Hunter
Science department chairman
Johnson Middle School, Westminster, Calif.

Bianca N. McRae
Science teacher, department chairwoman
Menifee Valley Middle School, Menifee, Calif.

Tia L. Shields
Life science/health and English language learning teacher
Nicolas Junior High School, Fullerton, Calif.

Kelly McAllister
Science teacher
Gage Middle School, Riverside, Calif.

Brad Joplin
Science teacher
Ray Wiltsey Middle School, Ontario, Calif.

Tony Heinzman
Science teacher
Apple Valley Middle School, Apple Valley, Calif.

Sylvia Gutman
Science teacher, department chairwoman
David A. Brown Middle School
Wildomar, Calif.
Lake Elsinore Unified School District

Erik Benton
Curriculum Writer
CPO Science

Special Thanks for Photos and Images

Dr. Geerat Vermeij
Professor of Marine Ecology and Paleoecology, University of California, Davis

Mary Doval Graziose
University of California, Davis

Curtis Ebbesmeyer
Beachcombers' and Oceanographers' International Association

Jim White
Beachcombers' and Oceanographers' International Association

Dr. Adam Dziewonski
Frank B. Baird, Jr. Professor of Science, Department of Earth and Planetary Science, Harvard University

Sarah Herve
John Day Fossil Beds National Monument

Joan Buhrman
American Society of Civil Engineers

John M. Watson
USGS

David A. Abel
Freelance photographer

Jim Sammons
Sammons' INK, Ltd.

ShutterStock, Inc.
Stock Photography

On each page of the student text, there are aids to help you find information, understand concepts, and answer questions. The following introduction includes sample pages with indicators that point out the page contents and reading aids.

Unit Pages and Chapter Pages

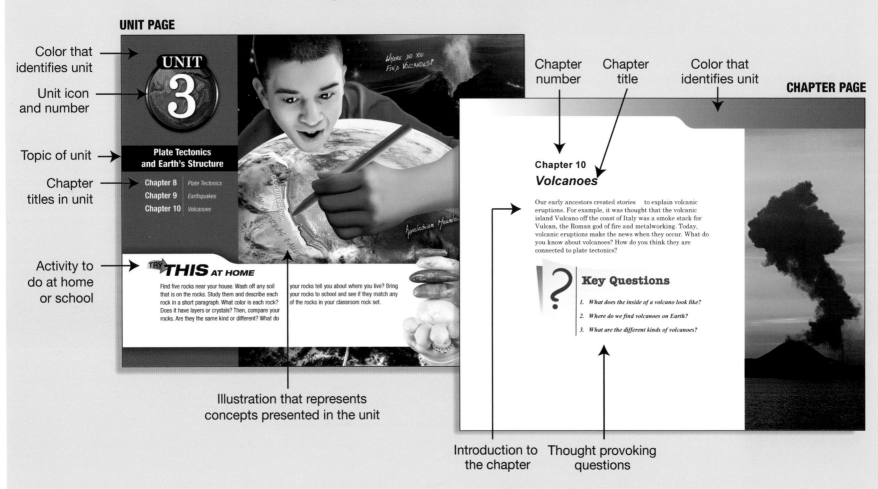

UNIT PAGE

Color that identifies unit

Unit icon and number

Topic of unit

Chapter titles in unit

Activity to do at home or school

UNIT 3

Plate Tectonics and Earth's Structure

Chapter 8 — Plate Tectonics
Chapter 9 — Earthquakes
Chapter 10 — Volcanoes

TRY THIS AT HOME

Find five rocks near your house. Wash off any soil that is on the rocks. Study them and describe each rock in a short paragraph. What color is each rock? Does it have layers or crystals? Then, compare your rocks. Are they the same kind or different? What do your rocks tell you about where you live? Bring your rocks to school and see if they match any of the rocks in your classroom rock set.

Illustration that represents concepts presented in the unit

Chapter number   Chapter title   Color that identifies unit

CHAPTER PAGE

Chapter 10
Volcanoes

Our early ancestors created stories to explain volcanic eruptions. For example, it was thought that the volcanic island Vulcano off the coast of Italy was a smoke stack for Vulcan, the Roman god of fire and metalworking. Today, volcanic eruptions make the news when they occur. What do you know about volcanoes? How do you think they are connected to plate tectonics?

? Key Questions

1. *What does the inside of a volcano look like?*
2. *Where do we find volcanoes on Earth?*
3. *What are the different kinds of volcanoes?*

Introduction to the chapter   Thought provoking questions

Student Text Pages

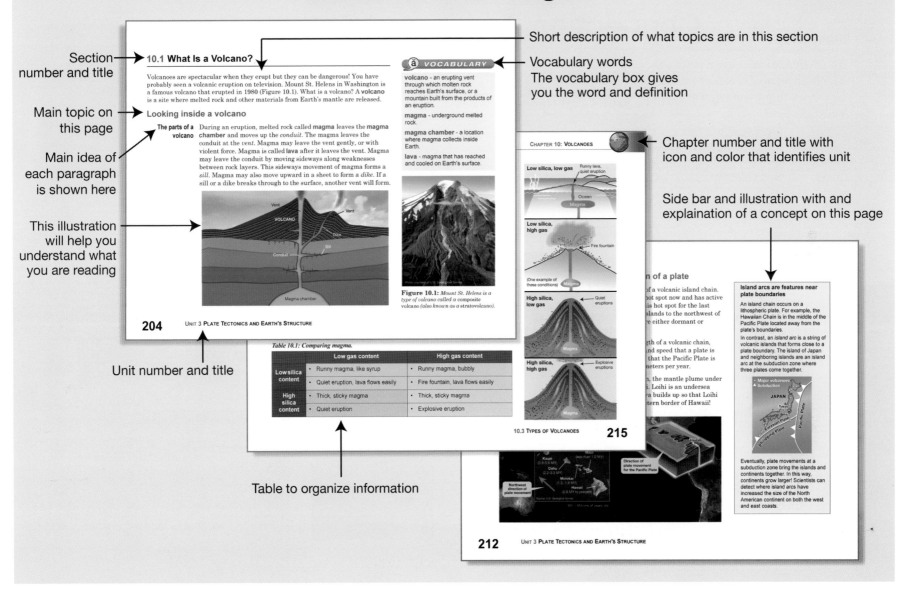

Section number and title

Main topic on this page

Main idea of each paragraph is shown here

This illustration will help you understand what you are reading

Unit number and title

Table to organize information

Short description of what topics are in this section

Vocabulary words
The vocabulary box gives you the word and definition

Chapter number and title with icon and color that identifies unit

Side bar and illustration with and explaination of a concept on this page

---

10.1 What Is a Volcano?

Volcanoes are spectacular when they erupt but they can be dangerous! You have probably seen a volcanic eruption on television. Mount St. Helens in Washington is a famous volcano that erupted in 1980 (Figure 10.1). What is a volcano? A **volcano** is a site where melted rock and other materials from Earth's mantle are released.

Looking inside a volcano

The parts of a volcano During an eruption, melted rock called **magma** leaves the **magma chamber** and moves up the *conduit*. The magma leaves the conduit at the *vent*. Magma may leave the vent gently, or with violent force. Magma is called **lava** after it leaves the vent. Magma may leave the conduit by moving sideways along weaknesses between rock layers. This sideways movement of magma forms a *sill*. Magma may also move upward in a sheet to form a *dike*. If a sill or a dike breaks through to the surface, another vent will form.

VOCABULARY

volcano - an erupting vent through which molten rock reaches Earth's surface, or a mountain built from the products of an eruption.

magma - underground melted rock.

magma chamber - a location where magma collects inside Earth.

lava - magma that has reached and cooled on Earth's surface.

Figure 10.1: *Mount St. Helens is a type of volcano called a composite volcano (also known as a stratovolcano).*

204 UNIT 3 PLATE TECTONICS AND EARTH'S STRUCTURE

Table 10.1: Comparing magma.

	Low gas content	High gas content
Low silica content	• Runny magma, like syrup	• Runny magma, bubbly
	• Quiet eruption, lava flows easily	• Fire fountain, lava flows easily
High silica content	• Thick, sticky magma	• Thick, sticky magma
	• Quiet eruption	• Explosive eruption

CHAPTER 10: VOLCANOES

Low silica, low gas — Runny lava, quiet eruption
Ocean
Magma

Low silica, high gas — Fire fountain
(One example of these conditions)
Magma

High silica, low gas — Quiet eruptions
Magma

High silica, high gas — Explosive eruptions
Magma

10.3 TYPES OF VOLCANOES **215**

n of a plate

of a volcanic island chain. hot spot now and has active is hot spot for the last slands to the northwest of re either dormant or

gth of a volcanic chain, nd speed that a plate is that the Pacific Plate is neters per year.

n, the mantle plume under i. Loihi is an undersea a builds up so that Loihi tern border of Hawaii!

Island arcs are features near plate boundaries

An island chain occurs on a lithospheric plate. For example, the Hawaiian Chain is in the middle of the Pacific Plate located away from the plate's boundaries.

In contrast, an *island arc* is a string of volcanic islands that forms close to a plate boundary. The island of Japan and neighboring islands are an island arc at the subduction zone where three plates come together.

JAPAN

Eventually, plate movements at a subduction zone bring the islands and continents together. In this way, continents grow larger! Scientists can detect where island arcs have increased the size of the North American continent on both the west and east coasts.

Kauai (5.6-5.5 MY)
Oahu (2.2-3.3 MY)
Molokai (1.3-1.8 MY)
Maui (less than 1.0 MY)
Hawaii (0.8 MY to present)
Direction of plate movement for the Pacific Plate
Northwest direction of plate movement

212 UNIT 3 PLATE TECTONICS AND EARTH'S STRUCTURE

Connection Pages and Activity Pages

CONNECTION

The **Connection** is like a magazine article about an interesting science fact. There is a Connection at the end of each chapter.

Title of the Connection

Main idea heading

Photos and illustrations to support your understanding

Unit color and Chapter number

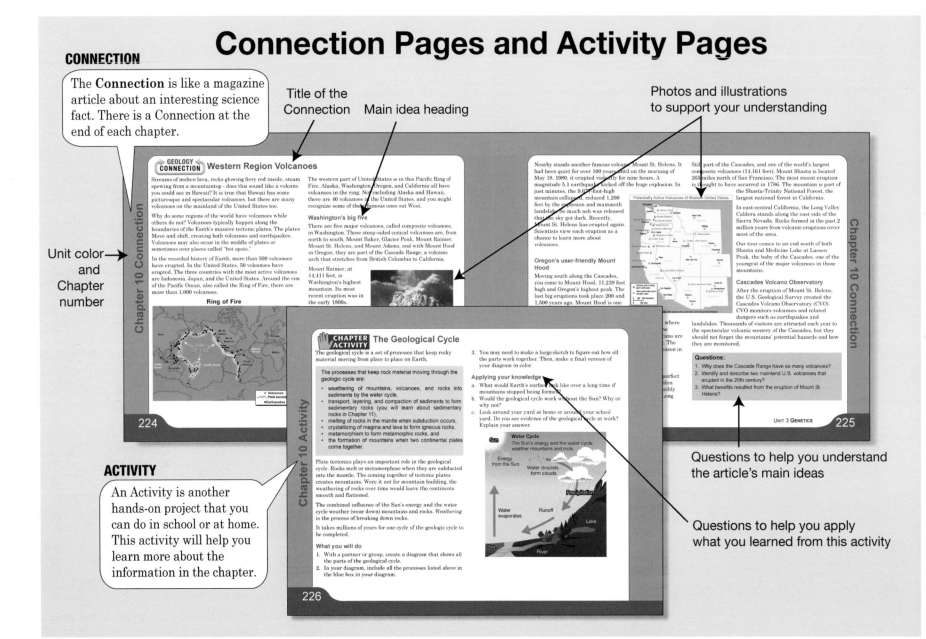

GEOLOGY CONNECTION Western Region Volcanoes

Streams of molten lava, rocks glowing fiery red inside, steam spewing from a mountaintop - does this sound like a volcano you could see in Hawaii? It is true that Hawaii has some picturesque and spectacular volcanoes, but there are many volcanoes on the mainland of the United States too.

Why do some regions of the world have volcanoes while others do not? Volcanoes typically happen along the boundaries of the Earth's massive tectonic plates. The plates Move and shift, creating both volcanoes and earthquakes. Volcanoes may also occur in the middle of plates or sometimes over places called "hot spots."

In the recorded history of Earth, more than 500 volcanoes have erupted. In the United States, 50 volcanoes have erupted. The three countries with the most active volcanoes are Indonesia, Japan, and the United States. Around the rim of the Pacific Ocean, also called the Ring of Fire, there are more than 1,000 volcanoes.

The western part of United States is in this Pacific Ring of Fire. Alaska, Washington, Oregon, and California all have volcanoes in the ring. Not including Alaska and Hawaii, there are 40 volcanoes in the United States, and you might recognize some of the famous ones out West.

Washington's big five

There are five major volcanoes, called composite volcanoes, in Washington. These steep-sided conical volcanoes are, from north to south, Mount Baker, Glacier Peak, Mount Rainier, Mount St. Helens, and Mount Adams, and with Mount Hood in Oregon, they are part of the Cascade Range, a volcanic arch that stretches from British Columbia to California.

Mount Rainier, at 14,411 feet, is Washington's highest mountain. Its most recent eruption was in the early 1800s.

Ring of Fire

Nearby stands another famous volcano, Mount St. Helens. It had been quiet for over 100 years until on the morning of May 18, 1980, it erupted violently for nine hours. A magnitude 5.1 earthquake kicked off the huge explosion. In just minutes, the 9,677-foot-high mountain collapsed, reduced 1,200 feet by the explosion and mammoth landslide. So much ash was released that the sky got dark. Recently, Mount St. Helens has erupted again. Scientists view each eruption as a chance to learn more about volcanoes.

Oregon's user-friendly Mount Hood

Moving south along the Cascades, you come to Mount Hood, 11,239 feet high and Oregon's highest peak. The last big eruptions took place 200 and 1,500 years ago. Mount Hood is one

Still part of the Cascades, and one of the world's largest composite volcanoes (14,161 feet), Mount Shasta is located 265 miles north of San Francisco. The most recent eruption is thought to have occurred in 1786. The mountain is part of the Shasta-Trinity National Forest, the largest national forest in California.

In east-central California, the Long Valley Caldera stands along the east side of the Sierra Nevada. Rocks formed in the past 2 million years from volcanic eruptions cover most of the area.

Our tour comes to an end south of both Shasta and Medicine Lake at Lassen Peak, the baby of the Cascades, one of the youngest of the major volcanoes in those mountains.

Cascades Volcano Observatory

After the eruption of Mount St. Helens, the U.S. Geological Survey created the Cascades Volcano Observatory (CVO). CVO monitors volcanoes and related dangers such as earthquakes and landslides. Thousands of visitors are attracted each year to the spectacular volcanic scenery of the Cascades, but they should not forget the mountains' potential hazards and how they are monitored.

Potentially Active Volcanoes of Western United States

Questions:
1. Why does the Cascade Range have so many volcanoes?
2. Identify and describe two mainland U.S. volcanoes that erupted in the 20th century?
3. What benefits resulted from the eruption of Mount St. Helens?

224

UNIT 3 GENETICS   225

Chapter 10 Connection

ACTIVITY

An Activity is another hands-on project that you can do in school or at home. This activity will help you learn more about the information in the chapter.

CHAPTER ACTIVITY The Geological Cycle

The geological cycle is a set of processes that keep rocky material moving from place to place on Earth.

The processes that keep rock material moving through the geologic cycle are:

- weathering of mountains, volcanoes, and rocks into sediments by the water cycle,
- transport, layering, and compaction of sediments to form sedimentary rocks (you will learn about sedimentary rocks in Chapter 11),
- melting of rocks in the mantle when subduction occurs,
- crystallizing of magma and lava to form igneous rocks,
- metamorphism to form metamorphic rocks, and
- the formation of mountains when two continental plates come together.

Plate tectonics plays an important role in the geological cycle. Rocks melt or metamorphose when they are subducted into the mantle. The coming together of tectonic plates creates mountains. Were it not for mountain building, the weathering of rocks over time would leave the continents smooth and flattened.

The combined influence of the Sun's energy and the water cycle weather (wear down) mountains and rocks. *Weathering* is the process of breaking down rocks.

It takes millions of years for one cycle of the geologic cycle to be completed.

What you will do
1. With a partner or group, create a diagram that shows all the parts of the geological cycle.
2. In your diagram, include all the processes listed above in the blue box in your diagram.

3. You may need to make a large sketch to figure out how all the parts work together. Then, make a final version of your diagram in color.

Applying your knowledge
a. What would Earth's surface look like over a long time if mountains stopped being formed?
b. Would the geological cycle work without the Sun? Why or why not?
c. Look around your yard at home or around your school yard. Do you see evidence of the geological cycle at work? Explain your answer.

Water Cycle
The Sun's energy and the water cycle weather mountains and rock.

226

Questions to help you understand the article's main ideas

Questions to help you apply what you learned from this activity

Assessment Pages

SECTION REVIEW

By answering these questions, you will have a quick check on what you remembered from the section.

This part of the review asks you to fill in sentences with vocabulary words

CHAPTER TEST

These questions are answered after reading the chapter.

10.2 Section Review

1. What did early map makers notice about the locations of volcanoes?
2. What causes the region called the Ring of Fire?
3. If you could melt a piece of quartz in some lava, would the lava get more sticky or less sticky? Explain your answer.
4. Where is runny lava found: (a) On a continental plate, or (b) on an oceanic plate?
5. Where is thick and sticky lava found: (a) On a continental plate, or (b) on an oceanic plate?
6. When volcanic island chains are formed, what moves? Pick the correct answer:

   a. the mantle plume   b. the plate above the mantle plume
   c. both the plate and the plume   d. nothing moves

7. Which of the Hawaiian Islands formed first and how long ago did it form?
8. What kind of geologic formation is Loihi? Is it a part of the Hawaiian Chain? Explain your answer.
9. How have scientists figured out that the Pacific Plate is moving at about 9 centimeters per year?
10. The Pacific Plate is moving at 9 centimeters per year.
    a. How long will it take for this plate to travel 4.5 meters?
    b. How far will the plate have travelled after 3 years?
11. What are the names of the items (A–C) on the graphic in Figure 10.10?
12. Name a difference between an island chain and an island arc.

Figure 10.10: *Use this graphic to answer question 11.*

MY JOURNAL

Write an essay about your observations and experiences during a visit to a [...] Write about Yose[...] Park if you have [...] write about anoth[...] you have visited. [...] write about the ge[...] park. Include dra[...] and/or photograp[...] essay.

214   UNIT 3 PLATE TECTONICS AND EARTH'S STRUCTURE

Graphs, diagrams or charts will help you in answering questions

You will be asked to think about something in the section and write about it in your journal

This tells you where to find the information

Chapter 10 Assessment

Vocabulary

Select the correct term to complete the sentences. Not all terms will be used.

volcano	geological cycle	magma	pyroclastic flow	Ring of Fire
cinder cone	lava	extinct volcano	shield volcanes	composite volcano
dormant volcano	magma chamber	volcanic neck	active volcano	volcanic island
resurgent dome	igneous rock	basalt	caldera	hot spot
lava lake	dormant volcano	silica	volcanic neck	volcanic island chain
lava bombs	lahars	pyroclastic flow		

Section 10.1

1. The products of an eruption can build a mountainous _____.
2. _____ is magma that has reached and cooled on Earth's surface.
3. A _____ is a place where magma collects underground.
4. A bowl-shaped volcanic feature is a _____.

12. After an explosive eruption, a _____ moves quickly down the side of a volcano and can cause a great deal of destruction.
13. Water released from a volcanic eruption can become part of _____, an important cycle energized by the Sun.

Section 10.3

14. Low gas, low silica magma forms _____ rocks.
[...] and a vent on a [...] a volcano. [...] considered to be [...]wer. [...]lting rock in the [...]ch of the Earth's

227

6. Mount St. Helens formed at what kind of plate boundary?

   a. a subduction zone   b. a transform plate boundary
   c. a divergent plate   c. where to continental plates
   boundary   came together

7. How is pressure involved in melting mantle material at a mid-ocean ridge?
8. How does plate tectonics cause volcanic islands to form in chain?
9. What volcanic land feature has helped the east and west coast of North America grow bigger?
10. Describe how the granite domes of Yosemite National Park were formed.

Section 10.3

11. Describe the magma of a fire fountain eruptions in terms of silica and gas content.
12. Explain how a shield volcano differs from a composite volcano.
13. Where do composite volcanoes tend to be found?

    a. a subduction zone   b. a transform plate boundary
    c. a divergent plate   c. where to continental plates
    boundary   came together

14. The Hawaiian Islands are what type of volcano? What causes these volcanoes to form?
15. Volcanoes found near subduction zones have:

    a. magma with high silica content
    b. an explosive eruption
    c. large amounts of gas released during the eruption
    d. All of the above

16. What is the difference between a pyroclastic flow and a lahar?

Section 10.4

17. How do igneous rocks form?
18. What about the appearance of an igneous rock gives you a clue about whether it cooled slowly or quickly?

Math and Writing Skills

Section 10.1

1. Mount Kilimanjaro in Tanzania is Africa's highest mountain is a controversial volcano. Research this volcano to find out whether experts think it is extinct, dormant, or active. Write your findings in a short paragraph.

Section 10.2

2. This image shows Hot Creek, a stream that is heated by volcanic activity below the surface. This creek is associated with the Long Valley Caldera in eastern California. The heat in the water is uneven. Some places are cool, but places where hot springs feed into the creek are so hot that you would be scalded. Nevertheless, the creek has fish! Research Hot Creek and describe what causes it to be hot.

Hot Creek, California

228   CHAPTER 10 VOLCANOES

Some questions ask you to write out short answers or solve a problem

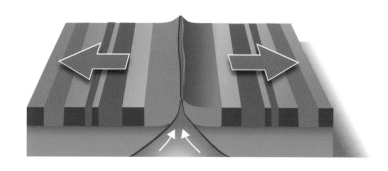

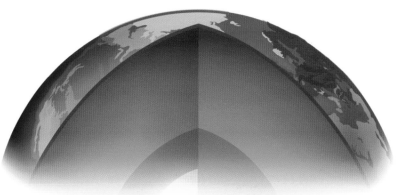

UNIT 3

Plate Tectonics and Earth's Structure

Photo courtesy U.S. Geological Survey

UNIT 4

The Shape of Earth's Surface

UNIT 5 — Ecology

WHAT IS EARTH'S LAND AREA?

WHAT IS EARTH'S DIAMETER AT THE EQUATOR?

VOLUME
LENGTH
WIDTH
HEIGHT

TRY THIS AT HOME

A map is a tool for traveling from one place to another on Earth's surface. Find a map and locate where you live. Locate another place on the map like your friend's house, your school, or a place in another state! Using the map, list the directions explaining how to get from your house to this other place. Use the scale at the bottom of the map to find out how far it is from your house to this other place. Is finding your way from one place to another similar or different from doing an experiment? What do you think?

Chapter 1
Science Is Everywhere

Your brain processes information all the time. You use this information to make choices and solve problems. What choices do you make when you eat lunch? How do you solve a problem like finding a missing sock?

Think about the title of this chapter. Is it true? Is science everywhere? Read Chapter 1 to find out!

Key Questions

1. *Is the science process like finding a lost sock?*

2. *What is the difference between an observation and an inference?*

3. *Are you a scientist?*

1.1 Learning about Science

How do you find a lost object? For example, what do you do if you can't find one of your favorite socks? Most likely you predict where it is based on your experience. A statement based on your experience is called an **inference**. You hear the clothes dryer running. Is your missing sock in the dryer? Asking questions and making inferences are important parts of the science process (Figure 1.1).

What is science?

Figure 1.1: *The science process is like looking for a lost sock.*

Observe **Science** is a process for answering questions. You start the science process by making observations. For example, look at the picture below. One observation about this picture is that the girl is reading a book. Another observation is that the girl is smiling.

Question Once you've made your observations, you continue the science process by forming a question. Why is the girl smiling?

Hypothesis Based on your observation, you might propose that the girl in the picture is smiling because she likes to read. An explanation, or a possible answer to a scientific question based on observations, is called a **hypothesis**. A hypothesis is not necessarily true or correct though. How can you find out if your hypothesis is correct?

VOCABULARY

inference - a statement based on experiences.

science - a process for answering questions.

hypothesis - a possible answer to a scientific question based on observations.

The scientific method

A testable hypothesis
Another quality of a hypothesis is that it must be testable. A hypothesis is tested to see if it is correct or not. Pieces of information that are collected to test a hypothesis are called **data**.

Collecting data
Scientists collect data to find out if a hypothesis is correct or not. You could ask the girl why she is smiling. She might say, "I like to read!" Or, you could ask her friends whether or not she likes to read. By collecting data, you learn if your hypothesis is correct.

Types of data
There are many different types of data. *Qualitative* data are in the form of words. *Quantitative* data are in the form of numbers. Here are some examples of data.

Examples of qualitative data	Examples of quantitative data
The girl likes to read science-fiction books.	The girl read 5 science-fiction books and 4 mystery novels last summer.
Some of the apples are red and some of the apples are green.	25 apples are red and 50 apples are green.
Some of the tomato plants are tall and some are short.	There are 40 tall tomato plants and 20 short tomato plants.
We caught a large fish.	The mass of the fish was 5 kilograms.

The scientific method
Scientists observe, form a question, state a hypothesis, and collect data by performing an experiment. Once these steps occur, the scientist studies the results of the experiment and reaches a conclusion. All together these steps are called the **scientific method**. The scientific method is summarized in Figure 1.2.

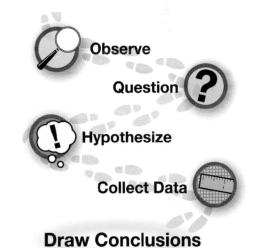

Observe

Question

Hypothesize

Collect Data

Draw Conclusions

Figure 1.2: *Basic steps in the scientific method.*

What is it like to be a scientist?

Looking through a keyhole
Jacques Cousteau, a famous marine biologist, described a scientist as a curious person who looks through a keyhole. What did he mean by this? When you look through a keyhole, you cannot see *everything,* only a few things (Figure 1.3). An experiment is like looking through a keyhole.

Experiments
An **experiment** is an activity performed to support or refute a hypothesis. Once a hypothesis is known to be correct or incorrect, it is time to perform another experiment. Scientists perform many experiments to understand complex issues. For example, many experiments have been performed to understand how to cure human diseases.

Anyone can be a scientist
Anyone can be a scientist. You have worked like a scientist if you have performed an experiment. Scientists are curious and they enjoy solving problems.

What is it like to be a scientist?
Scientists share information gained from experiments. A scientist might travel around the world. To study volcanoes, for instance, scientists may travel to locations where volcanoes are common like Iceland or Mexico. Scientists study volcanoes to learn how to predict eruptions. The work of scientists and local officials helped people evacuate in time when the Colima Volcano of Fire erupted in Mexico in June of 2005 (see photo at right).

Figure 1.3: *Can you tell what is happening on the other side of this keyhole? Performing an experiment is like looking through a keyhole. The results of the experiment give you only a small amount of information.*

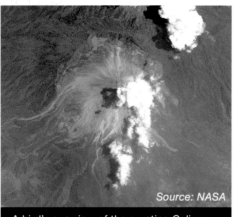

Source: NASA

A bird's eye view of the erupting Colima volcano, *June 2005.*

VOCABULARY

experiment - an activity performed to support or refute a hypothesis.

Fields of science

A list of sciences   Figure 1.4 lists some fields of science. Below you'll find examples of what scientists do in each field. All fields of science use the scientific method. Which field of science is most interesting to you?

Physics   Physics is the study of how and why things move. Physicists study motion, electricity, light, and sound. Marie Curie was a physicist who studied radioactive substances. In a physics class you might measure how fast something moves or learn how sound is made.

Chemistry   Chemistry is the study of matter. Here are some examples of matter: air, water, a book, a cat, and you! These things are all made up of small particles called *atoms*. Chemists are involved in activities like making new medicines and figuring out the best way to refine oil to make gasoline. In a chemistry class, you might study the properties of water or learn to perform chemical reactions.

Biology   Biology is the study of living things. Living things include bacteria, insects, fish, plants, animals, and people. If you take a biology class, you might learn about DNA or about how you digest your lunch!

Astronomy   Astronomy is the study of stars and planets and anything else that is in space. Astronomers discover new planets and galaxies and study objects that would take thousands of years to travel to.

Earth science   Earth science is the main focus of this textbook. Earth science includes the study of how Earth's surface changes, the study of rocks and rock formations, and the study of fossils.

Ecology   Ecology is the study of living things and how they interact with each other and their environment. Like earth science, ecology is taught in this textbook. You will have a good start on becoming an earth scientist or ecologist after you read this textbook!

Figure 1.4: *Different fields of science.*

How science affects your life

Science in the morning

Brushing your teeth is a daily activity that involves science. The fluoride in your toothpaste strengthens your tooth enamel so that you get fewer cavities (Figure 1.5). A chemist figures out how much fluoride to add to your toothpaste. Too much fluoride can discolor your teeth and too little will not help keep them strong.

Science at school

Check out your pencil. Making a pencil involves a range of sciences. A basic pencil is made of rubber, metal, wood, and graphite (Figure 1.5). The rubber for the eraser might be from a rubber plant or it could be a product derived from petroleum. Earth scientists often work in the petroleum industry. The wood of your pencil was probably harvested from a forest. Biologists play an important role in understanding the growth cycle of trees so that forests used for industry are sustainable. The "lead" of your pencil is a mixture of clay and graphite. The right mixture of these two materials was probably determined by a chemist.

Science after school

What kinds of activities do you do after school that involve science? If you play a sport, you'll be affected by the laws of physics. If you have a doctor or dentist appointment, you are benefiting from the science of biology. As you travel around your town, you might see mountains, lakes, ponds, forests, or other natural features that are studied by a range of scientists such as earth scientists and ecologists.

Science at meals

Do you eat a variety of foods each day? To help you make healthy choices, visit the website of the U.S. Department of Agriculture (USDA): http://www.mypyramid.gov. MyPyramid is based on the 2005 Dietary Guidelines set by the federal government, recommendations by the National Academy of Sciences, and the current eating patterns of people in the United States (Figure 1.5). MyPyramid is science in action to help you eat well!

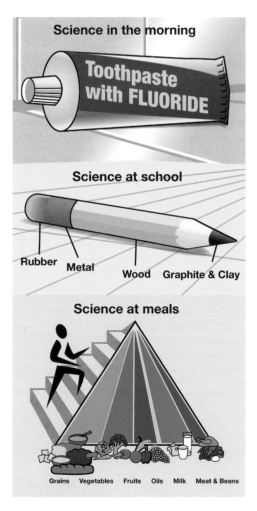

Figure 1.5: *Science during the day.*

1.1 Section Review

1. Write a short paragraph about how the science process is like finding a lost sock.

2. What is an inference?

3. Make inferences regarding the following situations:

   a. It is the start of a new school year. Make an inference about when the school day will end. On what experience is this inference based?

   b. Tomorrow is Saturday morning. What will you be doing at 10 a.m.? On what experience is this inference based?

4. You notice that the leaves on your houseplant are limp. Why are the leaves limp? Come up with a hypothesis.

5. List the steps of the scientific method. Draw a picture to illustrate each step. Write a caption for each picture.

6. Describe an experiment you have done on your own or in a science class. Be sure to include each of the steps of the scientific method in your description.

7. In 1847, Maria Mitchell discovered the Nantucket comet. It was the first time a comet had been discovered by a U.S. citizen and the first time a comet had been discovered by a woman. What kind of scientist was Maria Mitchell? How do you know?

8. Recently, scientists found that wolves are important as top carnivores in Banff National Park in Alberta, Canada. The scientists learned that in areas without wolves, the elk populations are 10 times higher. The elk eat all the plants, making it harder for other animals to survive. When wolves are around, they eat some of the elk. This means that more plants are available for other animals. What kind of scientists are studying the wolves in Banff National Park?

When you look at a slice of bread, you see little holes in it. Make a hypothesis about what causes these little holes.

Hint: Study a bread recipe to learn about the ingredients that are used to make a loaf of bread.

Question:
What causes these little holes in a slice of bread?

1.2 Observing the World

Chances are you have heard a person yell, "Watch me!" as he or she jumps off a diving board (Figure 1.6). Science involves observing events, but most things that you study in science, like a tree or a fish, don't yell, "Watch me!" Yet, you'll find that trees and fish do fascinating things if you use your senses to observe them. Use all of your senses to observe—sight, hearing, touch, taste, and smell!

Powers of observation

Making observations An observation is an accurate description of a thing or an event. "The sky is blue" is an observation. However, if you look at the sky every day, you will observe that it is not always blue. Some days it is grey, or it may be streaked with shades of red during a sunset.

Observations versus opinions What happens when a weather report predicts rain? Most likely, you form an opinion. Some people, especially farmers, like rain. A baseball team or a person who wants to have a yard sale might grumble, "I don't like rain!" What is your opinion when it rains?

- An observation is: It is raining.
- An opinion is: I like rain!

When practicing science, it is important to make observations without making opinions. Why do you think this is important?

An observation example Let's imagine your school wants to pick new school colors. The principal's opinion might be that the colors should be purple and red. A survey of all the students would allow the principal to pick the school colors based on an observation rather than his or her opinion. A survey might reveal that 90% of the students prefer blue and gold, 5% prefer blue and green, and 5% prefer purple and red. With the results of the survey, the principal can make the observation that the majority of students prefer blue and gold.

Figure 1.6: *People say "Watch me!" but fish, trees, and clouds, three things in nature that are worth studying, only say "Watch me!" in cartoons!*

MY JOURNAL

Interview a scientist or read about one. Write a paragraph about something you have learned.

Using all of your senses

The five senses   The five senses are seeing, hearing, touching, tasting, and smelling. Each of these senses is valuable in making observations. Making observations includes the use of one or all of the five senses depending on what you are observing.

Seeing   An astronomer looks through a telescope to see objects that are millions of miles away. A microbiologist looks through a microscope to study small organisms like amoebas and bacteria that are millions of times smaller than you are.

Hearing   *Acoustics* is the science of designing objects based on how sound travels. Hearing is important in this field of science. Hearing is also important in *ornithology,* the study of birds. Because birds are sometimes hard to see, they often have to be identified by their sound. Roger Tory Peterson, an ornithologist, had a keen ability to listen to nature. He once stated that he was able to identify nearly every bird in North America just by listening to their calls.

Touch   Geerat J. Vermeij, Ph.D., is a marine biologist who is blind. He relies on his sense of touch to study the shells of marine mollusks (Figure 1.7). His observations, based on touch, have helped him understand how mollusks protect themselves from predators.

Taste and smell   The senses of taste and smell are used when scientists develop new food products. How food tastes and smells determines whether it is enjoyable to eat. Let's say a company wants to develop a new brand of sugarless, cinnamon-flavored gum. Food scientists use chemistry to determine how to make the gum sugarless, taste good, and taste and smell like cinnamon. Look at some food labels. Can you tell which ingredients are added to improve the taste and which might be added to enhance the smell?

Photo courtesy of Mary Doval Graziose

Figure 1.7: *Geerat Vermeij uses his sense of touch to study the shells of marine mollusks. Examples of mollusks include snails, clams, conchs, and even those without shells like octopi!*

STUDY SKILLS

Use your powers of observation when you read. Look through the chapter for all the main titles and headings. Read those first before you begin reading paragraphs.

Each paragraph has a sidenote that highlights the main idea. Use this sidenote to form a question. Then ask yourself if you can answer the question after you have read the paragraph.

Recording observations

Keeping a notebook
Scientists write their observations in a notebook. A notebook is an important tool in science. Figure 1.8 shows Thomas Edison, inventor of the modern light bulb, writing in his notebook.

Format
A scientist's notebook contains observations, experiments, and drawings (Figure 1.9). The notebook may also contain mistakes! Mistakes show a thought process. Some mistakes spark new ideas or discoveries. When a mistake is made, a line is drawn through it so that the word or number is still readable (see example below).

SPEED DATA

Draw a line through mistakes.

DISTANCE (CM)	TIME (SECONDS)	SPEED (CM/SECOND)
16	0.1	160
32	0.3	~~170~~ 107

What do I write?
The science process helps you know what to write. First you record your observations, a question, and a hypothesis. Then you record the experiment procedure and data. Data can be descriptions or measurements. The table below lists measurements that you might make during an experiment. The table also lists the tools needed to make these different measurements. You write your conclusions last. Now, your experiment can be repeated by you or by other people because you have recorded everything you did!

If you need to measure...	Use a...
distance, length, or height	ruler, meter stick, or tape measure
mass and weight	balance or scale
volume	beaker or graduated cylinder
temperature	thermometer
time	stopwatch, watch, clock

U.S. Department of the Interior, National Park Service, Edison National Historic Site

Figure 1.8: *Thomas Edison wrote his ideas in a notebook.*

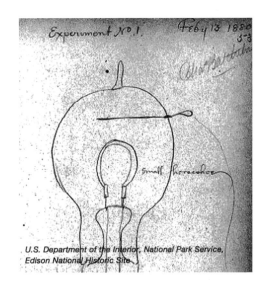

U.S. Department of the Interior, National Park Service, Edison National Historic Site

Figure 1.9: *Here is a page from one of Thomas Edison's notebooks. Thomas Edison invented the modern light bulb.*

1.2 Section Review

1. Choose an environment in which you can make observations. Write down as many observations as you can in one minute.
2. What is the difference between an observation and an opinion?
3. Think about your favorite food.
   a. Write an observation about your favorite food.
   b. Write an opinion about your favorite food.
4. List the five senses that you can use to collect data. List one observation for each sense.
5. Spend 10 minutes recording observations using all of your senses. Share your observations with your class.
6. Why is it important for a scientist to keep a notebook?
7. Why should you not erase mistakes from your science notebook? Make a list of reasons. Discuss these reasons with a partner or the class.
8. The word *science* is derived from a Latin word that means "to know."
   a. How does science help us know about the world?
   b. How is practicing science different from watching TV as a way to learn about the world?

Which pizza parlor in your neighborhood makes the best pizza?

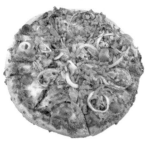

CHALLENGE

In the United Kingdom, there is a store that hires a person to travel the world to buy the world's best chocolate. This job requires that the person be good at judging the chocolate by taste! To do this job well, the person has to taste about a pound of chocolate a day!

Imagine that your job is to taste samples of your favorite food. You have five samples to taste and you have to pick the best one.

Examples:

- Which candy maker makes the best chocolate?
- You are the judge in a pie-baking contest. Which apple pie is the best?
- Which pizza parlor in your neighborhood makes the best pizza?

Write a description that explains how you would use the scientific method to pick the best sample.

Hint: Are there other senses in addition to taste that might be useful for picking the best sample?

1.3 Using the Scientific Method

Once you have made observations, how do you make a hypothesis? In this section, you will learn more about how to develop a hypothesis. You will also learn the difference between a scientific fact and a scientific theory.

Begin with an observation

An observation and a question Your friend Sam notices that the grass on the school ground is not green everywhere. In one place, where students wait for the bus, the grass is brown. Sam makes a diagram to illustrate his observations (Figure 1.10). His question is: Why is the grass brown near the bus waiting area?

The hypothesis Based on his observation, Sam states a hypothesis: *Students walk on the grass near the bus waiting area.* After making his hypothesis, Sam can complete the steps of the scientific method by collecting data and drawing conclusions (Table 1.1).

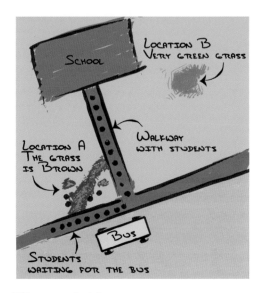

Figure 1.10: *Sam's diagram of the schoolyard.*

Table 1.1: Steps to the scientific method

1. Make observations	The grass is brown at the bus waiting area (location A) and green in an area closer to the school building (location B) (Figure 1.10).
2. Ask a question	Why is the grass brown near the bus waiting area?
3. State a hypothesis	The grass is brown at Location A (the bus waiting area) because students walk on the grass there.
4. Collect data	For his experiment, Sam observes students for three days while they wait for the bus. During this time, he records that students walk on the grass at location A, and no students walk on the grass at location B.
5. Draw conclusions	Sam concludes that his hypothesis is correct. The grass is brown at location A because students are walking on the grass.

Communicating research

Sam used the scientific method to learn why the grass in the school yard is brown. Imagine that you are on the student council. The student council wants to know the results of Sam's research. They also want to know what to do to make the grass green again.

Write an essay that explains Sam's research and list three ideas for protecting the grass.

What is a good hypothesis?

Making a good hypothesis Sam's hypothesis was good because it could be tested with an experiment. Sam tested his hypothesis by observing the students while they waited for the bus. Below are other testable hypotheses that Sam could have made.

The grass near the walkway is brown because:

1. It is not getting enough water.

2. It is not getting enough fertilizer.

Inference A good hypothesis is based on your experiences. As you have learned, an *inference* is a statement based on your experiences.

Here are some examples of inferences:

- For 5 weeks, the cafeteria has served ice cream on Friday. Therefore, my inference is that the cafeteria will serve ice cream next Friday.
- I have gone to 10 birthday parties. At each party, people sang *Happy Birthday to You*. My inference is that when I go to another birthday party, people will sing *Happy Birthday to You*.

What happens next? Sam made a hypothesis and documented evidence that his hypothesis was correct. Sam's next step might be to report the results of the experiment in a lab report (Figure 1.11). A lab report follows the steps of the scientific method.

What if your hypothesis is incorrect? An incorrect hypothesis is another piece of information that you can use to answer scientific questions. Let's say Sam wants to know why the grass near the school is so healthy. His question might be: What kind of treatment is applied to the grass? His hypothesis might be that the grass is fertilized. If this hypothesis is incorrect, Sam can use data from his experiment to make a new hypothesis about why the grass is healthy and run a new experiment.

MY JOURNAL

Pick one of the hypotheses listed at the left. Write a paragraph that describes what you would do to test this hypothesis in an experiment.

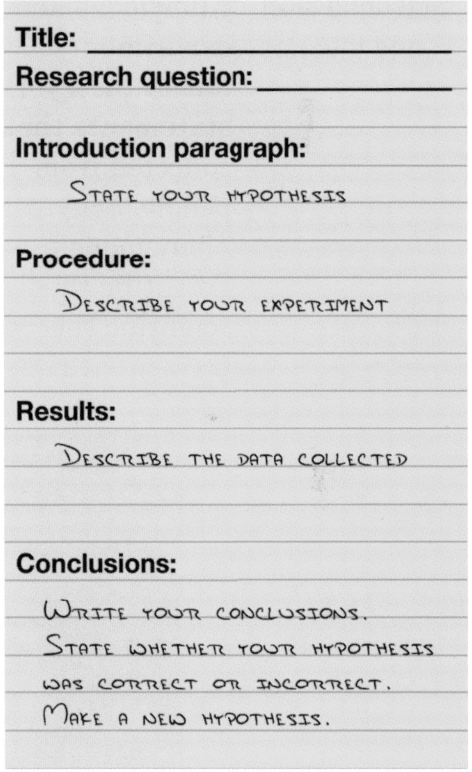

Title: _____

Research question: _____

Introduction paragraph:

State your hypothesis

Procedure:

Describe your experiment

Results:

Describe the data collected

Conclusions:

Write your conclusions.
State whether your hypothesis was correct or incorrect.
Make a new hypothesis.

Figure 1.11: *An example of a lab report. Note that the format of the lab report follows the steps of the scientific method.*

Scientific facts, laws, and theories

What is a scientific fact? Scientific facts are statements that are accepted as being true because the facts have been repeatedly measured or observed. Here are some scientific facts:

- The ocean is salty.
- It takes 365.25 Earth days for Earth to orbit around the Sun.
- Earth has one moon.

Scientific laws and theories Knowledge about a topic grows based on the results of experiments. Over time this knowledge may support a *scientific law* or *theory*. Both a **scientific law** and a **scientific theory** are statements that are supported by observations and evidence collected from many experiments performed by many different people. Scientific laws describe but do not explain an observed phenomenon. An example of a scientific law is the *law of gravity*. Scientific theories address more complex topics. An example of a scientific theory is the *theory of plate tectonics*. Scientific laws and theories are always being tested by experiments.

Location of tectonic plates on Earth's surface

North American Plate

Eurasian Plate

Eurasian Plate

Mid-Atlantic Ridge

Juan de Fuca Plate

Iranian Plate

Arabian Plate

Philippine Plate

Caribbean Plate

Cocos Plate

African Plate

Indo-Australian Plate

Pacific Plate

Nazca Plate

South American Plate

East Pacific Rise

Scotia Plate

Antarctic Plate

VOCABULARY

scientific law - a statement that describes an observed phenomenon; it is supported by evidence collected from many observations and experiments.

scientific theory - a statement that explains a complex idea; it is supported by evidence collected from many experiments.

What is the law of gravity?

The law of gravity states that objects attract other objects. Your pencil falls to the ground when you drop it because the mass of the pencil and the mass of Earth attract each other!

What is plate tectonics?

The surface of Earth is broken into many pieces like a giant jigsaw puzzle. These pieces are called tectonic plates. The graphic in the text (left) illustrates the location of the plates on Earth's surface.

The theory of plate tectonics describes how the plates move on Earth's surface. You'll learn about plate tectonics in Unit 3.

1.3 Section Review

1. Are you a scientist? The answer is yes! Each day you do things that are related to investigating the world in a scientific way. Write down activities that you did today that answer the questions in the table below.

	What did you do today?
What observations did you make?	
What questions did you ask?	
What problems did you solve?	
Did you make a hypothesis? If so, what was it?	
Did you perform an experiment and collect data? What data did you collect?	
What conclusions did you make today?	

2. Give an example of a scientific fact about the human body.

3. Give an example of an inference. Use your experiences from your favorite subject in school to come up with an inference.

4. You see small yellow flowers on a tomato plant. You also see that bees are attracted to these flowers. In a few weeks, you notice that the tomato plant has red tomatoes. What can you infer from this scenario?

5. Give an example of a question that you would like to answer by doing an experiment. State a hypothesis for your question.

6. What is the difference between a scientific fact and a scientific theory?

7. A very famous and important scientific law is the law of gravity. What is gravity? Do a test to see if gravity exists.

CHALLENGE

Before scientists accepted the theory of plate tectonics, another scientist, Alfred Wegener, proposed the idea of *continental drift.* This idea stated that continents like Africa and South America were once connected. The idea also stated that the continents pushed through the ocean floor when they moved apart.

Use the Internet or reference books to find out why continental drift was not accepted by scientists. Or you can read ahead to Unit 3!

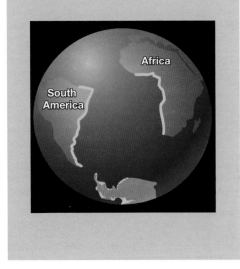

GEOLOGY CONNECTION — Dr. Rosaly Lopes—Volcano Scientist

What is it that you love? Playing baseball? Video games? Math? Spelling? Drama club? Singing? In-line skating? Volcanoes? Volcanoes! That just happens to be Rosaly Lopes's passion. She is a planetary volcanologist who searches for and studies volcanoes on Earth and elsewhere in the solar system. And at the National Aeronautic and Space Administration's Jet Propulsion Laboratory in Pasadena, California, she is considered an expert.

Dr. Rosaly Lopes standing on the Pu'u O'o eruption of the Kilauea volcano on Hawaii's Big Island.

Rosaly Lopes was born in Brazil and dreamed of being a scientist. As a child, she was fascinated by the study of space and the areas beyond Earth. At 18, she went to study astronomy at the University of London. Her original goal was to be an astronaut, but she found herself greatly influenced by a geology teacher who had visited Mount Etna, Europe's largest volcano, on the Italian island of Sicily. Lopes got hooked on the idea of traveling the world to study volcanoes.

She went on at the university to receive her doctorate degree in planetary geology and volcanology. In 1979, she found herself on Sicily doing fieldwork when Mount Etna erupted, killing several people. The experience taught her to truly appreciate and respect the power of volcanoes.

Thinking scientifically

Like most scientists, Dr. Lopes follows the scientific method in her research. The first step is to ask questions. For example, why are volcanoes important to understand? Scientists study volcanoes on Earth in the hope of being able to predict eruptions. Millions of people live near volcanoes. Their eruptions can cause great harm to local communities and the wider region. A volcano's eruption can cause climate changes and affects not only people, but also plants and animals.

Volcanoes are an important feature on Earth and other planets. Our planet has the most volcanoes in the solar system. Yet for Dr. Lopes, studying volcanoes on Earth was not enough. She recognized that by studying volcanoes on other planets, she could ask even more questions, and different kinds of questions. Meaningful questions can lead to a better understanding of the universe in which we live.

Mt. Etna, Sicily, Italy

Gathering data

On Earth, a lot of volcanic data is gathered by using satellites and aircraft. In space, volcanoes are studied mostly by using spacecraft, satellites, and radar images. NASA's Galileo mission to Jupiter provided information about that planet's moon Io. Dr. Lopes learned that the lava temperature on Io is nearly 2600 degrees Fahrenheit. She was amazed because this is almost 500 degrees hotter than lava here on Earth.

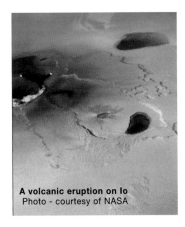

A volcanic eruption on Io
Photo - courtesy of NASA

Today, NASA's Cassini mission is gathering information about Saturn's largest moon, Titan. Dr. Lopes has learned that Titan has cold volcanoes with lava that is a slushy mixture of water, ice, and ammonia.

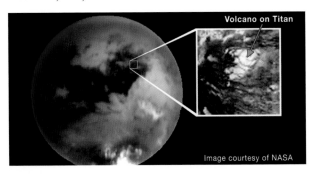

Volcano on Titan

Image courtesy of NASA

Presenting data

Scientists communicate their findings in many ways. Dr. Lopes writes papers that are published in scientific journals. She gives talks at scientific meetings. An important part of her job is speaking to the public and she often presents seminars at universities and astronomy clubs.

Television and books are ways to reach an even wider public. Dr. Lopes has appeared on the Discovery Channel and ABC News Nightline. She has filmed a program with National Geographic. She has written "The Volcano Adventure Guide" (Cambridge University Press, 2005) to advise people who want to safely explore some of the most famous volcanoes on Earth and explorers who may never get any closer to a volcano than in the pages of her book.

A record-breaking mom

Stop and think about what you could do to get in the Guinness World Records. Hop on one foot for a long time? Eat a lot of pies? What do you think Dr. Lopes did to get into the Guinness book?

She (not surprisingly) discovered volcanoes. Lopes's discovery of 71 active volcanoes on Io—which is about 500 million miles away from her Pasadena lab—is a world record. Her son thinks it is great to have his mom in the Guinness World Records.

When asked what is "the best part of her work," Dr. Lopes says: "The knowledge that I am exploring new places and seeing places that nobody has seen before. The thrill of discovery drives many of us scientists. It is not always a 'Wow, look at that,' though there is certainly plenty of that. Often discovery is the painstaking analysis of data, not unlike a detective unraveling a mystery."

Questions:
1. Why do scientists like Dr. Lopes study volcanoes?
2. How are volcanoes on Earth studied, compared with volcanoes on the other planets?
3. How does Dr. Lopes communicate her findings?
4. List the roles that Dr. Lopes has in her life.

CHAPTER ACTIVITY Observing The World Around You

One thing that all scientists have in common is that they make countless numbers of observations in their work. In order to be a scientist, you must practice the skill of making observations. It is a good idea to leave space for writing observations in your lab notebook.

During this activity, you will be asked to make as many observations as you can of what your teacher does in front of the classroom. The classroom needs to be silent so that all students can concentrate and be the best scientists they can be!

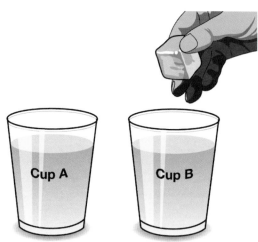

Procedure

1. Make a table like the one on this page on a separate sheet of paper.
2. There are two cups in front of the room, labeled A and B. There is a liquid in each of the cups. Write down your observations about these two liquids in the first row of your table. These are your initial observations before your teacher has conducted tests.
3. Now, your teacher will begin a series of tests on each of the liquids.

4. For each test, record your observations in the correct column. In the column labeled cup A, write observations about cup A. In the column labeled cup B, write observations about cup B.
5. Share your observations as a class. Your teacher will write all observations on the board.

Events conducted by the teacher	Observations	
	Cup A	Cup B
Initial observations (before any tests)		
Test 1		
Test 2		
Test 3		

Questions

a. How many senses did you use when making observations? Which sense/senses did you use the most?
b. How successful were you at making observations? What was your biggest problem?
c. What is the difference between an observation and an inference?
d. What are some inferences you could come up with about the various tests that were done in this experiment?
e. Was the liquid in cup A the same as the liquid in cup B? Explain your answer.

Chapter 1 Assessment

Vocabulary

Select the correct term to complete the sentences.

science	data	experiment
inference	scientific method	scientific theory
hypothesis	scientific law	

Section 1.1

1. You look up at the sky and see dark clouds. You predict that it might rain. A statement like this based on experience is called a(n) _____.

2. _____ is a process for answering questions. Astronomy is an example. Astronomy is a process for answering questions about stars and planets.

3. A(n) _____ is a predicted answer to a question based on observations. It must be testable and isn't always correct.

4. _____ are information that is collected in order to answer a question.

5. The _____ is a series of steps including observation, forming a question, stating a hypothesis, collecting data, and reaching a conclusion.

6. If you want to prove or disprove a hypothesis, you perform a(n) _____.

Section 1.2
There are no glossary words in this section.

Section 1.3

7. A(n) _____ is a statement that explains a complex idea such as a process for how Earth's surface has changed over time.

8. A(n) _____ is a statement that describes an observed phenomenon such as why an object falls when you drop it.

Concepts

Section 1.1

1. In the morning, you see a full glass of water on the kitchen table. By nighttime, the glass is almost empty. Is this statement a hypothesis or an observation?

2. In the morning, a jar is filled with water. By the afternoon the water level is lower. You propose that the water level has gone down because it was evaporated by the sun. Is this statement a hypothesis or an observation?

3. What are the different types of data that scientists collect during experiments? Give an example of each type of data.

4. Why is it important to perform many experiments?

5. Write a short paragraph that describes two characteristics that are important for a scientist to have.

Section 1.2

6. You are a judge at a contest to pick the best cake. Which senses do you use for making your observations? Explain how each sense that you list would be useful.

7. How is an observation different from an opinion? Give an example of an observation and an opinion.

8. What information should be recorded in a science notebook? Explain why each thing is important.

Section 1.3

9. Identify each statement as an observation or inference. If a statement is an inference, write an observation on which it may be based. If a statement is an observation, write an inference based on that observation.
   a. John is wearing red.
   b. The students will work hard during class tomorrow.
   c. It is going to be hot and humid tomorrow.
   d. Katie is smiling.

10. You observe that the plant in the window is turning brown. State a hypothesis to answer the question: Why is the plant in the window turning brown? Explain how you could test your hypothesis.

11. What do these three terms have in common: scientific fact, scientific law, and scientific theory?

Math and Writing Skills

Section 1.1

1. Choose two things that you do every day and explain how science relates to these things.

2. Write a paragraph about a famous scientist or a scientist whom you may know! In what field of science does this person work? How are you similar to this person?

3. In Section 1.1, you will find a bird's eye view of the erupting Colima volcano. This image shows what the volcano looks like if you were flying above it (like a bird). Draw a sketch that shows what this volcano might look like from the side.

Section 1.2

4. Write a story about a nature experience you have had at school, home, or on a trip. After you have written your story, list three observations and three opinions in your story.

5. Choose an interesting object from your home and gather measuring tools (such as a ruler, scale, and a calculator).

   a. Observe the object for 5 minutes. Write down everything you observe.

   b. Then, spend 5 minutes making measurements and recording those.

Section 1.3

6. Pretend you are Sam from Section 1.3. Write up a lab report based on the experiment he did.

7. Make an observation about something that happens in your classroom often. Formulate a hypothesis about why this thing or event happens. Design an experiment to test your hypothesis.

8. The text describes the law of gravity in words. What is the law of gravity in terms of a formula. See if you can find out the answer to this question by looking through resources including text books, the Internet, or in your school library. The complete name (to help you with your research) is the *Universal Law of Gravitation*.

Chapter Project—Observing Nature

Pick anything in nature at or outside your home. You may choose to observe the sunset, a tree, a garden, or even soil. There are countless things in nature that you can observe! Your teacher will approve your choice before you begin. Observe your piece of nature for 10 minutes every day for one week. Without stating what the object is, record all observations in your science notebook as words and drawings. Also, write down any questions you have throughout the observation period.

After you have collected your observations choose one of the questions you had, and answer it. You will need to use evidence from all of your observations to form inferences and opinions. Also, make predictions (based on your observations) about what will happen to that piece of nature over the next couple of months.

At the end of the week, bring your notebook of observations to class. Your teacher will collect your observations and redistribute them to other students. You will look at five other students' notebooks, and see if you can guess what other students have observed!

Chapter 2
The Science Toolbox

Many tools are used in science. What is the most important tool? It's your brain! Among other things, your brain allows you to ask questions and make hypotheses. Other science tools allow you to make measurements and collect data. An experiment is also a science tool. Some science tools are big and heavy like huge telescopes. Some are small and easy to carry like a ruler. Let's go look in the science toolbox and see what else is in there.

 **Key Questions**

1. *Why is your brain a good scientific tool?*

2. *Will a toy car go faster on a steeper ramp?*

3. *Can you design an experiment to find out the best tasting chocolate chip cookie?*

2.1 Measurement

An important step in the scientific method is collecting data. Measurements are one form of data. Measurements tell you how big or how small something is. Measurements also help you compare objects.

What is a measurement?

A number plus a unit
A **measurement** is a number that includes a *unit*. A **unit** is a specific quantity that is counted to make a measurement. The unit provides information about the type of measurement.

Why are units important?
Let's use an example. A basketball player might say, "I'm tall! I'm almost 2 high."

You might think "almost 2" doesn't sound very tall.

The basketball player is not tall if his height is almost 2 *feet*. A medium-sized dog is about two feet tall. However, the basketball player *is* tall if he is almost 2 *meters* tall. Two meters equals a height of about 6 feet 6 inches (Figure 2.1).

The words "meters" and "feet" are units. Always include a unit when making measurements. Do you see why this is important?

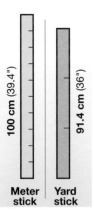

Meter stick / Yard stick — 100 cm (39.4") / 91.4 cm (36")

Activity: How tall are you in feet and meters?

Find a partner. You and your partner will need two measuring tools: a yardstick and a meter stick. Use the yardstick to measure height in feet and inches. Use the meter stick to measure height in meters and centimeters. Measure your partner's height. Your partner will measure your height.

How tall are you in feet and inches?
How tall are you in meters and centimeters?

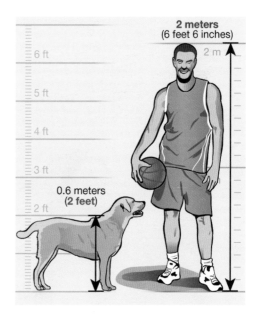

Figure 2.1: *A measurement includes a number and a unit. Two meters is much taller than two feet!*

A history of measuring systems

English System of measurement At one time, the English System of measurements included nearly a dozen units just for weight. For example, a pharmacist weighed medicine in *grains*, a jeweler weighed gold and gems in *carats*, and a carpenter weighed his nails in *kegs* (Figure 2.2). These units were hard to compare to each other.

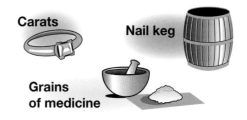

Figure 2.2: *Measurements in the early English system.*

The Metric System During the 1800s, a new system of measurement was developed in Europe and Great Britain—the Metric System. The goal of this system was for all units of measurement to be related to each other. It was a *base-10* system, meaning that all units were a factor of 10.

Comparing the systems Centimeters (cm) relate to liters in the Metric System. A 10 cm × 10 cm × 10 cm cube holds exactly 1 liter of liquid. However, in the English system, feet do not relate easily to gallons. A cube that is 1 foot × 1 foot × 1 foot holds about 7.48 gallons of liquid.

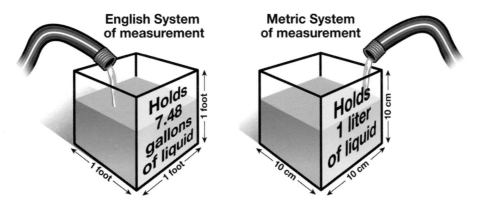

SI Units The General Conference on Weights and Measures changed the name of the Metric System to the International System of Units in 1960. Most people refer to it as SI units or SI measurements, from its official French name, Le Système International d'Unités. From now on, we will refer to this system as SI Units.

English and SI units

Imagine that you are working on your bicycle and find that the wrench that you have selected is one size too small. The graphic below shows that it is easier to pick the next bigger size if you use SI units than if you use English units.

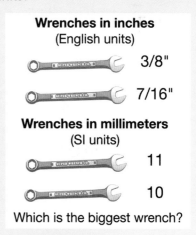

Wrenches in inches
(English units)

3/8"

7/16"

Wrenches in millimeters
(SI units)

11

10

Which is the biggest wrench?

More about SI units

The meter is the basic unit

The **meter** is the basic distance unit for the SI Units system of measurement. The meter is also the basis for this system. It was decided that the meter would be equal to one ten-millionth of the distance from the North Pole to the equator, measured along a line that passed through Paris, France (Figure 2.3).

There is nothing special about the length of the meter or how it was chosen. However, the meter was a good starting place for developing the rest of the SI Units system of measurement.

Useful prefixes

Prefixes are added to the names of basic units in the SI Units system. Prefixes describe very small or large measurements. There are many SI units prefixes. The good news is that only three prefixes are needed most of the time, even in science.

Prefixes	Prefix + meter	Compared to a meter
milli-	millimeter	1,000 times smaller
centi-	centimeter	100 times smaller
kilo-	kilometer	1,000 times bigger

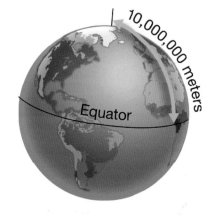

Figure 2.3: *In 1791, a meter was defined as 1 / 10,000,000 of the distance from the North Pole of Earth to its equator. Today a meter is defined more accurately using the speed of light.*

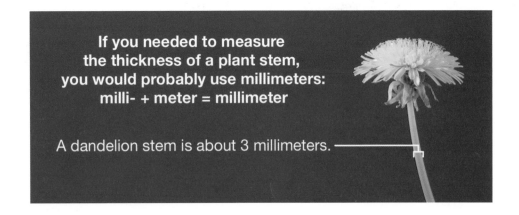

If you needed to measure the thickness of a plant stem, you would probably use millimeters:
milli- + meter = millimeter

A dandelion stem is about 3 millimeters.

Volume and mass

Volume **Volume** measures how much space is occupied by an object. One way to think of a volume measurement is as a measure with three distance measurements. The formula for the volume of a rectangular solid is length × width × height.

The liter The basic SI unit of volume is the **liter**. The liter is based on the centimeter. The prefix *centi-* means 1/100. A centimeter is one-hundredth of a meter—about the width of a pencil. A liter of volume is equal to the volume of a cube-shaped box that is 10 centimeters on each side (Figure 2.4).

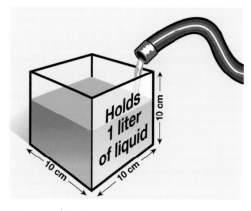

Figure 2.4: *A liter of volume is equal to the volume of a cube-shaped box that is 10 centimeters on each side.*

The gram A **gram** is the basic unit of *mass* in the SI Units measuring system. Water, a common substance, was wisely chosen as the material to define the gram. The water used to determine the mass of a gram must be pure, and the temperature and pressure have to be just right. A gram is defined as the mass of one-thousandth of a liter of pure water. Using prefixes, this means a gram is the mass of a *milliliter* of water. You will learn more about mass in Section 2.2.

Cooking with grams Around the world, many cooks measure the volume of ingredients in a mixing bowl using grams. They use a small electronic scale and weigh dry and wet ingredients in grams in the same bowl on the scale. This is possible because many wet ingredients are mostly water. Rather than measure 250 mL of milk into a cup, the cook adds 250 grams of milk to the bowl on the scale. This technique makes for a fast cleanup since only one bowl is needed for measuring all of the ingredients!

250 milliliters of milk equals 250 grams of milk

VOCABULARY

volume - a measurement of how much space is occupied by an object.

liter - the basic unit of volume in the SI Units measuring system.

gram - the basic unit of mass in the SI Units measuring system; one-thousandth of a liter.

Measuring volume with SI units

Measuring volume with distance

If an object is a solid cube or rectangle, you can measure its length, width, and height in SI units. These measurements are multiplied to find the volume in cubic SI units. If the measurements are taken in centimeters, the result of the multiplication will be in cubic centimeters or cm^3. This way of measuring SI volume is best suited for solid objects with parallel sides, but is also used for large volumes. For example, the volume of a lake may be measured in cubic meters (m^3) (Figure 2.5).

Measuring small volumes of liquid

The volume of liquids can be measured by pouring them into containers like beakers or graduated cylinders (Figure 2.6). Volume found this way is reported in milliliters (mL). This way of measuring SI volumes is best suited for small volumes of liquid.

The graphic below illustrates the two ways to measure volume in SI units. Regardless of the method chosen, the result is the same!

Volume = 3,200,000,000 m³

Source: U.S. Geological Survey Photographer: C.D. Miller

Mono Lake, California

Figure 2.5: *Large volumes are measured in cubic meters. The volume of Mono Lake in California is about 3,200,000,000 cubic meters (measurement made in 2002).*

A liter is a cube that measures 10 cm on each side.

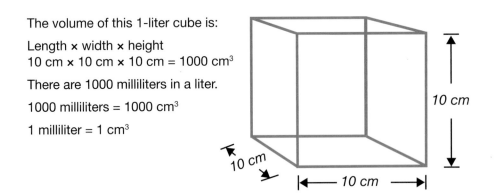

The volume of this 1-liter cube is:

Length × width × height
10 cm × 10 cm × 10 cm = 1000 cm³

There are 1000 milliliters in a liter.

1000 milliliters = 1000 cm³

1 milliliter = 1 cm³

10 cm

10 cm

10 cm

Figure 2.6: *A beaker and a graduated cylinder are used to measure small volumes.*

2.1 Section Review

Answer the following questions. For questions 3, 8, 9, and 10, assume that the water meets the special conditions that makes the mass of one milliliter of water equal to one gram.

1. What is the main difference between the SI Units measuring system and the English System of measurement?

2. What is the relationship between a cubic centimeter and a milliliter?

3. What is the mass of a cubic centimeter of pure water?

4. How many milliliters are in a liter?

5. What is the mass of a liter of water in grams? in kilograms?

6. What prefix increases an SI unit 1,000 times?

7. If you were going to measure the length of your foot, would you use millimeters, centimeters, or meters? Explain your answer.

8. How many liters of water are in a cubic meter?

9. What is the mass of a cubic meter of water in kilograms?

10. A metric ton equals 1,000 kilograms. What is the mass of a cubic meter of water in metric tons?

11. A room is 8 meters wide and 5 meters long. This room is 4 meters high. What is the volume of this room?

12. **Challenge:** Write a short story or describe a real-life story that illustrates why units are important.

SOLVE IT!

Use a metric ruler or a meter stick to measure the dimensions of your room at home. Record your measurements on a piece of paper. Then use a scale of 1 meter = 1 centimeter to make a map of your room on another piece of paper. Once you have drawn the shape of your room on the piece of paper, make the map. Where is your bed? Where do you keep your clothes? Where are your favorite things?

Example:

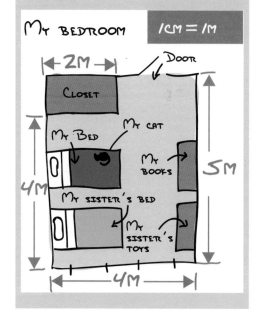

2.2 More Measurements

In this section you will learn more about measuring and measuring tools. You will learn the difference between measurements of mass and weight. And you will learn about measuring temperature and time.

Mass and weight

Matter Everything is made of **matter**. Your body, a book, an apple, a duck, water, and the air are all forms of matter. All matter is made of particles called **atoms**. Atoms are too small to see with your eyes. An atom is 10 million times smaller than a grain of sand.

Mass The **mass** of an object equals the amount of matter it has. A nutrition label includes measurements for the mass of carbohydrates, protein, and fat in the food. The "g" on the nutrition label stands for "gram."

Mass stays the same Mass and weight are not the same thing. One apple has a mass of about 150 grams. If you flew in a space ship to Mars, the apple would still have a mass of 150 grams. However, the weight of the apple would be different!

Weight **Weight** is a measure of the force of gravity. The more mass an object has, the greater the force of gravity on that object. Say you bought 15 apples. On Earth, 15 apples weigh about 5 pounds. On Mars, the force of gravity is less. Those same 15 apples would weigh only about 2 pounds (Figure 2.7)!

In science class, we will use the terms "grams" and "mass" instead of "pounds" and "weight."

pound = unit of weight	gram or kilogram = unit of mass
2.2 pounds on Earth = 1,000 grams = 1 kilogram	

VOCABULARY

matter - the substance of all objects; all matter is made of atoms and has mass.

atom - a particle of matter.

mass - the amount of matter that an object has.

weight - a measure of mass and the force of gravity on an object.

EARTH: 15 apples weigh 5 pounds

MARS: 15 apples weigh 2 pounds

Figure 2.7: *Fifteen apples on Earth weigh 5 pounds. The same 15 apples weigh 2 pounds on Mars! This is because the force of gravity is less on Mars.*

Measuring time

What time is it? What time does your school start in the morning? What time does school end? These questions ask about one moment in time. For example, one important moment each day is the start of lunch time. Many people are ready to eat lunch at 12:00 p.m. each day (Figure 2.8).

Measuring time It is often important to measure time in experiments. For example, it is important to know how long it takes for something to move or grow. It might take one hour for a car to travel 80 kilometers on a highway. It takes about 156 days from the time you plant a pumpkin seed until you have a big orange pumpkin (Figure 2.9).

Units for measuring time You are probably familiar with the common units for measuring time: seconds, hours, minutes, days, and years. But you may not know how these units relate to each other. The table below gives some useful relationships between units of time.

Figure 2.8: *12:00 p.m. is lunchtime.*

Time relationships
1 minute = 60 seconds
1 hour = 60 minutes
1 day = 24 hours
1 year = 365 days
1 century = 100 years

Figure 2.9: *156 days is about the amount of time it takes to grow a pumpkin from a seed.*

Measuring temperature

Two temperature scales
There are two commonly used temperature scales. If the temperature in England is 21 degrees Celsius, you can wear shorts and a T-shirt. If the temperature in the United States is 21 degrees Fahrenheit, you will need to wear a heavy coat, gloves, and a hat. The United States is one of few countries that still use the Fahrenheit scale. For this reason, it is useful to know both of these temperature scales (Figure 2.10).

Fahrenheit
On the Fahrenheit scale, water freezes at 32 degrees and boils at 212 degrees. A comfortable room temperature is 68°F. The normal temperature for a human body is 98.6°F.

Celsius
On the Celsius scale, water freezes at 0°C and boils at 100°C. The normal human body temperature on the Celsius scale is 37°C. Most science and engineering temperature measurements are in Celsius because 0° and 100° are easier to remember than 32° and 212°. Most other countries use the Celsius scale for descriptions of temperature, including weather reports.

Converting between the scales
You can convert between Fahrenheit and Celsius using these formulas.

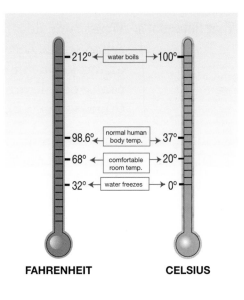

Figure 2.10: *The Celsius and Fahrenheit temperature scales.*

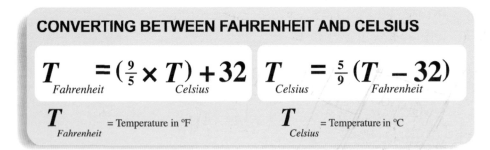

CONVERTING BETWEEN FAHRENHEIT AND CELSIUS

$$T_{Fahrenheit} = (\tfrac{9}{5} \times T_{Celsius}) + 32 \qquad T_{Celsius} = \tfrac{5}{9}(T_{Fahrenheit} - 32)$$

$T_{Fahrenheit}$ = Temperature in °F $T_{Celsius}$ = Temperature in °C

 **SOLVE IT!**

You are doing a science experiment with a Fahrenheit thermometer. Your data must be in degrees Celsius. If you measure a temperature of 86°F, what is this temperature in degrees Celsius?

How do you measure temperature?

Thermometers Humans can sense warmth or cold, but not very accurately. Accurate measurement of temperature requires a *thermometer*, an instrument that measures temperature. A thermometer that contains liquid alcohol uses the expansion of the alcohol to measure temperature changes (Figure 2.11).

When temperature increases As you have learned, matter is made of particles called *atoms*. Groups of atoms are called *molecules*. The volume of alcohol in a thermometer contains huge numbers of alcohol molecules. As temperature increases, the alcohol molecules move faster and bounce off each other. As a result, the liquid alcohol expands and takes up more space in the thermometer. For an alcohol thermometer, temperature is a measure of how much the alcohol expands. Even a small increase in volume inside the tube makes a visible change in the amount that the alcohol rises up the tube.

Different thermometers Thermometers are based on a physical property (such as color or volume) that changes with temperature. Alcohol thermometers measure temperature as a change in volume of the alcohol. Digital thermometers sense temperature by measuring the ability of electricity to pass through a part of the thermometer called a *probe*. Aquarium "sticker" thermometers use a chemical that changes color at different temperatures. The "sticker" thermometers like the one below are placed on the aquarium tank.

Digital thermometer

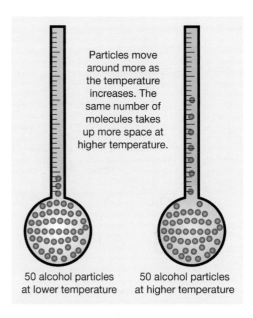

Particles move around more as the temperature increases. The same number of molecules takes up more space at higher temperature.

50 alcohol particles at lower temperature

50 alcohol particles at higher temperature

Figure 2.11: *Alcohol particles move faster at higher temperatures and spread out. The volume of alcohol expands, or takes up more space.*

STUDY SKILLS

A mathematical formula is easier to use the more you practice using it. Practice converting Celsius degrees to Fahrenheit degrees at least once a day. Pretty soon this conversion formula will be easy to use!

Aquarium thermometer

2.2 Section Review

1. Why is your brain a good scientific tool?

2. Describe three measuring tools that are used in science. The sidebar box at the right lists some of these tools.

3. A mathematical formula is one kind of tool. Use the temperature conversion formula below to fill in the following table. The first one is done for you.

	Celsius degrees	Converting	Fahrenheit degrees
a.	25°C	$(^9/_5 \times 25°C) + 32 =$ Multiply: $(9 \times 25) = 225$ Divide: $225 \div 5 = 45$ Add: $45 + 32 = 77°F$	77°F
b.	100°C		
c.	5°C		
d.			40°F
e.			100°F
f.			200°F

4. What is the difference between mass and weight?

MY JOURNAL

Write a short story about making an important scientific discovery. Include tools from the "science toolbox" in your story. Here is a list of important science tools:

- Your brain
- The scientific method
- An experiment
- Ruler, meter stick, tape measure
- Triple beam balance
- Beakers or graduated cylinders
- Thermometer
- Stopwatch
- Clock
- Calculator
- Graph paper
- Computer

CONVERTING BETWEEN FAHRENHEIT AND CELSIUS

$$T_{Fahrenheit} = (\tfrac{9}{5} \times T_{Celsius}) + 32 \qquad T_{Celsius} = \tfrac{5}{9}(T_{Fahrenheit} - 32)$$

$T_{Fahrenheit}$ = Temperature in °F

$T_{Celsius}$ = Temperature in °C

2.3 Systems and Variables

The universe is huge and complex. Therefore, it is useful to think about only a small part at a time. A toy car rolling down a ramp is a small part of the universe. In science, a group of objects, like a car and a ramp, is called a *system*.

What is a system?

A group of objects A **system** is a group of objects and the factors that affect these objects. Some systems are listed below:

- The respiratory system in the human body
- Bacteria in a petri dish
- A fish aquarium
- A car engine
- A car and ramp (see diagram below)

Variables A factor that affects an object is called a **variable**. A system can be affected by many variables. In an experiment, only a few variables are studied. Figure 2.12 lists variables that are part of the car and ramp system. Additional variables include color, light, the table and floor, and friction. These variables either stay constant or they do not affect the system.

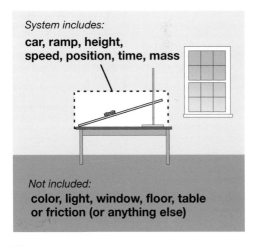

System includes:

car, ramp, height, speed, position, time, mass

Not included:
color, light, window, floor, table or friction (or anything else)

Figure 2.12: *A system includes objects and variables. Friction refers to how two objects interact. In the car and ramp system there is very little friction between the car and the ramp, so the car rolls very easily.*

Some important variables in this system

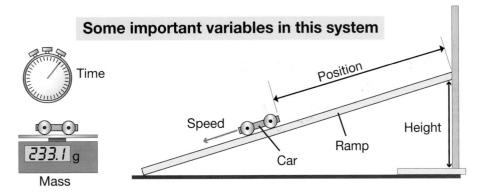

Systems and experiments

Start with a question
An experiment is an activity that follows the scientific method. An experiment can also be described as an activity that investigates the relationship between variables in a system. Experiments usually start with a question. An example is, "How does the height of a ramp affect the speed of a car?" (Figure 2.13)

independent variable - a variable that is changed in an experiment. The independent variable is sometimes called the *manipulated variable*.

An experiment is a tool
An experiment is a good scientific tool for answering the question, "How does ramp height affect speed?" An example of an experiment you could do would be to change the ramp height three times and measure the car's speed at the three different heights.

dependent variable - a variable that is affected by the change to the independent variable. The dependent variable is sometimes called the *responding variable*.

Independent and dependent variables
The variable that is changed in an experiment is the **independent variable**. The variable that is affected by the change to the independent variable is the **dependent variable**. In Figure 2.13, the height of the ramp is the independent variable and the speed of the car is the dependent variable.

control variable - a variable that is held constant in an experiment.

Change one variable at a time
There should only be one independent variable in an experiment. All of the other variables should stay the same so you know that your results are due to changes made to the independent variable.

Control variable
For example, to study height, you keep the other variables the same. A variable that is kept the same in an experiment is called a **control variable**. The mass of the car is a control variable. If you changed the height of the ramp *and* the mass of the car you would not know which variable affected the speed.

How does the height of the ramp affect the speed of the car?

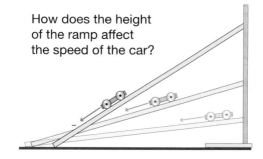

Figure 2.13: *State a hypothesis that answers this question. You will be able to test this hypothesis in your science lab class.*

State a hypothesis
A hypothesis is a statement describing how the independent variable will affect the dependent variable. (Note: The hypothesis is not necessarily correct. It must be tested.) One hypothesis is, "As height of the ramp increases, the car's speed increases." The hypothesis is made before the experiment takes place.

Energy in systems

Energy   Energy is an important variable in all systems. **Energy** is a measure of a system's ability to change or create change in other systems. Energy has many forms. Some examples of energy are heat, motion, light, height, pressure, electricity, and calories. Here are examples of energy and the resulting changes in the systems:

- Boiling (heat) changes the appearance of an egg.
- Kicking a ball (motion) moves it into a goal.
- Moving a book from a low to a high shelf (height) changes its position.
- Increasing the amount of air in a tire (pressure) makes it firm and able to support a car.
- Turning on a TV (electricity) causes an image to appear on a blank screen.
- Eating food provides energy (calories) to your body.

Energy in systems   Systems tend to move from high to low energy (Figure 2.14). A system at higher energy is unstable, while a system at lower energy is stable. The car is unstable at the top of the ramp where its energy of position (height) is greatest. It naturally rolls to a more stable position at the bottom of the ramp. Likewise, a child has more energy at the top of a playground slide. Once the child slides down, she is more stable and has less energy.

Friction   Energy is liberated due to *friction* when two objects rub against each other (Figure 2.15). The more friction there is between objects, the more energy builds up between them as they try to move past each other. Some of this energy is converted to heat. You can generate heat due to friction by rubbing your hands together really fast. If you wet your hands, it will be harder to generate heat. This is because the water reduces friction between your hands.

energy - a measure of a system's ability to change.

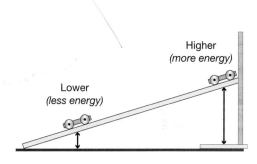

Figure 2.14: *A car at the top of a ramp has more height energy than a car at the bottom of the ramp.*

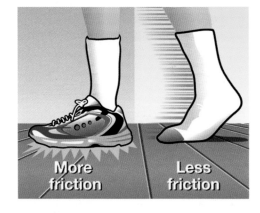

Figure 2.15: *There is more friction between a sneaker and a gym floor than between a sock and the gym floor.*

The scale of a system

An example of different scales　One characteristic of all systems is their scale. The word *scale* here refers to size. Figure 2.16 shows a road at three different scales. The bottom box shows a map, which is a system of roads shown at a large scale. You can see many roads in this large-scale model. The center box shows a road and a car at a human-scale, one road and one car, at the size that you see every day. The top box, showing a crack in the road, is using a smaller scale. Small scale is a close-up view, allowing you to see more detail than you'd see with a larger scale. The smallest scale involves atoms and molecules.

Large scale　Variables are on a large scale when you can see them with the naked eye, or measure them directly. The mass of a car and the temperature of a pot of water are large-scale variables. Most of the things you measure in classroom experiments are large-scale, or *macroscopic*.

The scale of atoms　Some variables are so small that they are not visible to the eye or readily measured. Temperature and energy are related variables, but it is not possible to understand how they are related using a macroscopic scale. To understand the connection between temperature and energy we must look using the *atomic scale,* the scale of atoms and molecules.

Atoms　Atoms are tiny particles, far too small to see without powerful magnification tools. Many of the large-scale properties of matter that you can observe depend on the behavior of atoms. To understand certain aspects of the world (such as temperature) we need to understand the behavior of atoms.

Figure 2.16: *Three different scales for looking at a road.*

Models

What is a model? Explanations in science typically come in the form of models. A *model* is an explanation that connects the variables in a system through cause and effect relationships. For example, if you increase the height of the ramp, the car's speed will increase. A model is a good science tool because it helps you think about how two variables are related. There are many types of models.

Mental models If you wanted to kick a soccer ball into a goal, you could come up with a mental model. You imagine the ball going into the goal and that helps you know how hard to kick the ball (Figure 2.17).

Physical models A physical model (or scale model) is a small version of something big. Engineers make small model bridges to learn how to make an actual bridge for a city. A scale model has to be proportional to the real object. For example, a scale of 1 centimeter = 10 meters means that an object 100 meters long in real life would be 10 centimeters long in a small-scale model.

Conceptual models A conceptual model is a way of using your existing knowledge to understand or remember a new concept. Earth scientists use a conceptual model called *theory of plate tectonics* to explain why earthquakes occur (see sidebar box). Comparing the Earth's plates to puzzle pieces makes the concept easier to understand.

Mathematical models An example of a mathematical model is $\mathbf{E = mc^2}$. This was a model that Albert Einstein discovered. $\mathbf{E}$ stands for energy, $\mathbf{m}$ stands for mass, and $\mathbf{c}$ stands for the speed of light. This mathematical model states that energy equals mass times the square of the speed of light. Graphs are another type of mathematical model that you'll learn about in the next section. A **graph** is a picture that shows how two variables are related.

Energy
Mass
$$E = mc^2$$
Speed of light

Figure 2.17: *Imagining how to kick a soccer ball to make a goal is a mental model.*

A conceptual model: The theory of plate tectonics

Earth's surface is like a giant puzzle with huge pieces called plates. The theory of plate tectonics describes how the plates move on Earth's surface. You will learn more about plate tectonics in Unit 3.

VOCABULARY

graph - a picture that shows how two variables are related.

2.3 Section Review

1. In Section 2.3, you learned that systems, experiments, and models are types of scientific tools. Explain why each of these things can be considered to be a scientific tool.

2. You read about an experiment that related the height of a ramp to the speed of a toy car. In the experiment, what kind of variables are the height of the ramp and the mass of the car?

3. Will a toy car go faster if the height of the ramp is raised from 20 centimeters to 50 centimeters? Explain your answer.

4. Refer to page 17 to answer these questions about energy:

   a. What kind of energy is involved in turning on a TV set?

   b. Your foot kicks a soccer ball into a goal. List the parts of this system. What kind of energy is involved in this system?

   c. Using an oven, you can turn cake batter into a delicious cake. What kind of energy is involved in this change?

5. You know that a toy car at the top of a ramp will always roll *down* the ramp. Why doesn't the car ever roll *up* the ramp?

6. Is the car and ramp system a macroscopic scale system or an atomic scale system?

7. Physical models are proportional to a real object. Imagine that you wanted to make a model of a car. The length of a real car is about 4 meters long. If the physical model has a scale of 10 centimeters = 1 meter, how long would the model car have to be?

8. What kind of model is a graph?

9. What kind of model is a globe of Earth?

Do an experiment

Below are two experiments for you to try. Be sure to state a hypothesis before you do your experiment, and follow the steps of the scientific method.

(1) Use the car and ramp to answer the following question: Does mass affect a car's speed on the ramp? Be very detailed in how you design your experiment and collect your data.

(2) Do an experiment to answer the following question: Does salty water freeze at a lower temperature than tap water? Here are some tips for this experiment. Place containers of salty water and tap water in a freezer. Use equal volumes of water. Observe the water samples at regular intervals and measure the temperature of each. Record the temperature at which ice forms on each sample.

2.4 Graphs

An experiment is an important scientific tool. One of the reasons it's a good tool is that it produces information or data. A graph is a mathematical model that helps you interpret the data you collect.

What is a graph?

A graph is a picture
A *graph* is a picture that shows how two variables are related. Graphs are easier to read than tables of numbers, so they are often used to display data collected during an experiment.

Independent variable
Graphs are drawn with the *independent variable* on the horizontal or *x*-axis. Independent variables are controlled by the experimenter. The independent variable in Graph A is the amount of gas in the car (Figure 2.18).

Dependent variable
The *dependent variable* goes on the vertical or *y*-axis. A dependent variable is affected by an independent variable. Distance is a good example of a dependent variable because distance traveled often depends on other things such as speed, type of vehicle, terrain, and amount of gas the vehicle has (Graph A).

Types of graphs
Types of graphs include line, bar, and pie graphs. A line graph is used when one variable causes a second variable to increase or decrease in value. For example, the more gas you put in a car, the farther it travels (Graph A). A bar graph compares categories of information. Graph B compares five places and their distances from home. A pie graph is a circular graph that also compares categories of information. The data in a pie graph is usually written in percentages. Graph C shows how a student spends her time during 24 hours. What would the graph look like if the student spent half her day in school and half her day asleep?

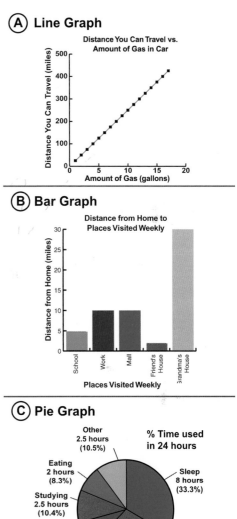

Figure 2.18: *Examples of graphs*

Parts of a graph

A picture of information A graph is a picture of information. All of the space on the graph should be used so that the data "picture" is easy to understand.

Example A car wash is being held to raise money for a school trip. The data set (Table 2.1) and the line graph below show the relationship between the amount of money in the cash box and the number of hours spent washing cars.

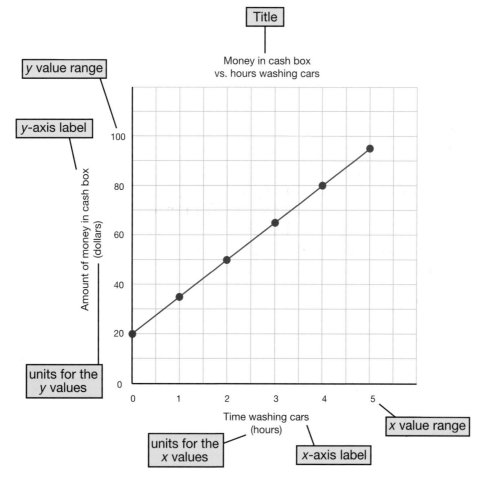

Title

y value range

y-axis label

Money in cash box
vs. hours washing cars

units for the
y values

units for the
x values

x-axis label

Time washing cars
(hours)

x value range

Data for a line graph

Table 2.1 contains a data set. A data set is organized into pairs of values. For every value in the "*x*" column, there is a value in the "*y*" column. Each pair of values can be represented by writing (x, y). A pair of values (x, y) represents a certain location or point on a graph. The *x* and *y* values are the *coordinates* of the point. The "picture" of points for this data set is the graph to the left.

Table 2.1: Money in cash box vs. number of hours washing cars.

x **# of hours washing cars**	*y* **Amount of money in cash box**	**(x, y) Coordinates**
0	20	(0, 20)
1	35	(1, 35)
2	50	(2, 50)
3	65	(3, 65)
4	80	(4, 80)
5	95	(5, 95)

How to make a line graph

Step 1 After you have collected your data, you compare independent and dependent variables. The independent variable always goes on the *x*-axis of a graph. The dependent variable always goes on the *y*-axis. Be sure to label each axis (see graph at right).

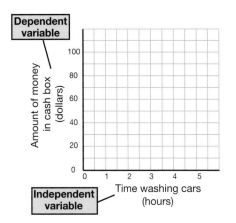

Step 2 The next step is to make a scale for each axis of the graph. Remember that the word *scale* refers to the size of something. When talking about a graph, scale refers to how each axis is divided up to fit the range of data values. For example, let's say we have a piece of graph paper that is 12 boxes by 12 boxes. The range of values for the *x*-axis is 0 to 5. The range of values for the *y*-axis is 20 to 95. To make a graph of this data, we need to figure out the value for each box on each axis.

To do this, you can use a formula:

Data range ÷ Number of boxes on the axis = Value per box

The scale for the *x*-axis is easier to determine. You have 12 boxes and values from 0 to 5 hours. The data range is 5 hours.

> **Data range ÷ Number of boxes on the axis = Value per box**
> **5 hours ÷ 12 boxes = 0.42 hour/box**

One box equals 0.42 hour per box. Round 0.42 to 0.5. This means every two boxes equals 1 hour.

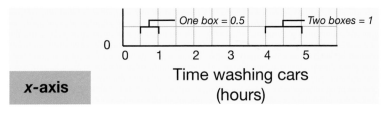

x-axis

For the *y*-axis, the data range is $20 to $95. To more easily calculate the scale, choose $0 to $100 as the data range. Calculate the scale this way:

> **Data range ÷ Number of boxes on the axis = Value per box**
> **$100 ÷ 12 boxes = $8.3/box**

Round $8.3 to $10. One box on the *y*-axis equals $10 (Figure 2.19).

Now, write the numbers of the data range on each axis at evenly spaced intervals. Label each axis with its corresponding variable and unit.

Step 3 Plot each point by finding the *x*-value and tracing the graph upward until you get to the correct *y*-value. Make a dot for each point. Draw a smooth curve that shows the pattern of the points (Figure 2.20).

Step 4 Create a title for your graph.

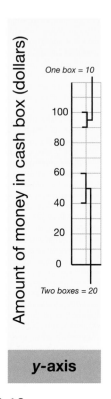

y-axis

Figure 2.19: *The scale of the y-axis for the graph.*

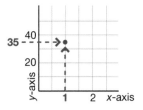

Figure 2.20: *Plot each point by finding the x-value and tracing the graph upward until you get to the correct y-value.*

2.4 Section Review

1. Why is it a good idea to make a graph of the data in a data table?

2. Questions and variables for different experiments are listed below. For each, determine which variable is independent and which is dependent.

	Question	Variables	Independent or dependent?
a.	Does getting more sleep help you do better on tests?	Test scores	
		Hours of sleep	
b.	Does the mass of a toy car affect its speed?	Mass	
		Speed of the car	
c.	Does the amount of sunshine increase the number of pieces of fruit per fruit tree?	Amount of sunshine	
		Pieces of fruit per tree	

3. Below is a list of data sets. State what kind of graph you would use for each.

   a. Favorite foods of a group of 100 students: 10% prefer steak, 20% prefer french fries, 20% prefer spaghetti, 25% prefer ice cream, and 25% prefer pizza

   b. Speed of a toy car on a ramp versus the height of the ramp

   c. Books in a library: 2,000 non-fiction books, 1,500 fiction books, 500 children's books

4. A blank graph is 10 boxes by 10 boxes (Figure 2.21). You want to plot a data set on this graph. The range of values for the *x*-axis is 0 to 20. The range of values for the *y*-axis is 0 to 10. Make a sketch that shows the scale that you would use for each axis.

CHALLENGE

Design three experiments to determine which of three chocolate chip cookie manufacturers makes the best cookie.

- One experiment should result in data that you can plot on a line graph.
- The second experiment should result in data that you can plot on a bar graph.
- And the third experiment should result in data that you can plot on a pie graph (or cookie graph)!

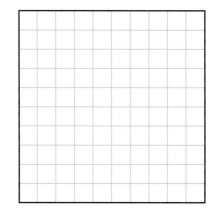

Figure 2.21: *A blank graph that is 10 boxes by 10 boxes.*

TECHNOLOGY CONNECTION   Modern Map-Making

Can you imagine trying to sail around the world without a map? The first Europeans to reach North America did just that. According to archaeologists, the history of mapmaking dates all the way back to early humans. They had the ability to produce a rough, but amazingly accurate drawing of their surroundings. Some of the first maps showed hunting and fishing areas with detailed drawings. A picture is really worth a thousand words when it comes to finding your way.

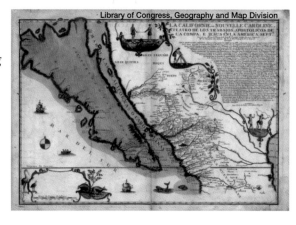

Library of Congress, Geography and Map Division

Mapmaking is known as *cartography*. The early European cartographers were often painters and artists. It was considered more of an art than a science.

How Things Have Changed

The first maps were probably drawn on animal skins. Later maps were made using brushes and parchment paper and then with pens and paper. Early maps were based on what people saw and what they were told. They were not nearly as accurate as they are today. Early map makers did not know the size or the shape of Earth. They were able to measure distances between points on Earth's surface, but not with great accuracy.

Now, thanks to sophisticated measuring devices, computers and satellites, mapmaking is truly a science. One thing that hasn't changed is the importance and the need for cartography.

Geographic Information System

The Geographic Information System (GIS) is a computer system that automates the production of mapmaking. GIS has the ability to measure distances. It can also calculate the area and borders of features.

The GIS technology is more than a computer system; it is a large collection of people, software, computers, information, and organizations. Every part of the system collects, stores, analyzes, and displays information about Earth. Every day, it seems, data about Earth's surface is added to GIS. It includes natural features, such as mountains, rivers, lakes, and streams. It also includes things people have built, such as roads, buildings, and bridges.

CAD and Cartography

Maps today are drawn on computers, often using CAD, a computer-aided design system. CAD systems are designed to show geographical features as drawings in a computer. Line thicknesses and colors can be changed easily. For example, a blue line might indicate water. These drawings are handled as separate layers that can easily be found and displayed for viewing alone or together. Because there are "layers" in the computer's files, they can be changed separately as well.

Technology Moves Mapping Forward

The use of aerial and satellite photography is one of the many ways maps are evolving. The earliest maps were made by measuring positions of latitude and longitude on Earth. Today remote sensing is used to gather information about Earth from a distance. Remote sensing devices can be used on airplanes as they fly above Earth's surface. Satellites are also used to gather information as they orbit around Earth.

Now, the view from the air or even from space gives map makers the ability to make every map exact, right down to the centimeter. Modern maps can be interactive and are easily updated. The best maps are just a mouse click away. In fact you can view The National Map at: *http://nmviewogc.cr.usgs.gov/viewer.htm*

A few clicks of the mouse allow you to interactively view, customize, and print a map of your choice. The National Map is a topographical map of the nation that provides the public with high quality data and information.

Where To Go For Answers

The National Map, maintained by the United States Geological Survey (USGS), provides critical up to date and accurate data. The USGS works with other federal, state, academic, and private mapmaking agencies. Maps are essential tools in the field of geology in that they are records of natural resources such as water, minerals, wildlife, and natural hazards such as earthquakes and volcanic activity.

Questions:

1. What is cartography?
2. Explain what the Geographic Information System is.
3. In what ways are GIS and CAD systems different?
4. What are the advantages of the National Map?

 **CHAPTER ACTIVITY** Measurement Olympics!

During the Measurement Olympics you and a partner will practice measurement and conversion skills.

Procedure

You will have 4 minutes at each event station. Your teacher will instruct you when it is time to move to a new station. Your partner will measure and record the results for you while you compete. Then, you will do the same for him/her.

Description of Events

- **Straw Javelin:** During this event, you will be throwing a straw as far as you can, like it is a javelin. Your front foot may not cross the start line, and you must throw the straw like a javelin with only one hand. Measure the distance of your throw in meters and centimeters.
- **Paper Cup Challenge:** How much water can you move from a tank to a beaker in 10 seconds using just one paper cup? Use a graduated cylinder to measure the volume of water you successfully transferred. Be careful so you don't spill any water!
- **Pebble Grab:** Who can grab the greatest mass of pebbles? Use ONLY ONE HAND to grab as many pebbles as you can out of a container. Transfer them to a triple beam balance to measure the mass. Be sure the balance is zeroed before you begin!
- **Side Step:** How far is your leg span? From a starting point step as far as you can to the side. Your partner will measure the length of your step in meters and centimeters.
- **Hoppity Hop:** Who can hop 10 meters the fastest on one foot? Your teacher has marked 10 meters on the floor. Using the timers provided, time how long it takes your partner to hop 10 meters on one foot!

Olympic Results

1. Record your results below. Any result with missing or incorrect units will be automatically disqualified from the Measurement Olympics!
2. After you have recorded your results there will be a class discussion about the winners. Record the winner's results for each event!

Olympic Event	My Results	Winners Results
Straw Javelin		
Paper Cup Challenge		
Pebble Grab		
Side Step		
Hoppity Hop		

Questions

a. Calculate the difference between the winner's results and your results for each event. (Don't forget units!)

Olympic Event	Difference
Straw Javelin	
Paper Cup Challenge	
Pebble Grab	
Side Step	
Hoppity Hop	

b. Which measurement were you most familiar with before The Olympics? Why?
c. Which measurement did you find easiest to do during The Olympics? Why was it so easy for you?
d. Which measurement did you find to be the most difficult during the Olympics? Why?

Chapter 2 Assessment

Vocabulary

Select the correct term to complete the sentences.

measurement	unit	atom
mass	gram	weight
dependent variable	variable	control variable
liter	energy	graph
meter	independent variable	system
volume		

Section 2.1

1. A(n) _____ includes a number and a unit.

2. My dog is 2 feet tall. The word "feet" in this sentence is an example of a _____.

3. A(n) _____ is a distance measurement that is a little longer than a yard.

4. The _____ is the basic unit of volume in the SI system of measurement.

5. A formula for _____ is length × width × height.

6. One _____ is the mass of one milliliter of pure water.

Section 2.2

7. A(n) _____ is a particle of matter.

8. Your _____ is the same on Earth and on Mars.

9. Your _____ is less on Mars than it is on Earth.

Section 2.3

10. In my experiment I studied a _____ that included a car, a ramp, and the height of the ramp.

11. The color of the car is an example of a _____ that I did not study in my experiment.

12. A(n) _____ is the variable that scientists change on purpose in an experiment.

13. The _____ is the variable in an experiment that changes as a result of how another variable is changed.

14. When doing an experiment it is important to keep one variable constant. This kind of variable is called a _____.

15. Systems tend to move from high to low _____.

16. A _____ is a picture that allows you to see how two variables relate to one another.

Concepts

Section 2.1

1. What is a unit? In your answer, give an example of an SI unit and an example of a unit from the English System of measurement.

2. Which statement is correct? Explain why it is the only correct statement?

    (a) I am 2 tall.   (c) I am 2 meters tall.

    (b) I am 2 kilograms tall.   (d) I weigh 30 milliliters.

3. You learned about two systems of measurement. Which of these systems is based on the number 10?

Section 2.2

4. An apple on the moon has the same mass as an apple on Earth, but the same apple weighs more on Earth than it does on the moon? Why?

5. The force of gravity on the moon is less than it is on Earth. Therefore, the weight of your body on Earth is _____ it is on the moon. Which statement goes in the blank: greater than, the same as, or less than?

6. You want to do an experiment to find out how long it takes for a bean plant to grow from a seed. What units of time would you use?

7. Below are pictures of different measurement tools. Identify whether the tool is used to measure length, volume or mass.

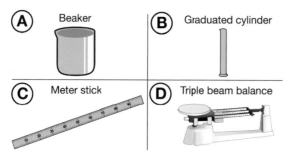

(A) Beaker

(B) Graduated cylinder

(C) Meter stick

(D) Triple beam balance

Section 2.3

8. Is an ant farm in an aquarium an example of a system? Use the definition of a system from the chapter to answer this question. Explain your answer in paragraph form.

An ant farm

9. You want to find out if light affects the growth of plants. To do your experiment, you use two plants. One plant is a bean plant and the other is a spider plant. Both plants are in the same size pot and the same type of soil. You put the bean plant in a

Does light affect the growth of plants?

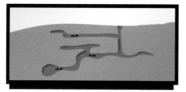

Spider plant in a dark room

Bean plant on window sill

window, and you put the spider plant in a closet, where the light will be turned off for the duration of the experiment. The experiment lasts one week. Each day at 9:00 am you measure the height of each plant and record your data using centimeters in your science notebook. At the same time, you water each of the plants with 500 mL of water.

Is your experiment a good scientific experiment? Why or why not?

10. Identify the independent variable, dependent variable, and the control variable(s) in this experiment. Explain your reasoning.

Question: How does wheel size affect the speed of carts moving down a ramp?

In the experiment, there are 5 carts that are all identical, except for the wheels. Each cart had a different size wheel with diameters as follows: 5 cm, 7 cm, 9 cm, 11 cm and 13 cm. The carts were placed one at a time on a ramp and released. The carts were released from the same starting point. The time for each cart to roll 2 meters down the ramp was recorded. There were 3 trials for each cart, and the same ramp was used for the entire experiment.

11. You are doing a presentation about The Golden Gate Bridge in your social studies class. Since you can't bring the bridge to class, you want to make a model of the bridge for your classmates. In a paragraph, describe the best model you could use. What type of model is this? What is one essential component to your model, so your classmates get an accurate depiction of the bridge?

12. Friction is known to:

    a. increase the amount of energy in a system.

    b. cause a loss of energy in a system through heat.

    c. do nothing to the energy in a system.

    d. None of the above. There is little known about friction.

Section 2.4

13. There are 3 graphs below. Identify each type of graph:

Ⓐ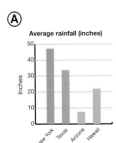

Ⓑ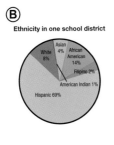

Ⓒ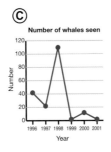

14. When graphing you should always:

   a. put the independent variable on the *x*-axis.

   b. put the dependent variable on the *x*-axis.

   c. put the independent variable on the *y*-axis.

   d. put the control variable on the *y*-axis.

15. Below are three data sets. What kind of graph would you use to plot each data set? Explain your answer.

   a. Student grades on a science test

Grade	Percent of students who earned this grade
A	25%
B	35%
C	35%
D	5%
F	0%

b. The favorite foods of students in a 6th grade class

Favorite food	Number of students who say that this food is their favorite
Pizza	10
Ice cream	3
Tacos	5
Chocolate	2
Spaghetti	3

c. The height of a plant each day

Day number	Height (cm)
1	3
2	3.2
3	4
4	4.5
5	6

Math and Writing Skills

Section 2.1

1. How many meters does each value represent?

   a. 1,000 millimeters

   b. 300 centimeters

   c. 2 kilometers

2. A book is on a shelf that is 2.5 meters high. How high is the book in centimeters?

3. How long is this wrench in centimeters?

4. You have a box that measures 5 cm × 5 cm × 3 cm. How many milliliters of water would fit in this box?

5. Which box would hold 100 milliliters of water?

    a. A box that measures 2 cm × 2 cm × 2 cm

    b. A box that measures 4 cm × 5 cm × 5 cm

    c. A box that measures 20 cm × 2 cm × 1 cm

6. Your mother gives you 1000 mL of your favorite soda and says "You are only allowed to drink half of a liter of that soda." How many milliliters are you allowed to drink? How much soda will be left over after you drink half a liter?

Section 2.2

7. A grocery store wants to sell 100 pounds of bananas. What is the mass of these bananas in kilograms?

8. Calculate how many seconds are in 2 hours and 5 minutes.

9. What is the typical body temperature of the human body in Fahrenheit? Now, convert this to Celsius and report typical human body temperature in Celsius.

Section 2.3

10. Here are some examples of systems: the Earth and moon system, the digestive system in your body, and a fish in an aquarium. Choose one of these systems and write a paragraph about it that answers these questions:
    What are the different parts of the system?
    Why is it a system?
    What variables affect the function of the system?

Section 2.4

11. Make 3 graphs of the data that were reported in Concept question #15. Make one graph for each data set, and be sure it has all of the proper components.

12. Below is a bar graph for climate data in Los Angeles over one year. Answer the following questions about the graph.

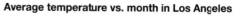
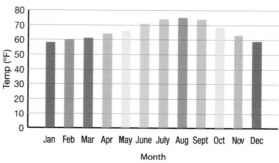

    a. When was the highest average temperature?

    b. When was the lowest average temperature?

    c. What does the graph show about the trends in temperature in Los Angeles over one year?

    d. What do you predict the average temperature will be in May of the following year?

Chapter Project—Conduct an Experiment

Design and conduct your own scientific experiment. What do you want to find out? The experiment can take up to one week to perform, or can take only a couple of hours to perform. Here is what you need to keep in mind:

- Ask a question about which you are curious.
- Your hypothesis must be testable.
- You need an independent and a dependent variable.
- Are all other variables controlled?
- How are you going to collect data, make measurements, and record results?

Be sure to check with your teacher about your question and your hypothesis before continuing with your experiment.

Chapter 3
Introducing Earth

Earth is an enormous system. Studying such a large system can be difficult. Through observations, scientists have come up with techniques to make the study of Earth easier. A couple of techniques that you will learn about in this chapter are relative dating and tree-ring dating. Scientists also use maps to study Earth. Look at a map of your town. What conclusions can you draw about Earth's surface and geology from that map?

Key Questions

1. *How is the Grand Canyon like a history book?*

2. *How old is Earth?*

3. *What is a topographic map?*

3.1 Observing Earth

You have learned about systems and how they are used in experiments. In this book you will learn about Earth, a huge system! Earth science is a large field of science that includes **geology**, the study of rocks and rock formations (Figure 3.1). This section is about geology and the scientific methods used to study it.

The beginnings of geology

Shark's teeth In 1666, Nicolas Steno, a Danish anatomist, studied a shark's head and noticed that the shark's teeth resembled mysterious stones called "tonguestones" that were found inside of local rocks. At that time, people believed that tonguestones had either fallen from the moon, or that they grew inside the rocks. Steno theorized that tonguestones looked like shark's teeth because they actually *were* shark's teeth that had been buried and became fossils!

How did teeth get inside a rock? Steno realized that when an animal dies it is eventually covered by layers of soil. The animal's soft parts decay quickly, but bones and teeth do not. Over a long period of time, the soil around the dead animal becomes rock with the bones and teeth inside.

Figure 3.1: *Examples of rock formations*

Relative dating

What is relative dating? Steno's thoughts and observations helped him develop ideas about how rocks and fossils form. His ideas are used today in the study of geology as a technique called relative dating. **Relative dating** is a method of putting events in the order in which they happened.

Relative dating is used by geologists as they study rock formations, and also by scientists called *paleontologists* who study and identify fossils. A **fossil** is a part of a dead animal or plant that has been preserved for a long time.

How is relative dating used? Relative dating can be used to determine the general age of a rock, rock formation, or fossil. Relative dating does not try to determine the exact age of an object, but instead uses clues to figure out the order of events over time. A simple example of relative dating is presented in Figure 3.2. Which event occurred first?

The present explains the past Like Steno, Scottish geologist James Hutton (1726–1797) was an important figure in the development of modern geology. Hutton believed that if you understand processes that are happening now, you can use that knowledge to explain what happened a long time ago. The short form of his idea is: *The present explains the past.*

For example, think of the last time it rained really hard. What happened to the ground? You might have seen small rivers of water washing away soil. When the rain stopped, there may have been grooves left behind by the rivers of rain. The way water affects the land is seen every time it rains. We can use the observations that we make in the present to figure out how the Grand Canyon was formed in the past! The Grand Canyon was formed by the Colorado River (see next page).

VOCABULARY

relative dating - a method of putting events in the order in which they happened.

fossil - a part of a dead animal or plant that has been preserved for a long time.

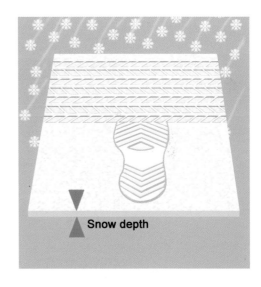

Snow depth

Figure 3.2: *This graphic illustrates three events: a footstep, a tire track, and snowfall. Which event happened first? Sequencing these events in the correct order is a form of relative dating.*

Steno's ideas

Steno's ideas for relative dating include superposition, original horizontality, and lateral continuity. These ideas help identify the clues you need to put events in the order in which they happened.

What is superposition? *Superposition* means that the bottom layer of a rock formation is older than the layer on top, because the bottom layer formed first. A stack of old newspapers illustrates superposition (Figure 3.3).

Original horizontality Sediment particles fall to the bottom of a body of water, such as a riverbed, in response to gravity. The result is horizontal layers of sediment. Over time, these layers can become layers of rock. Sometimes rock layers are found in a vertical position. Steno realized that movements of the Earth could slowly move horizontal rock layers into a vertical position. This theory is called *original horizontality*.

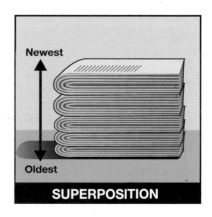

Figure 3.3: *A stack of old newspapers illustrates superposition. The oldest newspaper is usually on the bottom of the stack.*

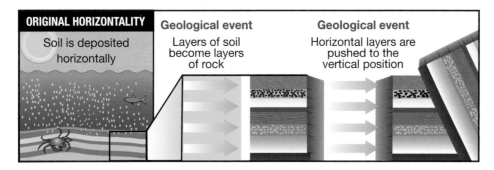

Lateral continuity *Lateral continuity* is the idea that when layers of sediment are formed, they extend in all directions horizontally. Subsequently, a separation may be caused by erosion or an earthquake. The Colorado River created the gap that is now the Grand Canyon. If you were to compare rock layers in the Grand Canyon, you would find that the layers on one side of the canyon match up with the layers on the other side (Figure 3.4).

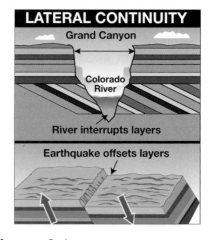

Figure 3.4: *Layers of rock are continuous unless a river interrupts the layers or an earthquake moves them.*

More relative dating

Cross-cutting relationships

The theory of *cross-cutting relationships* states that a vein of rock that cuts across a rock's layers is younger than the layers. Figure 3.5 shows a rock formation with three layers and a cross-cutting vein. The rock layers formed first. The vein formed when melted rock oozed into a crack in the original rock, cutting across the layers. Then the melted rock solidified. The bottom layer is the oldest part of the rock formation and the vein is the youngest. The middle and top layers formed after the bottom layer but before the vein.

Inclusions

Sometimes rock pieces called *inclusions* are found inside another rock. During the formation of a rock with inclusions, sediments or melted rock surrounded the inclusion and then solidified. Therefore, the inclusions are older than the surrounding rock (Figure 3.5). A rock with inclusions is like a chocolate chip cookie. The chocolate chips (inclusions) are made first. Then they are added to the batter (melted rock or sediment) before being baked (hardened) into a cookie (rock).

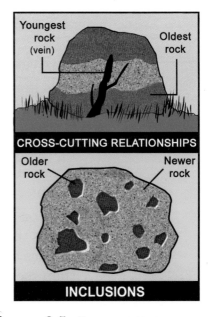

Figure 3.5: *Cross-cutting relationships and inclusions.*

Faunal succession

Faunal succession means that fossils can be used to identify the relative age of the layers of a rock formation (Figure 3.6). For example, dinosaur fossils are found in rock that is about 65 to 200 million years old because these animals lived that long ago. The fossils of modern human beings (*Homo sapiens*) are found in rock that is about 40,000 years old, but not in rock that is 65 to 251 million years old. And dinosaur fossils are not found in rock that is 40,000 years old. This means that human beings did not live at the same time as the dinosaurs. How might you learn which plants and animals *did* live at the same time as the dinosaurs?

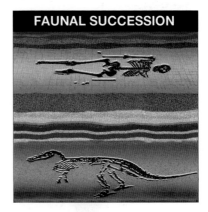

Figure 3.6: *Faunal succession.*

3.1 Section Review

1. Who is Nicolas Steno? What ideas did he come up with that have contributed to modern geology?

2. How are a vein of rock and an inclusion similar? How are they different? Describe a vein and an inclusion in your answer.

3. What idea is represented in the figure at the right? Which organism is oldest? Which is youngest? How can you tell?

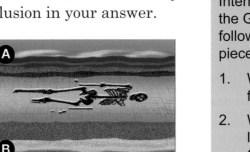

4. True or False: Superposition states that rock layers near the surface of Earth are younger than rock layers further from the surface. Explain your reasoning.

5. How is the Grand Canyon like a history book?

6. Study the following picture. Which is the oldest layer of rock? Which layer is the youngest?

3.2 Geologic Time

When we talk about Earth's history, we use the term "geologic." The geologic time scale is a model of Earth's history. In this model, time is divided into eras and periods. Figure 3.7 includes pictures of organisms and events that characterize the periods. How old do you think Earth is? In this section you will learn about Earth's age and how it was determined.

The geologic time scale

Precambrian era The Precambrian era lasted from 4,570 to 542 million years ago (mya). During this earliest time, layers of rock formed the Grand Canyon and only single-celled organisms lived on Earth.

Paleozoic era The Paleozoic era lasted from 542 to 251 mya. During the Cambrian period many new, complex life forms developed, but glaciers covered the Earth in the Ordovician period, causing many of these new organisms to become extinct. Fish, reptiles, and amphibians developed during the rest of the Paleozoic era.

Mesozoic era The Mesozoic era lasted from 251 to 65 mya. At the beginning of this era, Earth's continents were connected in one "supercontinent" called *Pangaea*. During the Triassic period, pieces of Pangaea moved apart. The Jurassic period was marked by the dinosaurs and the appearance of the first birds. During the Cretaceous period, the Rocky Mountains in the western part of the United States formed. Flowering plants also evolved during the Cretaceous period.

Cenozoic era The Cenozoic era began 65 mya and is still going on. A giant meteor hit Earth at the beginning of the Tertiary period. Scientists believe this event may have ended the existence of the dinosaurs. Modern humans appeared 40,000 years ago during the Quanternary period.

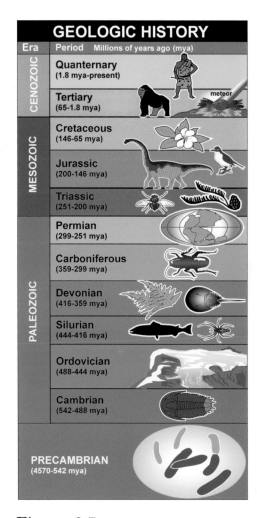

Figure 3.7: *Earth's geologic history.*

The age of Earth

An early calculation William Thomson Kelvin (1824–1907), was a physicist who did important work in the study of temperature. In 1862, Kelvin calculated Earth's age to be between 10 million and 100 million years. His calculations were based on his belief that Earth was once a "red-hot globe" and his prediction of how long it took for the Earth to cool enough to sustain life as we know it.

Radioactive decay Lord Kelvin's calculations were proven incorrect in the early 1900s, when the concept of radioactive decay was discovered. **Radioactive decay** refers to how unstable atoms lose energy and matter over time. As a result of radioactive decay, an element turns into another element over a period of time. An **element** is a substance composed of only one kind of atom. For example, uranium is a radioactive element that decays in several steps, eventually becoming lead, a stable, nonradioactive element.

The half-life of uranium Scientists know that it takes 4.5 billion years for one half of the uranium atoms in a specimen to turn into lead. We say that 4.5 billion years is the *half-life* for the radioactive decay of uranium (Figure 3.8).When scientists study rocks that contain uranium, they can determine a rock's age by the ratio of uranium to lead atoms found in the sample. Understanding radioactive decay has allowed scientists to accurately determine the age of rocks and fossils found on Earth.

Earth is around 4.6 billion years old The oldest rocks found on Earth so far are around 4 billion years old. Scientists can't determine Earth's exact age by dating Earth's rocks because the oldest rocks have been destroyed. But scientists have found moon rocks and meteorites that are around 4.6 billion years old, and since it is believed Earth was formed at the same time as the rest of the solar system, that would make Earth around 4.6 billion years old as well.

radioactive decay - refers to how unstable atoms lose energy and matter over time.

element - a substance composed of only one kind of atom.

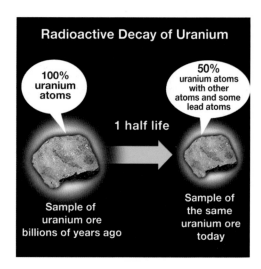

Figure 3.8: *The radioactive decay of uranium to lead. Radioactive decay is measured in half-lives. After one half-life, 50% of the atoms have decayed.*

Learning from trees

One tree ring equals one year

Have you ever looked at a tree stump or a log of wood? You may have noticed that the wood forms circular layers. These layers are called *tree rings*. For pine trees, one tree ring includes two bands—one light and one dark. A tree grows one tree ring for every year that it is alive (Figure 3.9).

Very old trees

The oldest tree that we know about, a bristlecone pine called "Methuselah," is 4,765 years old. It is located in the White Mountains of California. A bristlecone pine is pictured in Figure 3.10. Redwood trees, the world's tallest trees at about 300 feet tall, are found in California and can live to be 2,000 years old. This means that there are some trees that have been living on Earth for longer than any human being or animal!

Trees are like history books. Each tree ring is a record of what the environment was like that year. For example, even though no one living today was around in the 1800s, we can guess what the environment might have been like back then by studying a 200-year-old tree.

Tree-ring dating

Andrew Douglass (1867–1962) was an astronomer who discovered the significance of tree rings. In the early 1900s, Douglass hypothesized that trees might record what Earth's climate was like in the past. He began to test his hypothesis by recording the tree rings of pines and Douglas firs and eventually sequoia trees. By 1911, he had proven that trees within a similar area had matching tree ring patterns. Wide tree rings indicated a very wet year and narrow rings indicated a dry year. Douglass named this new field of science *dendrochronology* (tree-ring dating). Douglass founded the Tree-Ring Research Laboratory at the University of Arizona in 1937.

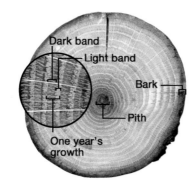

Figure 3.9: *A cross-section of a tree shows tree rings. Each ring is composed of two bands—a dark and a light band. One tree ring equals one year's growth.*

Photo: David A. Abel

Figure 3.10: *A bristlecone pine.*

3.2 Section Review

1. How old is Earth? What methods have scientists used to determine this?

2. Which answer is correct? During the Precambrian era:

   a. Human beings lived and thrived.

   b. Dinosaurs became extinct.

   c. Only single-celled organisms lived.

   d. Flowering plants evolved.

3. List two events of the Mesozoic era.

4. How much uranium is left if a solid piece goes through:

   a. one half-life?

   b. two half-lives?

5. If a tree has 25 rings, how old is it?

6. Figure 3.11 shows cross-sections from two trees that grew in different environments.

   a. The trees were the same age when they were cut. How old are these trees?

   b. Write a description that explains the wet and dry conditions for each tree during each year of its lifetime.

7. Research bristlecone pines. What kind of environment do they live in? Where do you find bristlecone pines? Are they all over the world or just in certain locations?

Earth has been in existence for 4.6 billion years. Many changes have occurred in its geology, climate, and in the organisms that have lived here during this time.

Since there have been so many changes, scientists have divided the 4.6 billion years of Earth's existence into 4 eras. Each era is different in length. Construct a timeline of Earth's history including all 4 eras. Your timeline must be drawn to scale, accurately representing the amount of time for each era. Use Figure 3.7 to help you make your timeline.

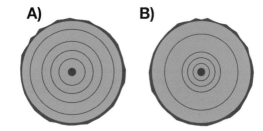

Figure 3.11: *Cross-sections of two trees.*

3.3 Mapping Earth

A **map** is a representational drawing of a location. You may be familiar with road maps or state maps. On a local weather report, you might see a map of the United States. There are also world maps. In this section, you will learn about two kinds of maps that represent the surface of the Earth: topographic and bathymetric maps.

Elevation and depth

Mapping concepts Before learning about topographic and bathymetric maps, we need to review a few concepts that are used to make these maps. These concepts are elevation, depth, and scale of maps.

Elevation **Elevation** means the height of an object measured from a reference level. Usually the reference level that is used on maps is called sea level. **Sea level** is an average level of the ocean (Figure 3.12).

Depth The depth of rivers, lakes, and oceans is important information for certain maps. The depth of these features is compared to sea level.

Scale of maps The *scale* of a map helps you relate the small distances on the map to the larger real-life distances. There are three kinds of map scales. A *fractional scale* shows the ratio of the map distance to the real-life distance as a fraction. The scale 1/100,000 means that 1 unit on the map is equal to 100,000 units in real life. A *verbal scale* expresses the relationship in words, "1 centimeter is equal to 1 kilometer." A bar scale is simply a bar drawn on the map with the size of the bar equal to a distance in real life.

Types of map scales		
Fractional 1/1,000,000	**Verbal** 1 cm = 1 km	**Bar** 1 2 3 4 5 kilometers

map - a representational drawing of a location.

elevation - the height of an object measured from a reference level.

sea level - the average level of the ocean; the halfway point between high tide and low tide.

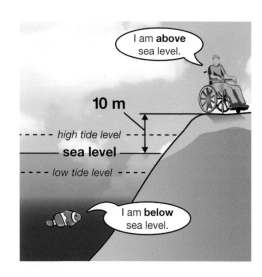

Figure 3.12: *Elevation and sea level. You may know that oceans experience tides—sea level is the halfway point between high tide and low tide.*

Topographic maps

What is a topographic map?

A topographic map is a map that shows elevation. Since a map is often a flat piece of paper, you may wonder how you can show a mountain on a map. **Topographic maps** use special lines called contour lines to show mountains and other land features.

Contour lines

Contour lines indicate all points where the elevation is the same. The zero contour line on a topographic map indicates sea level (Figure 3.13). A 100-meter contour line indicates points that are 100 meters above sea level.

Direction and map symbols

Maps show direction—north, south, east, and west. An example of the direction symbol you might see on a map is shown at the left. A **legend** is a special area on the map that lists the symbols that are used. Topographic maps (and bathymetric maps) use a range of symbols to show contour lines, rivers and lakes, roads and train tracks, airports, types of plants, buildings, and many other things.

North

West ⊕ East

South

Topographic contour	── 6000 ──	**River**	
Bathymetric contour		**Lake**	⬭
Campground	△	**Highway**	═══════
Railroad track	──┼──┼──┼──	**Woodland**	▬

National Map Accuracy Standards

The United States Geological Survey (USGS) publishes about 57,000 topographic maps of the United States. These maps are drawn according to the National Map Accuracy Standards. The standards define accurate measurements for map making so that any map you read can be compared to another map. The scales of most USGS topographic maps are 1:24,000, 1:100,000, 1:250,000, or 1:500,000.

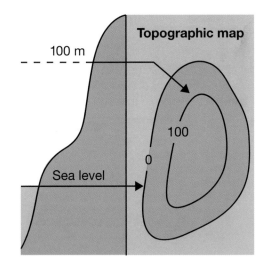

Figure 3.13: *The 0 contour line is always at sea level.*

VOCABULARY

topographic map - maps that use contour lines to show elevation.

contour lines - curved lines on a topographic (or bathymetric) map that indicate all the points where the elevation is the same.

legend - a special area on a map that lists the symbols that are used.

Making a topographic map

Drawing contour lines

To understand how to add contour lines to a topographic map, imagine you have a shape in a box that you will fill with water. The shape will represent an island. The starting level of water in the box equals zero or sea level. You will add water to the box four times. Each time will represent a water level increase of 10 meters.

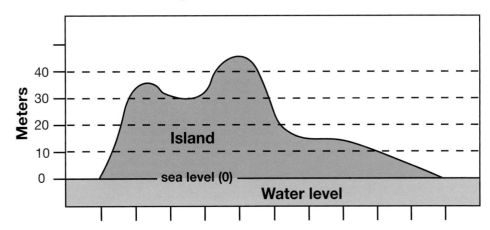

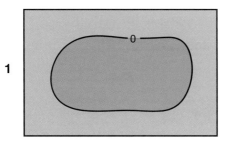

1

0 contour line

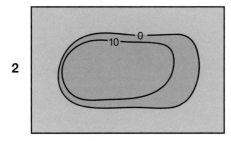

2

0 and 10 contour lines

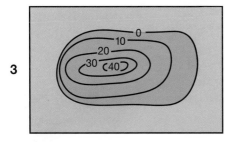

3

Topographic map of the island

What does the map look like?

Figure 3.14 illustrates how contour lines are used to make a topographic map. The first line—the 0 contour line—shows the outline of the island when the water is at sea level. At the 10-meter mark, the outline of the island is smaller and lies inside the 0-meter contour. On the right side of the map, the space between the 10- and 20-meter contour is wider than on the left. This shows that the right side of the island is not as steep as the left side. When contour lines are close together, you know that the land is steep. When contour lines are farther apart, the land is not as steep—it slopes gradually. Only the highest of the two peaks is shown on this topographic map. The second peak is less than 40 meters high but taller than 30 meters. We would need a contour line at 35 meters to see this peak.

Figure 3.14: *Drawing contour lines to make a topographic map. Note that the space between the 10- and 20-meter contour is narrower on the left than the right. This shows that the left side of the island is steeper.*

Bathymetric maps

What is a bathymetric map?

A **bathymetric map** shows the depths of a body of water such as a lake or an ocean. Bathymetric maps use contour lines to show depth (Figure 3.15). However, depth can also be shown using color. The map below shows land elevation and ocean depth using color.

Longitude and latitude

The bathymetric map below has numbers on the top, sides, and bottom. These numbers are part of a grid system that helps describe locations on Earth. There are two starting places for this grid. The **equator** is an imaginary line around Earth's middle and between the north and south poles. The **prime meridian** is an imaginary line that goes through Greenwich, England, and is perpendicular to the equator.

Latitude lines are north or south of the equator (the zero line) and run east-west (left to right on the map below). **Longitude** lines (or meridians) are east or west of the Prime meridian (the zero meridian) and run north-south (top to bottom on the map below). Both latitude and longitude lines are measured in degrees. The star on the map indicates the location of the Hawaiian volcano, Mauna Loa: Latitude 19.5° north, Longitude 155.5° west.

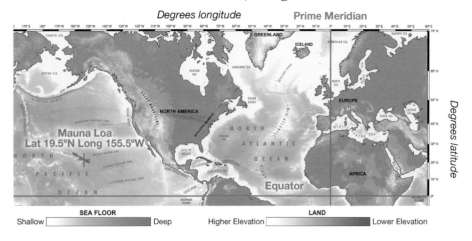

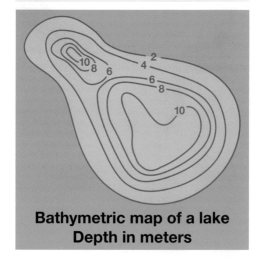

Bathymetric map of a lake
Depth in meters

Figure 3.15: *A bathymetric map of a lake. Where is the lake the deepest? Where is the lake the shallowest?*

3.3 Section Review

1. Answer the following questions using the map below.

   a. Using the two-lane road, how many kilometers is it from point A to point B?

   b. Which point is the furthest east on the map?

   c. Which map location would have no cars?

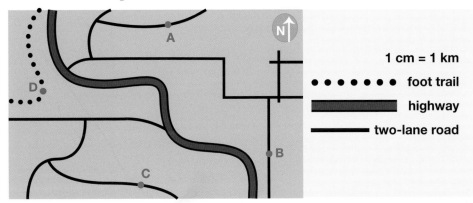

2. On what kind of maps are contour lines found? What are contour lines?

3. What information does a map legend give you?

4. Match these islands (A, B, and C) with their topographic map.

5. Compare and contrast bathymetric and topographic maps.

6. The scale of a topographic map is 1:24,000 which means one centimeter on the map equals 24,000 centimeters on land. How many kilometers is 24,000 centimeters?

7. What is the difference between latitude and longitude lines?

Study your town's location on several maps. Use a world map, a country map, a state map, and a topographic map.

- In what hemisphere is your town?
- What is the latitude and longitude of the town in which you live?
- In what area of the state is your town located? (north, south, east, west, etc.)
- How far is your town from the nearest state border? What direction is this border from your town?
- What other towns are directly surrounding your town? What direction are each of these towns from your town?
- What is the elevation of the town in which you live?

BIOLOGY CONNECTION — It's All in the Rings

How old are you? Can you think of how you changed between your last two birthdays (other than to add a candle to your cake, that is)? As children grow, they get taller, or more muscular, or acquire other characteristics that indicate they are getting older. Trees get older and taller each year, too, and their years are marked by growth rings. *Dendrochronologists* are scientists who study tree rings to date past events. By studying the rings, they can tell how old the wood is to the exact year. Imagine finding trees that are 500, 1,000, or even more than 4,000 years old!

Tree rings

Generally, trees growing in mild climates produce one growth ring per year. Tree-ring growth is affected by rainfall, temperature, and nutrients in the soil. Trees that grow under good conditions have wide ring growth. Those growing under poor conditions produce narrow rings. Each tree ring typically represents an annual growth cycle.

One growth ring

However, counting tree rings to determine a tree's age is not enough. Occasionally, a tree may grow more than one ring or none at all over a year. Dendrochronologists use cross-dating (matching patterns among tree samples) to make sure dates are accurate. This means studying 20 or more trees of the same species growing under similar conditions.

Bristlecone pines—the oldest living trees

Conifers are cone-bearing, needle trees that are often chosen for research. Fir and pine trees are easy to work with because they have clear rings and they grow quite old. Some trees, such as maples and oaks, may live 250 years. But conifers may live thousands of years.

Bristlecone Pine

Bristlecone pines are the oldest living trees on Earth. People often think that big trees with big, wide trunks are old. But big does not necessarily mean old. Bristlecone pines grow slowly and are not that large. They are able to ward off insects and disease and that allows them to live a long, long time. A bristlecone pine named Methuselah is growing in the White Mountains of California and is the oldest living tree in the world. Discovered in 1953 by Edmund Schulman, this tree is more than 4,750 years old.

Clues from the past

We can learn a lot about the past from tree rings. Scientists use tree-ring data to understand past climates, glacier movements, fires, droughts, and insect outbreaks. This information can be used to solve problems in other areas of science such as ecology, climatology, geology, and anthropology. For ecologists studying living things and their environment, tree-ring analysis provides information about insect outbreaks and fires. Climatologists (who study climates) learn about droughts and cold spells. Geologists studying Earth's structure use the data to learn about volcanic eruptions and earthquakes. Anthropologists studying human societies learn how they lived in the past, using tree-ring data to understand historical buildings and ruins. Scientists have used tree rings to date ruins from Ancestral Puebloans in the Southwest United States.

Laboratory of Tree-Ring Research: touchdown!

Who would expect to find scientific research going on under a football stadium? The Laboratory of Tree-Ring Research (LTRR) at the University of Arizona in Tucson has been exactly there for years. In 1937, Andrew Ellicott Douglass founded the lab—the first of its kind in the country—and became the father of dendrochronology. Douglass, an astronomer, hoped tree rings would provide records about past sunspot cycles. He found a link among the Sun, climate, and tree-ring growth.

Douglass needed space for his tree-ring samples and a sports stadium seemed to be the answer. Today, the lab occupies two floors under the stadium, and contains over 600,000 tree-ring samples.

At LTRR, researchers, professors, and students are involved in many projects. Rex Adams, senior research specialist (seen in this photo), takes field trips across the western United States for climate, fire, and ecology studies.

Photo - courtesy of Melanie Lenart, Laboratory of Tree Ring Research, University of Arizona

He studies the tree-ring samples he brings back to unlock past events. For Adams, the best part of his job is working in the field collecting samples. He compares his work to doing a crossword puzzle or solving a mystery. And, yes, if Adams or others work on a Saturday afternoon in the fall, the lab does rock a bit during a football game. But how much sturdier many of those old tree samples must seem compared even with a concrete stadium.

Questions:

1. What do wide and narrow tree rings mean?
2. Count the tree rings in the cross-section on the previous page. How old was this tree when it was cut down?
3. Why are fir and pine trees commonly used for tree-ring analysis?
4. How is tree-ring data used?
5. Who was Andrew Ellicott Douglass?

CHAPTER ACTIVITY Trees and Maps

Activity 1—How tall is a tree?

You know that counting tree rings gives the age of a tree. Now, you will measure the height of a tree.

Materials

Thin cardboard; measuring tape; drinking straw; string; clay; tape; scissors, protractor, and T-square

What you will do

1. Use the T-square to mark out a right triangle on the cardboard. The triangle should have 2 equal sides that are each 20 cm long. Cut out the triangle.
2. Cut the straw to 10 cm long and tape it to the longest side of the triangle.
3. Tape a 30-cm piece of string to one of the 45 degree angles of the triangle. Fix a ball of clay to the other end of the string. The clay acts as a weight for the string.
4. Look through the straw to the top of the tree, and have someone check the position of the string.
5. Walk forward and backward until the string hangs in line with the side of the triangle and you can see the top of the tree through the straw.
6. When this happens, you can figure out the height of the tree. Take the distance you are away from the tree (in meters), and add it to the height of your eye from the ground (in meters). This gives you the height of the tree!

Activity 2—Making a land form

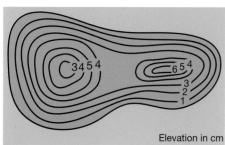

Elevation in cm

During this activity, you will create a land form that matches this topographic map.

Materials

The materials used for Investigation 3B; modeling clay and a rectangular piece of cardboard (with the same dimensions as the bottom of the GeoBox)

What you will do

1. Study the topographic map on this page. Each contour line represents an elevation of 1 centimeter.
2. Then, use the modeling clay to create a model land formation in the GeoBox that matches the topographic map.
3. To see if your land form matches the map, add water to the 0-cm mark on the GeoBox and trace the outline of your land formation on the lid. This is the 0-cm contour line and represents sea level.
4. Pour colored water into the tray until it reaches the 1-cm mark.
5. Now, trace the outline the water makes around the edges of the model land formation on the lid.
6. Repeat this procedure until you have poured 8 cm of water into the tray.
7. Finally, trace the outlines from the plastic sheet onto a piece of tracing paper.
8. Label the contour lines on your topographic map with the proper elevations.

Applying your knowledge

a. Activity 1: How high was the tree you measured?
b. Activity 2: Does your topographic map of your land formation match the topographic map on this page? Why or why not? If your map does not match the one on this page, make improvements to your model landform and try the activity again.

Chapter 3 Assessment

Vocabulary

Select the correct term to complete the sentences.

geology	relative dating	topographic map
legend	bathymetric map	radioactive decay
equator	contour line	elevation
latitude	map	sea level
longitude	prime meridian	element
fossil		

Section 3.1

1. Through their observations of rock formations, Nicholas Steno and James Hutton helped develop the field of _____.

2. _____ is a method that involves putting events in the order in which they happened.

3. An ancient shark tooth is an example of a(n) _____.

Section 3.2

4. Uranium is a(n) _____ that has a half-life of 4.5 billion years.

5. Uranium is an unstable element, which decays to a more stable element, lead. This process is an example of _____.

Section 3.3

6. A(n) _____ is a representational drawing of a location.

7. The average level of the ocean along a coastline is called _____.

8. On a mountain top, _____ is much higher than at sea level.

9. A(n) _____ is list of symbols used on a map.

10. A(n) _____ indicates the location on a map where elevation is the same.

11. A _____ is a map that shows the surface features of an area and shows elevation by using contour lines.

12. A _____ is a map that shows the depths of bodies of water.

13. _____ lines are imaginary lines on Earth's surface that run east-west and represent north and south locations.

14. _____ lines are imaginary lines on Earth's surface that run north-south and represent east and west locations.

15. The _____ is a line that falls between the north and south poles on Earth and that represents 0° latitude.

16. The _____ is a line that is perpendicular to the equator and that represents 0° longitude.

Concepts

Section 3.1

1. Use relative dating to identify the order in which each line was drawn. Which line was drawn first? Which line was drawn last?

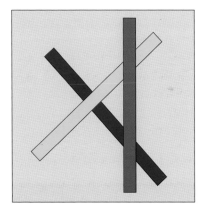

2. Define superposition and lateral continuity. Why are these ideas useful in interpreting how the Grand Canyon formed?

3. An inclusion is:

   a. younger than surrounding rock.

   b. the same age as surrounding rock.

   c. older than surrounding rock.

4. Put the rock bodies (A, B, C, and D) illustrated below in order from oldest (formed first) to youngest (formed last). Explain your reasoning.

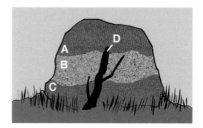

5. How do scientists use the ideas of faunal succession to identify how long ago different animals lived?

Section 3.2

6. How old is Earth? How old is the solar system and the moon?

7. Uranium decays into a more stable element called:

    a. lead   c. carbon

    b. nitrogen   d. phosphorous

8. What range of time is known as the Precambrian Era? What kinds of organisms lived during this era?

9. During what era did humans first appear?

10. How might a tree fossil help a scientist understand the climate of certain places millions of years ago?

11. You notice that a tree cross section has very wide tree ring that occurred in 1985 and a very narrow tree ring that occurred in 1992.
    a. From this information, what can you infer about the tree's environment in 1985?
    b. What can you infer about the tree's environment in 1992?

Section 3.3

12. Why is a legend an important part of a map? What would happen if a map did not include a legend?

13. Look at the topographic map below.

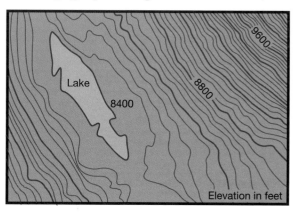

    a. Where are the steepest slopes on the map?
    b. Where is the lowest elevation shown on this map?
    c. What is the lowest elevation?
    d. Where are the gentlest slopes?

14. What do latitude and longitude lines represent?

Math and Writing Skills

Section 3.1

1. Both Nicolas Steno and James Hutton contributed to the development of modern geology. What important things did each scientist do? Through research, find a fact about each of these scientists that was not mentioned in the chapter.

2. Imagine you have to explain superposition to a group of second graders. Think of a creative model you could use that would help them understand this concept. Describe your model and how you would teach superposition in a paragraph.

3. How do scientists know which plants and animals lived at the same time as the dinosaurs?

Section 3.2

4. A scientist discovers that a certain rock is 25% uranium and 75% lead and other elements. If the rock started out as being 100% uranium, How many half-lives has the rock gone through?

5. A rock that is 100% uranium goes through three half-lives.

   a. How many years is three uranium half-lives?

   b. How much uranium is left after three half-lives: 2%, 10%, or 12.5%?

6. Which era took up the most time during geologic history?

7. Imagine you could go back in time and visit any period of Earth's geologic history. Which period would you want to visit? Why would you want to visit this time in geologic history?

Section 3.3

8. A map is drawn with 1 centimeter equal to 2 miles.

   a. How many centimeters equal 10 miles?

   b. How many miles does 4 centimeters represent?

9. The scale of a topographic map is 1:250,000 which means one centimeter on the map equals 250,000 centimeters on land. How many kilometers is 250,000 centimeters?

10. Choose an object in your classroom.

    a. Measure the dimensions of this object. Sketch the object and write its dimensions.

    b. Imagine that the dimensions of the object were half of what they are now. What would the dimensions be?

    c. Now, imagine that the dimensions of the object were twice as big. What would the dimensions be?

11. Look at the topographic map from Concepts question 13. How many feet does each contour line represent? (Hint: Subtract 8400 from 8800 and divide the answer by the number of lines between these two elevations.)

12. Below is a diagram of a tree core. Use this diagram to answer the following questions. Do not count the bark or the pith when figuring out how old the tree is. One tree ring equals a white area and one dark line.

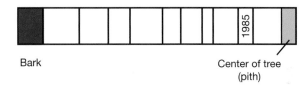

Bark   Center of tree (pith)

   a. How old is this tree?

   b. What year was this tree cut down?

   c. Give an example of a year that was probably warm with a lot of rainfall.

   d. Name a year that was probably cool and dry.

Chapter Project—Making Maps

Now it's your turn to make maps.

   a. You want your friends to come to a party at your house after school. They have never been to your house before, so you have decided that the best way to give them directions is to create a map from school to your house. Include all important features along the route. Be sure your map is to scale, has a legend, symbols and other important map features. Remember, it must be accurate and easy to read!

   b. You decide that you want your party to have a pirate theme. You hide a treasure and draw a map for your friends to use to find it. Make your treasure map easy to follow.

UNIT 2

Energy in Earth's Systems

WHY DOES THIS HOT-AIR BALLOON RISE?

WHAT HAPPENS TO INCOMING SOLAR RADIATION?

WHAT IS A GYRE?

TRY THIS AT HOME

The next time you have spaghetti for dinner, observe the process for boiling the noodles. Make sure you have an adult nearby the whole time! Record your observations including how the stove, pot, water, and heat are used to cook the noodles. Try to come up with at least ten observations.

After you have enjoyed your spaghetti dinner write down what you learned about how heat gets from the the stove to the noodles.
How is the water in the pot heated?
How are the noodles cooked?

Chapter 4

Heat

Have you ever seen a hot air balloon float high above Earth's surface? What about a hang glider or a soaring bird of prey like a hawk? Each of these objects—a hot air balloon, a hang glider, and a hawk—take advantage of heat to "fly." In this chapter, you will learn about heat and temperature and how they affect natural events and human activities.

Key Questions

1. *What is the difference between heat and temperature?*

2. *Why does an ice cube melt in your hand?*

3. *Does the Sun help a hawk to fly?*

4.1 What Is Heat?

What happens to an ice cube when you hold it in your hand? The ice melts because heat flows from your hand to the ice cube. We've all experienced the effects of heat, but what exactly *is* heat?

Atoms and molecules

Particles of matter move constantly
Matter is made of tiny particles called *atoms* that are too small to see with your eyes or even with a magnifying glass (Figure 4.1). In most matter, atoms occur in a group called a **molecule**. Atoms and molecules move constantly. The molecules of the water you drink and the air you breathe are moving. Molecules in an ice cube are moving. All of the atoms of your body are moving constantly, too—even when you are asleep!

Kinetic energy
Imagine what it would be like to live in an atom-sized world. If you were suddenly shrunk to the size of an atom, you would be pushed and shoved by all the atoms and molecules around you. Watch out! Atoms and molecules whiz by at amazingly fast speeds! The constant motion of atoms is a form of energy. The energy of motion is called **kinetic energy**. Faster atoms have more kinetic energy than slower atoms.

molecule - a group of atoms.
kinetic energy - energy of motion.

Atoms are so small that 200,000 could fit across the thickness of a piece of aluminum foil.

ALUMINUM FOIL

Figure 4.1: *The thickness of a sheet of aluminum foil is about 200,000 atoms across. Important note: Atoms are too small to see with your eyes or a magnifying glass!*

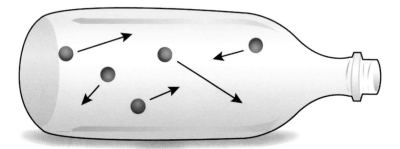

Imagine atoms were big enough to see. In this diagram, arrow length shows atom speeds. Which atoms have the most kinetic energy?

Heat and temperature

What is heat? **Heat** is a form of energy caused by the motion of atoms and molecules.* Heat is the sum of the kinetic energy of each atom in a sample. This means that a bucket of hot water has more heat energy than a cup of hot water. The bucket contains more hot water molecules than the cup. More molecules means more motion and more heat energy.

What is temperature? Temperature is related to heat, but it isn't the same thing. **Temperature** is a measure of the *average* speed of atoms in a sample. The average speed of the atoms in a hot object is fast. The average speed in a cold object is slow (Figure 4.2).

What is your temperature? Sometimes when you are sick, your forehead feels very warm and a thermometer might show a temperature of 100°F or more. The normal temperature for the human body is 98.6°F. A thermometer measures the average kinetic energy of the atoms in your body.

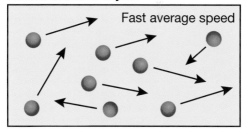

heat - a form of energy caused by the motion of atoms and molecules.

temperature - a measure of the average speed of a sample containing lots of atoms.

Atoms in a hot object

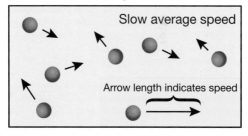

Atoms in a cold object

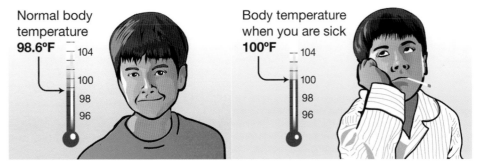

Normal body temperature **98.6°F**

Body temperature when you are sick **100°F**

The average speed of atoms in your body is higher when you are sick.

Figure 4.2: *The average speed of atoms in a hot object is fast. The average speed of atoms in a cold object is slow.*

* Footnote: This definition of heat was adapted to be appropriate for the level and content of this text.

Summary of heat and temperature

An example If you wanted to warm up a swimming pool of water you need heat energy. Here are two methods for warming the water. Which method is the best?

- Warm the water with a teacup of water at 100°C, or
- Warm the water with a bucket of water at 50°C

The water in the teacup has a higher temperature, but there are fewer molecules than in the bucket of water. This means that the teacup water has less heat energy than the water in the bucket.

Even though the teacup has a higher temperature, the bucket is a better choice for warming the pool water because it contains more total heat energy!

The best method for warming the water in the pool is to add the bucket of water at 50°C.

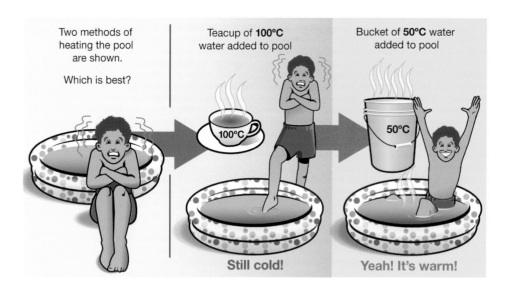

Two methods of heating the pool are shown.

Which is best?

Teacup of **100°C** water added to pool

100°C

Still cold!

Bucket of **50°C** water added to pool

50°C

Yeah! It's warm!

 SOLVE IT!

When two equal volumes of water are mixed, the final temperature of the mixture is halfway between the two original temperatures.

This is because molecules collide and exchange energy. Fast molecules slow down while the slow ones speed up. Eventually, all the molecules are going at about the same speed.

Use this information to solve this problem:

A cup of water at 20°C is mixed with a second cup of 80°C water. Both cups have the same amount of water. What will the temperature of the final mixture be?

What is the final temperature?

Heat is a form of energy

From warmer to cooler objects

Heat, as a form of energy, can be transferred from one object to another. Heat moves from warmer to cooler objects. For example, if Michelle accidentally touches a hot dinner plate, heat from the plate moves to her cooler finger. Fast-moving atoms of the plate push against the slower atoms of her finger. As a result, the nerves in her finger send a warning message to her brain. Her brain sends a message to the hand to pull away from the plate as quickly as possible. If Michelle didn't remove her finger from the plate, she might get burned!

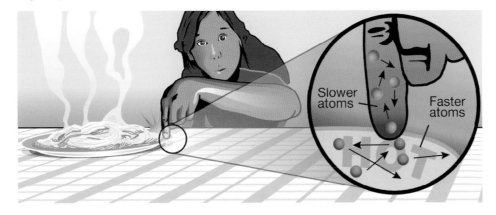

Slower atoms

Faster atoms

Fortunately, the hot dinner plate will not stay too hot forever. Eventually, as heat from the plate transfers to the cooler air around it, the plate cools down to the temperature of the room.

Usable energy and heat

Michelle will eat the spaghetti on her plate to get energy to do her homework. Some of that energy will be used by Michelle to do her homework. Some of that energy will become heat and Michelle cannot get back the lost heat. To get more energy, she needs to eat more food!

MY JOURNAL

1. Place an ice cube in a plastic sandwich bag and seal the bag tightly. What happens to the ice cube when you let it sit on the table (in the bag)?

2. Sketch a "before" and "after" picture in your journal. Record the time it took for the ice cube to melt.

3. What could you have done to shorten the melting time? List all possibilities.

Energy flow and heat loss

Heat and light bulbs
The source of energy for a light bulb is electricity. A light bulb produces energy in the form of light. The light bulb might feel hot to the touch after it has been lit for awhile. This is because only 2% of the energy produced by a regular (or incandescent) light bulb is light energy and 98% of the energy produced is heat energy. Only a small amount of the energy produced by the bulb is useful for brightening a room (Figure 4.3).

Heat and cars
The source of energy for a car is gasoline. For most cars, about 20% of the gasoline burned by the engine is used to move the car. Eighty percent of the energy from the gasoline is given off as heat energy (Figure 4.4).

Heat and fuels
Like a light bulb or a car, a power plant loses some of the energy it produces as heat. A **power plant** is a place where electricity is generated. Fossil fuels like coal, oil, and natural gas are common sources of energy for power plants. The first step of producing electricity involves burning the fossil fuels to boil water. The resulting steam turns a turbine. The *turbine* converts the energy from the steam into energy that turns a generator. The generator then converts this kinetic energy into electricity. The electricity is carried to your house by wires. Some heat is lost at each step in the process of converting fuel energy into useful electricity.

VOCABULARY

power plant - a place where electricity is generated.

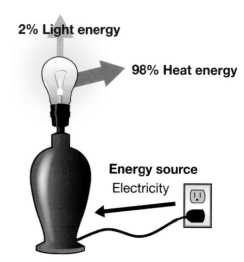

Figure 4.3: *Most of the energy used by a light bulb becomes heat energy.*

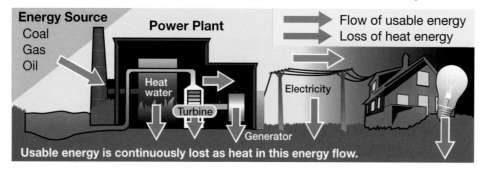

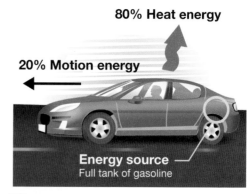

Figure 4.4: *Most of the energy from gasoline becomes heat energy.*

4.1 Section Review

1. What are atoms and molecules?

2. Relate the amount of kinetic energy to the speed of atoms.

3. Fill in the blank. Faster atoms have _____ (more/less) kinetic energy than slower atoms.

4. Figure 4.5 lists the speeds of students running in a gymnasium. Find the average speed of the students by adding the speeds and dividing by five. If the group of students represents a group of atoms, what does their average speed represent?

5. What is the difference between heat and temperature?

6. Will 1 liter of hot water have more or less heat energy than 2 liters of hot water? Explain your answer.

7. In which direction is heat transferred—from warm to cool or from cool to warm?

8. You mix 100 milliliters of 10°C water and 100 milliliters of 90°C water. What is the final temperature of the mixture?

9. What kind of energy is used to keep a light bulb lit?

10. Name three fossil fuels that are used as the source of energy at many power plants.

11. Describe the process by which electricity is made at a power plant that uses fossil fuels.

12. In a light bulb, car, and power plant, what type of energy is lost?

13. Research the answers to the following questions using your school library or the Internet. In terms of energy produced:

    a. What is the main difference between an incandescent light bulb and a compact fluorescent light bulb?

    b. What is the main difference between gasoline-powered and electric hybrid cars?

Student	Speed (cm/s)
Alice	100 cm/s
Bernard	150 cm/s
Chloe	50 cm/s
Dev	75 cm/s
Eduardo	125 cm/s
AVERAGE (sum of five speeds ÷ 5)	

Figure 4.5: *The speeds of five students running in a gymnasium.*

Compare and contrast this hydroelectric power plant with a fossil fuel burning power plant.

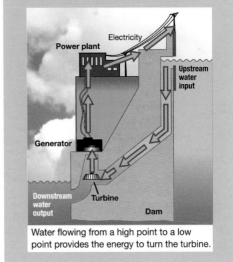

Water flowing from a high point to a low point provides the energy to turn the turbine.

4.2 How Does Heat Move?

Ice cream will melt when it comes in contact with warm air molecules. How does this happen? This section describes how heat is transferred.

Heat transfer by convection

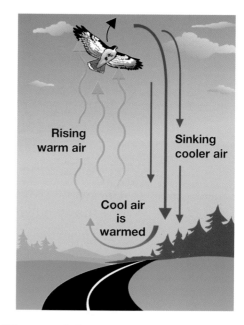

VOCABULARY

convection - transfer of heat through the motion of liquids and gases.

What is convection? **Convection** is the transfer of heat through the motion of gases and liquids such as air and water. Warm air tends to rise and cold air tends to sink. Convection occurs naturally in Earth's atmosphere. Convection also occurs in homes. To understand convection, let's think of how a room gets heated.

Convection is used to heat rooms A radiator is a device used to heat a room. Heat from a radiator warms nearby air atoms. The warmed atoms move quickly and carry heat energy as they rise above the radiator. A curtain above the radiator flutters as fast-moving atoms collide with it. Eventually, heat from the radiator and convection of the air make the room comfortably warm.

Figure 4.6: *Hawks use convection to soar. They are lifted higher in the sky by rising warm air.*

Convection is used to fly Air near Earth's surface gets warm and rises. Hawks make use of convection to soar in the sky. Rising warm air provides lift so that hawks can soar. Eventually, the rising warm air cools down and sinks back to the ground where it may get reheated.

Heat transfer by conduction

What is conduction? **Conduction** is the transfer of heat by the direct contact of atoms and molecules in solids. Heat is transferred from atom to atom by direct contact. If you hold an ice cube in your hand, warmer hand atoms will transfer heat by conduction to the cooler ice cube atoms.

Example of heat transfer by conduction Unlike the atoms in liquids and gases, the atoms in solids are anchored in place. They can wiggle and push each other, but they do not move freely. If you place a cold spoon into a mug of hot cocoa, you may notice that the handle of the spoon becomes warm. If solid atoms can't move freely, how does the *handle* of a spoon resting in a mug of hot cocoa get warm? Imagine the spoon handle as a long line of atoms. At first, all of the atoms are moving at similar speeds. You know this because the whole handle is at the same temperature. Soon the part of the handle closest to the surface of the cocoa heats up. This means that the handle's atoms close to the surface of the cocoa are now wiggling and pushing at a higher speed. As these atoms push other atoms further along the handle, these more distant atoms speed up in turn. In a similar fashion, the atoms are sped up all along the handle. Transferring heat this way is an example of conduction.

VOCABULARY

conduction - transfer of heat by direct contact of atoms and molecules.

MY JOURNAL

Where is conduction in your house? Walk through your house. In each room, observe whether or not there are objects that are involved in conduction. Based on your observations, make a list of as many examples of heat transfer by conduction as you can. Remember, heat transfer by conduction works in solids, because direct contact of atoms and molecules must occur.

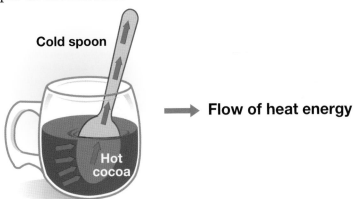

Cold spoon

→ **Flow of heat energy**

Hot cocoa

Heat transfer by radiation

What is radiation?
The warmth of the Sun on your face feels good on a cool day. The heat from the Sun is necessary for life to exist on Earth (Figure 4.7). This heat is not transferred to Earth by conduction or convection. Instead, the Sun's heat reaches Earth by a heat transfer process called radiation. **Radiation** is heat transfer through empty space. Heat transfer by radiation occurs without direct contact or movement of atoms.

Summary of convection, conduction, and radiation
All three forms of heat transfer are often working at the same time to transfer energy from warmer objects to cooler objects. A pot of water being heated by a campfire is warmed through the process of conduction, convection, and radiation!

VOCABULARY

radiation - heat transfer that involves energy waves and no direct contact or movement by atoms.

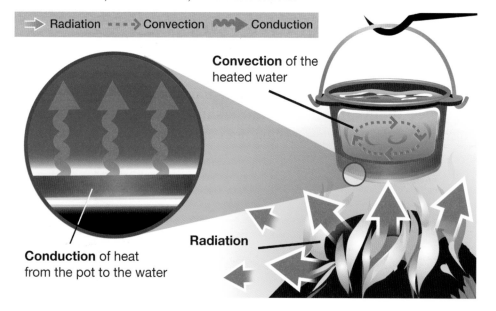

Radiation ----> Convection ∿∿∿ Conduction

Convection of the heated water

Radiation

Conduction of heat from the pot to the water

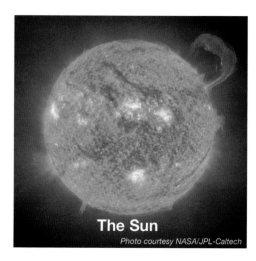

The Sun
Photo courtesy NASA/JPL-Caltech

Figure 4.7: *The Sun's heat is the product of nuclear reactions between atoms in the Sun. The Sun's heat reaches Earth by radiation.*

4.2 Section Review

1. Why does an ice cube melt in your hand?
2. State the type of heat transfer that is occurring in each situation:
   a. Warm air rises.
   b. You feel the heat on your feet as you walk barefoot across a driveway in the summertime.
   c. You feel the warmth of the Sun on your face.
3. A hawk gets some help while flying by using convection currents (air currents created by rising warm air). How is the Sun involved in creating convection currents?
4. How would heat transfer occur in the following substances or objects?
   a. The atmosphere
   b. A metal rod
   c. Water in a pot
   d. An empty pot on a hot stove
   e. The air inside a hot-air balloon
5. You mom is cooking a pot of spaghetti on the stove. You observe that the spaghetti moves all around the pot even though she isn't stirring. What makes the spaghetti move?
6. How is radiation different from heat transfer by convection and conduction?
7. A thermostat controls the switches on a furnace or air conditioner by sensing room temperature. Explain, using conduction, convection, and radiation, where you would place the thermostat in your classroom. Consider windows, outside and inside walls, and the locations of heating and cooling ducts.

Another type of power plant

You have probably heard of nuclear power plants. These power plants produce heat using radioactivity. When unstable atoms undergo radioactive decay, they also happen to produce heat. This heat can be used to heat water. As with power plants that use fossil fuels, nuclear power plants work by using the steam from heated water to turn a turbine. The turbine converts the energy from the steam into energy that turns a generator. The generator then converts this kinetic energy into electricity.

A nuclear power plant

4.3 Earth's Heat Energy

Heat energy is necessary for life on Earth to exist. Even in the coldest parts of Antarctica, heat energy due to the motion of molecules can be found. Do you know where most of Earth's heat energy comes from?

Where does Earth's heat come from?

Surface heat energy
Most of Earth's surface heat energy comes from the Sun, and a little comes from volcanoes and geysers. About 5 million tons of the Sun's mass is converted to energy every second through nuclear reactions. This energy leaves the Sun as radiant energy that is mostly visible light, but also includes infrared radiation (heat) and ultraviolet light. Visible and ultraviolet light, and infrared radiation are part of the *electromagnetic spectrum.*

Radiation from the Sun

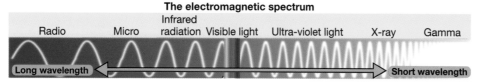

When the Sun's radiation arrives at Earth, it is reflected or absorbed by the atmosphere or the surface (Figure 4.8). For example, our sky looks blue and our Sun seems yellow because blue visible light is scattered by the atmosphere more than yellow light. *(Safety note: Never look at the Sun. Its radiation can harm your eyes.)* Fortunately, ozone in our atmosphere absorbs most of the ultraviolet light which can cause sunburns and skin cancer.

Internal heat energy
The Earth's internal heat energy mostly comes from its *core* (Figure 4.9). Much of this heat energy is left over from when Earth first formed. Some of the core's heat energy comes from the breakdown of radioactive atoms. Radioactive atoms are unstable and undergo changes that produce heat and other products.

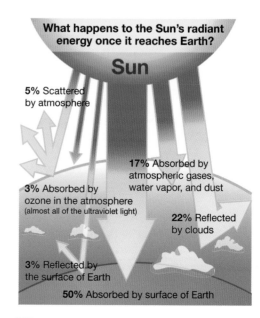

Figure 4.8: *The Sun's radiant energy at Earth's surface.*

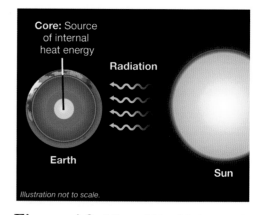

Figure 4.9: *Most of Earth's internal heat comes from the core. Most of Earth's surface heat comes from the Sun's radiation.*

4.3 Section Review

1. How much of the Sun's mass is converted to energy every second?
2. From where and in what form does Earth get most of its surface energy?
3. How much of the Sun's radiant energy is absorbed by Earth's surface?
4. How much of the Sun's radiant energy is reflected by clouds or scattered by the atmosphere?
5. List two other sources of heat energy at Earth's surface.
6. Some of the radiation that reaches Earth's surface from the Sun is *ultraviolet* radiation. This type of radiation causes skin cancer. Look at Figure 4.8. Why is Earth's ozone layer so important?
7. From where does Earth get most of its internal energy?
8. Why is Earth's core so hot? List two reasons.
9. The electromagnetic spectrum is the range of energy waves called electromagnetic waves. Name the type of electromagnetic waves:
   a. that we can see.
   b. that are the main component of solar radiation.
10. What is a volcano? What is a geyser? Define these terms in your own words, using knowledge you already have. These features provide some energy at Earth's surface, but where do they get their source of heat energy?
    (Note: You will learn more about the heat source for volcanoes and geysers in chapter 10).

SOLVE IT!

Make a graph of the information in Figure 4.8. What kind of graph should you make? Make your graph easy to read and understand.

CHALLENGE

Like Earth, you produce internal heat and you also get heat from outside sources. Following are some questions about heat and how you stay warm. Use your school library or the Internet to find the answers to these questions.

(1) Your body is 98.6°F most of the time. How does it stay so warm?

(2) What sources of energy do you use to stay warm indoors? What sources of energy do you use to stay warm outdoors?

Body temperature: **98.6°F**

GEOLOGY CONNECTION — Earth's Energy

Remember the last time you dipped your foot into a bathtub of hot water? Or how good it feels to take a hot shower on a cold rainy day? The hot water we use every day has to be heated by a system. Your home probably has a hot water heater to heat water. However, there are places on Earth, like Iceland, that use Earth's plumbing and heating system to get hot water. Parts of this system are geysers and hot springs. The source of heat is *geothermal energy*—heat that comes from inside our planet.

At Earth's core, temperatures can reach 4982°C (9,000°F). Heat from the core travels to the next layer of rock, the mantle. Mantle rock that melts becomes magma. Magma, lighter than the surrounding rock, travels upward carrying heat. This upward movement and transfer of heat through a fluid is called convection. Convection moves heat away from its source at a lower, hotter area to a higher, cooler area.

Magma that reaches the Earth's surface is lava, but most magma stays below the surface. That underground magma heats nearby water and rocks.

Hot springs and geysers are created by surface water that seeps into the ground and finally reaches those hot rocks. When that heated water rises by convection back to the surface, hot springs and geysers are created.

Hot water from Earth

Rocks are hotter the deeper they are inside Earth. In areas where there is no volcanic activity, those hot rocks heat the hot springs. In areas with volcanic activity, the hot springs are heated by magma. Extremely hot magma can cause the water in a hot spring to boil.

Water temperatures in hot springs vary. Usually the water is warmer than body temperature—37°C (98.6°F)—which makes it feel hot to the skin. In hot springs with high temperatures, the water is usually clear because the water is too hot for algae or bacteria grow. However, this water may not be safe to drink because of the minerals dissolved in it.

Hot spring

Photo courtesy of Geoff Tierney

Things come to a boil

Geyser is an Icelandic word meaning "roarer." A geyser is a type of hot spring that shoots water and steam into the air. The roaring sound comes from the eruption of the water and steam. As it does with a hot spring, water seeps into the ground until it reaches hot rocks. Most geysers are located in areas of volcanic activity. One big difference between a hot spring and a geyser is constriction, which is a narrowed area of plumbing that causes pressure to build.

Far below Earth's surface, geysers fill with water. Near the top of the geyser, a constricted area forms a seal and pressure is created. Pressure also differentiates a hot spring from a geyser. Cooler water sitting in the area pushes down on the hot reservoir of water. Under increased pressure, the reservoir below heats up even more. As the temperature rises, the reservoir starts to boil.

The building pressure of the boiling water causes an eruption. Water and steam is forced out of the geyser to the surface through an opening called a vent. Pressure is released—and, naturally, the process begins again.

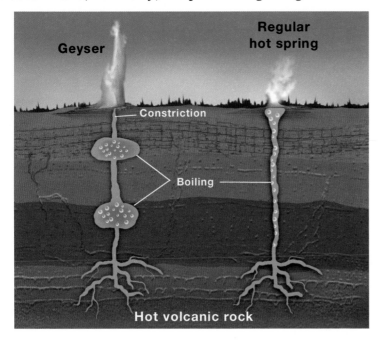

Old Faithful

There are four big locations for geysers on the planet: Iceland (where they got their name), Yellowstone National Park in Wyoming, North Island in New Zealand, and Kamchatka Peninsula in Russia. Old Faithful in Yellowstone is one of the world's famous geysers. Just about every 35 to 120 minutes, it shoots water 100 to 200 feet into the air. Yellowstone is located over a hot spot in the planet's

mantle and this makes it one of the richest locations for geysers—nearly 500 of them in all.

Old Faithful

Photo: Geoff Tierney

Importance of geothermal energy

Hot springs and geysers are more than rare natural attractions. They also can be sources of energy. In the 1970s, Iceland started to use its hot springs and geysers to provide energy for power, heat, and hot water. Today, Iceland uses geothermal energy to provide heat to nearly 87 percent of its homes. In Northern California, geothermal geyser fields have been used for nearly 40 years and produce electricity for San Francisco. Earth's energy can provide a safe, low-cost, and environmentally sound source of power.

Questions:
1. What is geothermal energy?
2. What is the difference between a hot spring and a geyser?
3. Why is "geyser" a good term for Old Faithful?

CHAPTER ACTIVITY Energy at the Surface of Earth

In this activity you will model radiation of heat energy from the Sun to Earth.

Materials

- Two 16- or 24-ounce soda bottles with some sand for stability
- Two digital thermometers and paper towels
- Light source
- Black paper and white paper
- Stopwatch (or use the CPO Science timer)
- Tape, pencil, and a metric ruler

What you will do

1. Pour a handful of sand into each of the soda bottles. The sand steadies the empty bottle by adding a little weight.
2. Wrap a strip of paper towel around the thermometers at the zero degree mark. Insert a thermometer into each bottle so that it snugly fits into the neck.

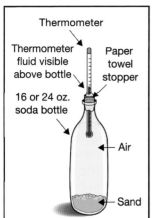

Thermometer

Thermometer fluid visible above bottle

Paper towel stopper

16 or 24 oz. soda bottle

Air

Sand

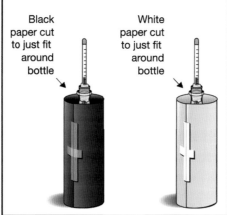

Black paper cut to just fit around bottle

White paper cut to just fit around bottle

3. Practice fitting a piece of black paper around one of the bottles so that the bottle is completely surrounded, but with no overlap. Mark the paper with a pencil, and cut the paper as necessary so that there is no overlap.

4. Tape the black paper to the bottle. Wrap the paper snugly around the bottle, and tape it in place.
5. Repeat steps 3 and 4 for the other bottle, substituting the white paper for the black paper.
6. Place each bottle 10 cm away from the light source.
7. Record the initial temperature of the bottles in Table 1.
8. Turn on the light source and record temperatures in both bottles every minute for 10 minutes in the table.
9. Graph your data. Use the time as the x-axis data and the temperature as the y-axis data.
10. Make a legend to indicate the curves for the black bottle and white bottle. Don't forget to label your axes, to use units, and to title your graph.

Table 1: Radiation data

| | Temperature at each minute (°C) | | | | | | | | | | |
	0	1	2	3	4	5	6	7	8	9	10
Black bottle											
White bottle											

Applying your knowledge

a. What form of heat transfer occurs between the light source and the bottles?
b. Which of the bottles reached a higher temperature?
c. What was the difference in the final temperatures of the two bottles?
d. Which bottle absorbed more energy from the light source? How do you know this?
e. Describe what happened to the energy from the light source when it reached the black bottle and the white bottle. Think about how the two bottles each absorbed and reflected radiation.
f. Based on your results, what types of surfaces on Earth would absorb more radiation from the Sun? What is the light source modeling in the Earth-Sun system?

Chapter 4 Assessment

Vocabulary

Select the correct term to complete the sentences.

heat	molecules	kinetic energy
convection	temperature	power plant
radiation	conduction	

Section 4.1

1. A place that produces electricity is called a _____.

2. The normal _____ for the human body is 98.6°F.

3. Atoms occur in groups called _____.

4. _____ is the energy of motion.

5. Twenty five grams of hot water has more _____ energy than fifteen grams of hot water.

Section 4.2

6. _____ is heat transfer through empty space.

7. The transfer of heat by the direct contact of atoms and molecules is called _____.

8. _____ is the transfer of heat through the motion of gases and liquids.

Concepts

Section 4.1

1. Use the terms in the box below to answer these questions.

   a. Two hydrogen atoms and one oxygen atom make one water _____.

   b. _____ move constantly, make up matter, and are too small to see with your eyes or a magnifying glass.

atom(s)	molecule(s)	power plant(s)

2. Which of the following would be an example of kinetic energy?

   a. Energy stored in the muscles of a cat
   b. Energy from the wind
   c. Energy in a battery

3. An iceberg has more heat in it than a cup of boiling water. Explain why this is true based on what you understand about heat energy.

4. Give an example of heat moving from a warmer object to a cooler object.

5. For a hot air balloon to work, the air molecules inside the balloon must be heated. Explain how these molecules behave when they are heated. Use your new vocabulary to explain.

6. Give an example of energy being lost as heat.

Section 4.2

7. Saucepans are made of metal so they heat up quickly. This takes advantage of the process of:

   a. radiation
   b. convection
   c. conduction

8. Birds use this type of heat transfer to lift them in the air.

   a. radiation
   b. convection
   c. conduction

9. The transfer of heat energy through space from the Sun comes in the form of:

   a. radiation
   b. convection
   c. conduction

Section 4.3

10. From where and in what form does Earth get most of its surface energy?

11. From where does Earth get its internal energy?

12. What is the main type of electromagnetic radiation that makes up the solar radiation that reaches Earth?

13. **Challenge question:** The solar energy that reaches Earth does so in such a way that some places on Earth are cooler or warmer than others. Why do you think this happens?

Math and Writing Skills

Section 4.1

1. The normal human body temperature in Fahrenheit is 98.6°F. What is the normal human body temperature in Celsius. Use this conversion formula to help you:

$$T_{°F} = (\tfrac{9}{5} \times T_{°C}) + 32 \qquad T_{°C} = \tfrac{5}{9}(T_{°F} - 32)$$

$T_{°F}$ = Temperature in °F $\qquad$ $T_{°C}$ = Temperature in °C

2. A cup of water at 5°C is mixed with a cup of water at 25°C. Both cups have the same amount of water. What will the temperature of the final mixture be?

3. The final temperature of a mixture is 60°C and the volume of the mixture is 200 milliliters. To make the mixture, a 100-milliliter sample of water at 30°C water was used. What was the temperature and volume of the other sample of water that was used to make the mixture?

4. What would the temperature in Celsius be if you mixed 50 milliliters of water at 32°F with 50 milliliters of water at 0°C? Explain your answer.

Section 4.2

5. The Sun is 151,000,000 kilometers from Earth. Light travels at approximately 300,000 kilometers per second. How many seconds does it take for the Sun's light to get to Earth? How many minutes does it take?

6. Sunscreen protects your skin from the Sun's energy. Research how sunscreens work and write up your findings in a paragraph.

Section 4.3

7. What percentage of Earth's diameter does the core take up, given that it provides most of the internal energy for Earth? The radius of Earth is 6,371 kilometers. The diameter of the core is 2,462 kilometers.

8. Ultraviolet light is one kind of radiation that reaches Earth's surface. What other kinds of radiation reach Earth's surface? What form is most common?

Chapter Project—Exploring Radiation

1. Use a digital thermometer to record air temperatures near the surface in different areas of your school. Examples include the parking lot, a sidewalk, and a grassy field. What does your data this tell you about the amount of solar radiation that is absorbed in and around your school by different types of surfaces? Present your data as a poster.

2. Solar radiation includes visible light, ultraviolet light, and infrared radiation. Research these types of radiation. Make a poster to present your findings. Use these questions to guide your research: (1) How much of each kind of radiation reaches Earth? (2) Which form of radiation has the highest energy? The lowest energy? (3) What is the relationship between white light and colors of light?

Chapter 5
Density and Buoyancy

You read about heat in Chapter 4. In this chapter, you'll learn a little more about heat and learn about two new concepts—*density* and *buoyancy*. Take a guess at what these terms mean. You may have heard them before. Here are a couple of hints: Density helps explain why a piece of steel sinks in water and a beach ball floats. And, buoyancy explains why a huge piece of steel in the shape of a ship floats!

Key Questions

1. *How does the density of a block of steel compare to the density of a steel boat?*

2. *Why do beach balls float?*

3. *How does a scuba diver sink and float?*

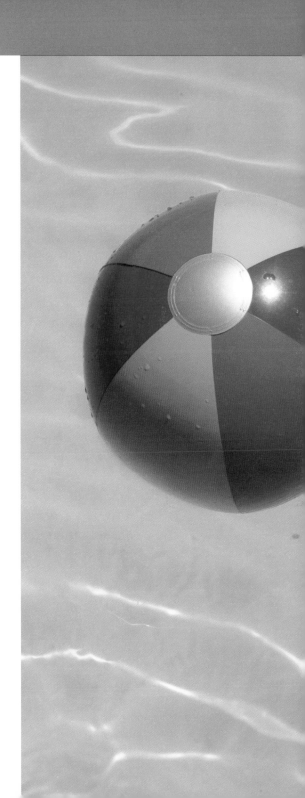

5.1 Density

It's impossible for a person to lift real boulders because they're so heavy (Figure 5.1). However, in the movies, superheroes move huge boulders all the time. And at the end of a scene, a stagehand can pick up the boulder and carry it away under one arm. How is this possible?

Mass and weight

Mass is the amount of matter in an object
Can you lift a huge boulder? You could if the boulder was made of plastic foam! A fake boulder has much less mass than a real boulder, even when both boulders are the same size. *Mass* is the amount of matter in an object. Remember, in the SI Units measurement system, mass is measured in kilograms and grams. A kilogram is 1,000 times bigger than a gram. While kilograms are used to measure the mass of boulders, grams are used to measure small objects. You will usually use the gram unit in science class.

Mass vs. weight
What is the mass of your body? You are probably familiar with measuring your weight, but not your mass. Mass and weight are not the same thing. *Mass* is the amount of matter in an object. *Weight* is a measure of the pulling force of gravity on mass. In the English system, weight is measured in pounds. The SI unit is called a *newton*. It takes 4.448 newtons to make one pound. You can think of a newton as a little less than a quarter-pound.

Weight on other planets
The force of gravity is different on every planet in our solar system. As a result, your weight would change if you visited another planet. A boy who weighs 445 newtons (100 pounds) on Earth would weigh 1,125 newtons on Jupiter! However, his mass stays the same on both planets (Figure 5.2). This is because mass measures the amount of matter a body contains, not how much that matter is pulled by gravity.

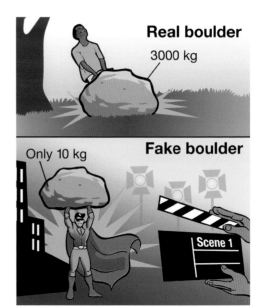

Figure 5.1: *A real boulder versus a fake boulder.*

	Mass (kg)	Weight (newtons)
Earth	45.5	445
Jupiter	45.5	1,125

Figure 5.2: *Mass versus weight on Earth and Jupiter. Weight changes from place to place, but mass stays the same.*

Volume

A solid cube or rectangle *Volume* is the space that something takes up. To find the volume of a solid cube or rectangle, you measure the length, width, and height of the object. Then you multiply the length, width, and height together. If your measurements are in centimeters, the volume unit will be cubic centimeters, or cm^3.

Volume of a rectangular box:

5 cm × 3 cm × 1 cm = 15 cm³

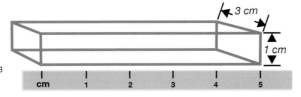

Odd-shaped objects You can find the volume of an odd-shaped object, like a key, by placing it in water. This is often done in a container called a *graduated cylinder*. First, the volume of water in the graduated cylinder is noted. Then, the key is placed in the graduated cylinder. The key pushes aside an amount of water equal to its volume, causing the water level to rise. The volume of the key is equal to the volume of the water with the key in it (28 mL) minus the volume of the water without the key (25 mL).

What is the volume of the key?

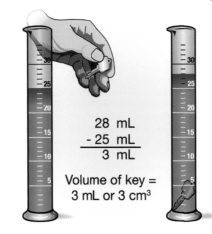

28 mL
- 25 mL
_____
3 mL

Volume of key =
3 mL or 3 cm³

SOLVE IT!

On Great Skies Airlines a carry-on suitcase can be no more than 12 kg and 30,000 cm³. Does the following suitcase qualify as a carry-on? Explain your answer.

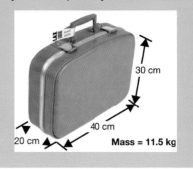

30 cm
40 cm
20 cm
Mass = 11.5 kg

STUDY SKILLS

Remember important information by writing it down on flash cards.

VOLUME

1 MILLILITER = 1 CUBIC CENTIMETER

1 mL = 1 cm³

Keep your flash cards with you so that you can study them when you have free time.

Density

What is density? Think again about the fake boulder mentioned earlier. A fake boulder has to have the same volume as a real boulder, so it will look realistic. However, for a person to be able to lift the fake boulder, it must have a much lower mass than a real boulder. **Density** is the word used to describe the comparison between an object's mass and its volume. Specifically, density is the mass of an object divided by the volume of the object. A real boulder has a greater density than a fake boulder made of plastic foam.

Density depends on two things All matter is made of tiny particles called atoms. The density of a material depends on two things:

1. The mass of each atom or molecule that makes up the material.

2. The volume or amount of space the material takes up. This is related to how closely the atoms or molecules are "packed" in the material.

A material like plastic foam has low density. Plastic foam has individual molecules that are low in mass and not packed very close together. Additionally, plastic foam has air pockets. A material like rock has individual molecules that are higher in mass than the atoms of plastic foam, and they are packed more closely to one another. This means rock has a higher density than plastic foam (Figure 5.3).

Solids, liquids, and gases Like solid objects, liquids and gases are made up of atoms and molecules and have mass and volume. As with solids, you can find the density of a liquid or a gas too!

density - the mass of an object divided by the object's volume.

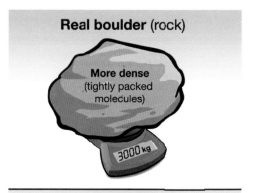

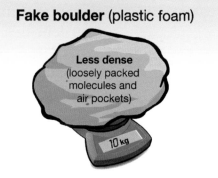

Figure 5.3: *The density of a real boulder is greater than the density of a fake boulder.*

Finding density

Doing the math The density of an object is found by measuring the object's mass and volume then dividing the mass by the volume. Division can be shown with a slash mark (/). The slash is read as the word "per." A density of 2.7 g/cm^3 is read as: two point seven grams per cubic centimeter.

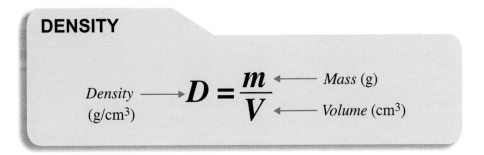

DENSITY

$$Density\ (g/cm^3) \longrightarrow D = \frac{m}{V} \begin{array}{l} \longleftarrow Mass\ (g) \\ \longleftarrow Volume\ (cm^3) \end{array}$$

What is the density of an aluminum metal block that has a mass of 27.0 g and a volume of 10.0 cm^3 ?

$$D = m/V$$
$$D = 27.0\ g/10.0\ cm^3$$
$$D = 2.7\ g/cm^3$$

The density of a material is always the same The density of a material is always the same under the same conditions. This is true regardless of how much of the material you have. For example, the density of aluminum metal is always 2.7 g/cm^3. Aluminum foil, aluminum wire, or an aluminum brick all have the same density. This is true as long as you have a sample of aluminum metal that is not hollow and does not have any other materials mixed with it.

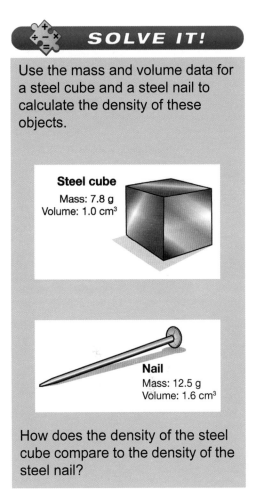

SOLVE IT!

Use the mass and volume data for a steel cube and a steel nail to calculate the density of these objects.

Steel cube
Mass: 7.8 g
Volume: 1.0 cm^3

Nail
Mass: 12.5 g
Volume: 1.6 cm^3

How does the density of the steel cube compare to the density of the steel nail?

5.1 Section Review

1. How does measuring mass differ from measuring the weight of an object?

2. On Earth a package weighs 19.6 newtons. What is the mass of this package on Earth? (Hint: On Earth, 1 kilogram weighs 9.8 newtons.)

3. Imagine you could mail this package to Neptune. What would the mass of the package be on Neptune?

4. What is the volume of a solid rectangle with dimensions of 2 cm × 5 cm × 8 cm?

5. The volume of water in a graduated cylinder is 88 mL. After a small object is placed in the cylinder, the volume increases to 100 mL. What is the volume of the object? First give your answer in milliliters, then in cubic centimeters.

6. Density relates what two measurements to each other?

7. What is the density of an object with a mass of 35 grams and a volume of 7 cm^3?

8. Will the density of a material always be the same, regardless of its size? If so, why?

9. Use Table 5.1 to help you answer the following questions.

   a. The volume of 100 grams of a substance is 100 milliliters. Calculate the density. What might this substance be?

   b. The volume of 5 grams of a substance is 2 cm^3. Calculate the density. What might this substance be?

   c. What is the volume of 10 grams of air?

Table 5.1: Densities of common materials

	Rock (granite)	Water	Air
Average density (g/cm^3)	2.5	1.0	0.001

Very dense wood!

Tabebuia trees, commonly called "Ipe" (pronounced e-pay), grow in the Amazon rainforest. The wood of these trees is extremely hard and dense. In fact, *Tabebuia* wood is so dense that it sinks in water. A single plank can have a mass of as much as 159 kilograms. That's more than the mass of an average household refrigerator (about 100 kilograms)!.

Tabebuia trees grow in the Amazon Rainforest.

Photo: Don Deering, NASA/LBA Project

5.2 Buoyancy

Why do some things float and others sink? Ice cubes can float in a glass of water, but a pebble will sink. People usually float in water, but scuba divers can sink to different depths to explore a coral reef or a sunken ship. What causes things to float and sink?

Floating and sinking

Fluids Matter that can flow is called a **fluid**. "Fluid" does not mean the same thing as "liquid." Liquids and gases are both fluids. Under the right conditions, solid matter that is made of small particles also can flow. The ground shaking during an earthquake can turn soil into a fluid! When this happens, cars and other solid objects can sink into the ground.

Solids, liquids, and gases can float and sink We are used to talking about a solid object, like a boat, floating or sinking in a fluid like water. Figure 5.4 gives examples of objects that help people float safely in water. But other examples of floating and sinking exist. Vinegar sinks to the bottom of a bottle of oil-and-vinegar salad dressing. This is a liquid-in-a-liquid example of sinking. A balloon filled with helium gas floats in air. This is a gas-in-a-gas example of floating.

VOCABULARY

fluid - matter that can flow, usually a liquid or a gas.

MY JOURNAL

Make a list of five objects (all made of different materials) that float in water, and a list of five objects (all made of different materials) that sink in water.

Several ways to help people float better in the water

Figure 5.4: *A foam life preserver, a life vest, and a raft all help people float!*

Floating and sinking in fluids

Solid in liquid   Gas in gas   Liquid in liquid

Sinking and buoyant force

A 400 cm³ rock displaces 400 cm³ of water
The illustration below shows a 400 cm³ rock that has sunk to the bottom of a pond. When the rock is completely underwater, it displaces (pushes aside) an amount of water that is equal to its volume. The rock displaces 400 cm³ of water.

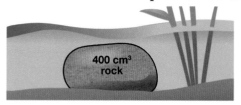
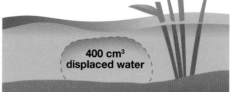

The rock weighs 9.8 newtons
On Earth, this 400 cm³ rock weighs 9.8 newtons. This means that if you are holding the rock, you use 9.8 newtons of force to support it so it doesn't fall to the ground.

The water weighs 3.9 newtons
On Earth, the 400 cm³ of water displaced by the rock weighs 3.9 newtons. This means that it takes 3.9 newtons of force to support the displaced water.

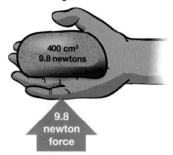
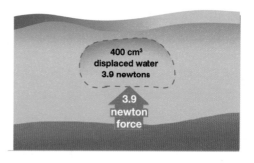

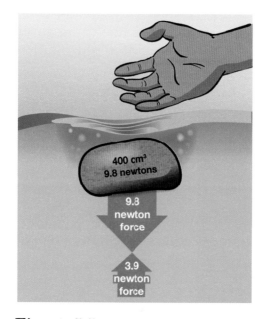

Figure 5.5: *The buoyant force of the water displaced by this rock is not enough to support it so that it floats. Therefore, the rock sinks!*

The water pushes on the rock with a 3.9 newton force
When the rock is dropped into water, the water pushes back on the rock with a force *equal to the weight* of the displaced water. The upward force shown in Figure 5.5 is called **buoyant force**. The buoyant force is always equal to the weight of the displaced fluid.

Why does the rock sink?
The rock sinks because its weight is greater than the displaced water's weight. The 9.8-newton downward force acting on the rock is greater than the water's 3.9-newton upward force.

Floating

A beach ball It is nearly impossible to get on top of a floating beach ball in a swimming pool. It takes a lot of weight to push it underwater. Why do you need to work so hard to push a beach ball underwater?

Why does a beach ball float? A beach ball seems to float on top of the water. In other words, it does not displace a lot of water. Why? The answer is easy. The weight of the ball is small. Therefore, the amount of water that needs to be displaced (to provide enough upward buoyant force to keep it afloat) is also small.

How do you get a beach ball underwater? If you pushed a large beach ball completely underwater, it would displace a volume of water equal to about 30,000 cm³! This amount of water weighs 294 newtons. If the beach ball weighs only 4 newtons, you need to push down with at least 290 newtons (about 65 pounds) of your weight to get the ball underwater! In the example below, the girl is pushing down with only 150 newtons of weight so the beach ball is still partially above water. Keep in mind that any object or material floats if it pushes aside enough water to give an upward buoyant force that supports its weight.

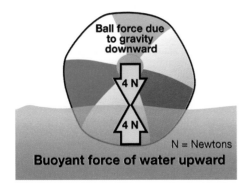

Ball force due to gravity downward

4 N

4 N

N = Newtons

Buoyant force of water upward

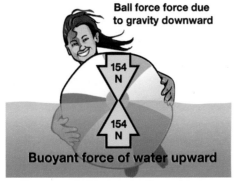

Ball force force due to gravity downward

154 N

154 N

Buoyant force of water upward

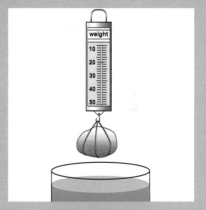

Buoyancy and density

Review floating and sinking
What determines whether an object will float or sink? Look back at the beach ball and rock examples. What happens to an object depends on the object's weight and how much fluid it displaces.

The density connection
The amount of fluid pushed aside by an object (buoyancy) depends on the space an object takes up (its volume). You already know that density depends on mass and volume ($D = m/V$), so there must be a connection between buoyancy and density.

Floating, sinking, and density
Examine each test tube in the graphic below to determine whether the object sank or floated. Density values for wood, glass, water, and mercury are listed in Figure 5.6. Complete these sentences to make two rules that use density to predict floating or sinking.

1. When an object is *less dense* than the fluid it is in, the object will _____ (sink/float).

2. When an object is *more dense* than the fluid it is in, the object will _____ (sink/float).

	Density (g/cm³)
air	0.001
wood	0.9
water	1.0
glass	2.3
mercury	11.0

Figure 5.6: *Density values for common materials*

STUDY SKILLS

Draw your own diagrams!

If you have a lot of information to keep track of in a problem, it helps to make a drawing to organize your thoughts.

For example, make your own sketch of the diagram at the left. Label each object and fluid on your sketch with the density values from Table 5.2. This will make it easier for you to compare the objects and fluids, and complete the two rules.

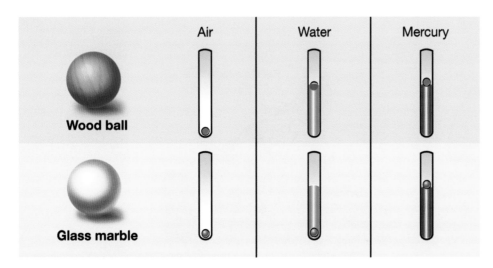

Rules for floating and sinking

What happened? Low-density objects have a *large volume* for their mass. If a low-density object is placed in a higher-density fluid, it will be able to push aside enough fluid so it can float. High-density objects have a *small volume* for their mass. If a high-density object is placed in a lower-density fluid, it will not be able to push aside enough fluid to float.

The rules When an object is:

1. *less dense* than the fluid it is in, the object will **float**.

2. *more dense* than the fluid it is in, the object will **sink**.

Neutral buoyancy A scuba diver uses a buoyancy control device (BCD) to sink or float in water. To sink, a scuba diver releases air from the BCD to decrease her volume. This *reduces* her buoyant force and makes her *more dense*. To rise to the water's surface, she has to become *less dense* by *increasing* her buoyant force. So, she increases her volume by filling her BCD with air from her scuba tank. She can stay in one place underwater if she has *neutral buoyancy*. This means she has the same density as the water around her! She can be neutrally buoyant by controlling the amount of air in her BCD.

Buoyancy Control Device (BCD)

Weights

Sinking | Floating | Neutral Buoyancy

An "Eggs-periment"

Will an egg sink or float in water?

1. Place a egg (uncooked and in its shell) in a wide-mouth glass containing 1¼ cup of warm* tap water.

2. Does the egg sink or float?

3. Remove the egg and add three tablespoons of salt to the warm tap water. Stir until the salt has dissolved.

4. Place the egg back into the glass of water.

5. Does the egg sink or float?

Explain your results by using the density prediction rules for floating and sinking.

*Using warm water the salt dissolve in step 3.

5.2 Section Review

1. Define the term "fluid." Which of the follow substances are fluids?

a. light	b. concrete	c. water
d. air	e. orange juice	f. helium

2. Give an example of an object (solid, liquid, or gas) that floats on a fluid.

3. What is buoyancy? Against what other force does it act?

4. A 10-newton object displaces 12 newtons of water. Will this object sink or float?

5. Ben's model boat weighs 4 newtons. When he places it in the water it sinks! Explain what happened and what he can do to make it boat float.

6. What makes an object float rather than sink? Answer this question using the terms weight and buoyant force. Then, answer in terms of the density of the object and the density of the fluid.

7. A beach ball that is full of air floats in a swimming pool. However, a ball that is not inflated sinks to the bottom of the pool. Why?

8. In order for an object to have neutral buoyancy, what would the relationship between the density of the object and the density of the fluid have to be?

9. Research questions:
   a. If you went for a swim in the Dead Sea in Israel, you would discover that it is very easy to float! Find out why.
   b. What percent of an iceberg is below water and why?

SOLVE IT!

National Concrete Canoe Competition

Photo © Bart Boatwright, courtesy of the American Society of Civil Engineers

Concrete is a heavy construction material made from sand, gravel, and stone. If you toss a piece of concrete into a pond, it sinks. So, how can you make concrete float? The American Society of Civil Engineers (ASCE) sponsors an annual contest for college-level engineering students. The goal is to build a concrete canoe that displaces enough water so that up to four adults can be in it without it sinking. The contestants race the canoes to win scholarships. To make concrete float, it must be shaped so that it pushes aside enough water to create enough buoyant force to support the boat's weight.

Make a sketch that explains why a block of concrete sinks, but a concrete canoe floats!

5.3 Heat Affects Density and Buoyancy

How does a hot-air balloon float? The word "hot" is important. See if you can explain how hot-air balloons can float after you read this section. Hint: Helium isn't involved!

Warm air

Warm air from a candle Look at the picture of the candle below. As the candle burns, the ribbons of mylar (the shiny, thin material that is often used to make silvery birthday balloons) mysteriously flutter and move. If you try this experiment, make sure the mylar is placed far enough from the candle so it doesn't burn!

Rising warm air

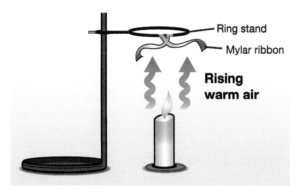

Ring stand
Mylar ribbon

Rising warm air

Figure 5.7: *How does a candle carousel work? The burning candles heat the air. The warmed air rises and encounters the wooden paddles of the fan. The fan turns. Since the base of the carousel is connected to the fan, it also turns, like a carousel or merry-go-round. Important: This type of decoration can never be left unattended!*

A mystery Why do the mylar ribbons move when there is no breeze from an open window or a fan? The candle simply sits there, warming the air around it. Look at Figure 5.7. The carousel moves using only the heat from candles too. How?

Mystery solved— warm air rises The air above a candle feels warmer than the air below the table on which it has been placed. Therefore, warm air must move upward. Mystery solved! In the graphic above, the current of rising warm air causes the mylar ribbons to move. In Figure 5.7, the current of rising warm air causes the fan to move. The first mystery is solved, but now there is a new mystery—why does warm air rise?

Why does warm air rise?

Warm air is less dense
Since warm air rises, the warm air must float on top of the cooler air. Therefore, we know the density of warm air is *less than* the density of cool air.

Mass or volume?
You know that density is the relationship between the mass and the volume of matter. In the examples on the previous page, the burning candle warmed the air around the flame so that the air became less dense than the cool air. To make the density of any material smaller, you would need to either make the mass smaller, or make the volume bigger. So, did the burning candle *decrease the mass* or *increase the volume* of the warm air so that it became less dense than the cool air?

Fast-moving warm air molecules
Warm air molecules move faster than cool air molecules. Faster-moving warm molecules push against each other with more force than cold molecules. This causes warm molecules to be pushed farther apart. Warm molecules that have been pushed farther apart take up more space. We know that volume is the space that atoms take up so we now have the answer to our question. The burning candle *increased the volume* of the warm air, making it less dense. This is why warm air rises.

Earth's enormous energy
We have just studied an example of heat affecting air density in a simple candle system. We studied it in detail because, as you will learn, this process is also at the heart of many important Earth systems. In our candle example, the energy source was a candle flame. On the surface of Earth, the Sun is the energy source and it can affect wind and weather. Below the surface, heat from the Earth's core drives the movement of large pieces of Earth's crust. These Earth systems are huge and involve enormous energy, but they work much like the simple candle system. The same rules of buoyancy, density, and heat energy apply!

Blimps: No Hot Air!

Have you ever seen a blimp in the sky, or have you seen one on television? Do you know how a blimp stays in the air? If you guessed that the blimp floats because the gas inside it is less dense than the surrounding air, you're right! Hot-air balloons heat up ordinary air molecules to make them less dense so the balloon can float. Blimps, however, don't use warm air. A blimp is filled with helium (a gaseous element)! Helium gas has the same volume, but less mass, than regular air. That's why helium floats in air.

5.3 Section Review

1. Which is less dense, warm air or cool air? What does your answer tell you about how warm air and cool air will move relative to each other?

2. An empty party balloon will float to the ceiling of a room once it is filled with helium.

   a. What does this tell you about the density of air in the room compared to the density of helium?

   b. For the balloon to float in air, what two factors might have changed about the balloon?

3. Why does a group of warmer atoms take up more volume than a group of cooler atoms?

4. Name the two energy sources for Earth's systems.

5. Write a paragraph that explains why hot-air balloons float.

   a. Once you have written your paragraph, compare it to the list of information on the right. How did you do?

   b. Use the list of steps at the right and your paragraph to make a poster that explains why hot-air balloons float. Your poster should be creative and easy to understand.

Why hot-air balloons float

Answer question 5a before you read this sidebar!

1. The hot-air balloon pilot allows the gas burner flame to heat the air inside the balloon.

2. The now-warm air molecules are traveling at a higher speed than they had been.

3. The warm air molecules collide with greater impact.

4. The warm air molecules push each other farther apart, taking up more space.

5. The volume of the air in the balloon increases. Some air is forced out of the opening at the bottom because the envelope of the balloon doesn't stretch very much.

6. The mass of the remaining air is less, but the volume is about the same. This makes the density of the balloon less.

7. Buoyancy says that less-dense objects (the warm air in the balloon) will float in more-dense fluids (the cool surrounding air). Therefore, the hot-air balloon floats high above the ground.

Why do hot-air balloons float?

PHYSICS CONNECTION — Full of Hot Air

Do you know what the oldest form of aircraft is? You may think it is the airplane flown by the Wright brothers in 1903. The hot-air balloon dates back much earlier than the Wright brothers. In 1783, the first passengers in a hot-air balloon were a duck, rooster, and a sheep.

Several months later, the Montgolfier brothers of France made a balloon of paper and silk. This flight carried two men for 25 minutes across 5½ miles. Ballooning has come a long way since that historic flight. Balloons are used to forecast weather, explore space, perform science experiments, and flying in them is considered a sport.

The science behind hot-air balloons

Hot-air balloons have three major parts: envelope, basket, and burner. The envelope is the colorful part of the balloon. It is made of heat resistant nylon with a special liner to hold in the heat. The basket is made of strong wicker that will not crack upon landing. Before takeoff, inflator fans are used to fill the envelope with air. Once the envelope is filled with air, burners heat the air. Just as smoke rises, the heated air makes the balloon rise.

An increase in the temperature of a gas causes an increase in the movement of gas molecules. A molecule is a tiny particle in motion. When molecules move around more, they move further apart. Gas molecules that are farther apart decrease gas density.

In a hot-air balloon, the heat from the burners makes the envelope air less dense. The air inside the envelope is now lighter than the air outside. These temperature and density differences create a force called buoyancy. Buoyancy is an upward force.

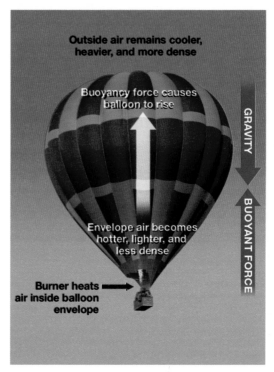

When you are in a swimming pool, buoyancy helps you to float. For hot-air balloons, buoyancy pushes the lighter, hotter air up. The result is the hot-air balloon rises.

Hot-air balloons depend on the wind to travel. The pilot controls the burner to raise or lower the balloon to catch these winds. Balloons move wherever the wind blows!

Hot-air balloons used for science

The National Scientific Balloon Facility in Palestine, Texas is a National Aeronautics and Space Administration (NASA) facility. NASA launches about 25 science balloons each year. Science balloons do not carry people, but carry a "payload." The payload carries equipment for experiments and may weigh up to 8,000 pounds. These experiments help scientists study earth and space. Airplanes usually fly five to six miles above the ground. Science balloons fly up to 26 miles high!

An Ultra Long Duration Balloon (ULDB)

Photo - courtesy of NASA

NASA is developing an Ultra-Long Duration Balloon (ULDB). The ULDB envelope is made of a material that is as thin as sandwich wrap. Scientists hope the ULDB will be able to fly up to 100 days. Longer balloon flights will let scientists carry out more advanced science experiments.

Steve Fossett

Steve Fossett is the first person to fly solo around the world in a hot-air balloon. He is an adventurer who worked 10 years to achieve this goal. On June 19, 2002, Fossett completed his trip. His journey lasted 14 days, 19 hours, and 51 minutes. Fossett did run into problems during his great balloon adventure. At one point, he had to fly as low as 500 feet to avoid very high winds.

Although Fossett was alone in the balloon, he did not work alone to complete the trip. He had a team that included meteorologists, engineers, scientists, and balloonists. Fossett's balloon was equipped with computers, telephone, radio, and almost 20 pounds of maps. He also had oxygen available for high altitudes. The air at high altitudes is very thin and does not have enough oxygen for normal breathing.

Balloon festivals

In the United States, there are more than 4,000 balloon pilots. Pilots from around the world love to gather, race, and fly. The Albuquerque International Balloon Fiesta in New Mexico has been held annually for over 30 years. This fiesta is the largest balloon festival in the world with over 500 balloons. The Helen to the Atlantic Balloon Race and Festival in Georgia is the oldest in the south. It is also the only long distance hot-air balloon race in the United States.

Imagine floating above some of the most spectacular views from coast to coast. Ballooning in New Hampshire offers views of the White Mountains. The Sonoma County Hot-air Balloon Classic, held in Windsor, California offers balloonists early morning rides over the vineyards of Northern California. hot-air ballooning is not just full of hot-air. The wind welcomes the balloonists and provides an experience unlike any other of its kind.

Questions:

1. How does heat affect air density?
2. Describe buoyancy and its effect on a hot-air balloon.
3. How do you steer a hot-air balloon?

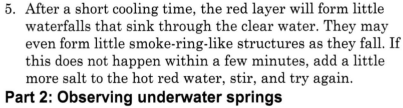

CHAPTER ACTIVITY — Observing Density Effects

The density of water changes depending on its temperature and how salty it might be. In this activity you will observe how these two variables—temperature and saltiness—affect the density and movement of water.

Materials

- Clear plastic cups and foam cups
- Table salt
- Red and blue food coloring
- Eye dropper
- Cool and hot water

What you will do

Part 1: Creating an underwater waterfall

1. Fill a clear plastic cup nearly full with cool water.
2. Fill a foam cup half-full with hot water. Add a pinch of salt. Add 6 drops of red food coloring. Stir until the salt dissolves.
3. Place the eyedropper into the hot red water to warm it up. After a minute, fill the dropper barrel with the water.
4. Hold the dropper so that it lies at a flat angle at the surface of the clear water with the tip just under the surface. Gently squeeze out a layer of hot red water onto the surface of the clear water.

Eyedropper

5. After a short cooling time, the red layer will form little waterfalls that sink through the clear water. They may even form little smoke-ring-like structures as they fall. If this does not happen within a few minutes, add a little more salt to the hot red water, stir, and try again.

Part 2: Observing underwater springs

6. Fill a clear cup three-quarters full with cool water. Add a heaping teaspoon of salt to the water. Stir until the salt dissolves.
7. Fill a foam cup half-full with cool water. Add 6 drops of blue food coloring. Stir to mix.
8. Fill the eyedropper with cool blue water.
9. Gently lower the dropper into the salt water so that the tip is near the bottom. Gently squeeze the dropper so that a small stream of blue water is released.

Applying your knowledge

For part 1:

a. Explain why the red water floats at first.
b. Explain why the red water eventually sinks.

For part 2:

c. Where did the blue water go? Why?
d. In this model, the blue water was less salty than the surrounding water. Think of another way you could cause the results seen in this activity. Write your own procedure, test it, and explain what happened.

Chapter 5 Assessment

Vocabulary

Select the correct term to complete the sentences.

fluid	density	buoyant force

Section 5.1 and Section 5.2

1. Matter that can flow is called a _____.

2. An object which has a weight (downward force) of 20 newtons displaces a volume of water that weighs 8 newtons. This object will sink because the _____ is not enough to help it float.

3. The _____ of a wooden ball is less than water so it floats.

Concepts

Section 5.1

1. Fill in the blanks using the terms *mass* or *weight*:

   a. Your _____ is always the same regardless of gravity.

   b. Your _____ on Earth is different than on the moon because of the moon's weaker gravitational force.

   c. On Earth the _____ of an object is 10 newtons.

   d. On Jupiter the _____ of an elephant would be greater than it is on Earth, but its _____ would be the same.

2. Describe how you would find the volume of these two objects: (a) A cardboard box, and (b) A marble.

3. Density is the ratio between which two properties an object (see box below)? Write the formula for density.

mass	temperature	weight
heat energy	volume	buoyant force

4. The _____ (mass, weight, or density) of a material is the same no matter how much of the material you have.

Section 5.2

5. Define the term fluid and give three examples of fluids.

6. When talking about buoyant force, why is the weight of an object talked about instead of its mass?

7. If the weight of an object was 500 newtons and the buoyant force was 75 newtons, would the object sink or float?

8. Why is it so easy to float in the very salty Dead Sea?

9. True or false? This is an example of a gas floating on another gas—warm air rising above cooler air because it is less dense.

10. True or false? You can increase the volume of a balloon by heating up the air inside.

Section 5.3

11. You want to heat a cold room. You place a space heater in a corner. Using what you know about the density of warm air versus cool air, explain what happens in the room when the space heater is turned on.

12. What are two ways to make the density of an object smaller? Give your own example.

Math and Writing Skills

Section 5.1

1. The moon's gravity is one sixth that of the gravity experienced on Earth, If an object's weight on Earth is 1,200 newtons, what would be its weight on the moon?

2. The volume of a solid 4 cm × 6 cm × 10 cm is:

   a. 24 cm

   b. 240 cm

   c. 240 cm^3

   d. 100 cm^3

3. What is the volume of a box that measures 10 meters long by 5 meters wide by 2 meters high?

4. You know that a box can contain 150 cm^3 of water. Give an example of what the dimensions of the box might be.

5. The volume of a 20-gram object is 5 cm^3. What is its density?

Section 5.2

6. If an object has a buoyant force acting on it of 320 newtons, would the weight of the object have to be more or less than 320 newtons in order to float?

7. An object weighs 135 newtons. What would the buoyant force have to be in order for the object to have neutral buoyancy?

Section 5.3

8. If you have a hot-air balloon, how does heating up the air inside decrease the density of the hot air balloon? Explain using the concepts of volume and mass.

9. At the top of the highest mountain on Earth, the force of gravity is a little less than it is at sea level. Would your weight be a little greater or a little less at the top of the highest mountain on Earth?

10. The density of water is 1.0 g/cm^3 and the density of wax is 0.9 g/cm^3. Would wax float or sink in water?

Chapter Project—How Do Animals Float?

Marine mammals live in water all the time. Have you ever wondered how these animals stay afloat? Why don't they sink to the bottom of the ocean? Especially, why doesn't a 150-metric ton animal like the blue whale sink?

For this project, pick any marine animal. Then, research facts about this animal to find out why this animal doesn't sink. Do an oral presentation in front of your class to describe what you learn from your research.

Here are some questions to guide your research:

- What is the name of your marine mammal?
- What is the mass of the animal in kilograms or metric tons (one metric ton = 1,000 kilograms)?
- What are the dimensions of this animal? Use these dimensions to estimate the volume of this animal.
- See if you can use the mass and volume of the animal to calculate the density of this animal.

  Note: The density of salt water is 1,028 kg/m^3. The density of pure water is 1,000 kg/m^3.
- Why does this animal float instead of sink?
- What does this animal do when it sleeps?

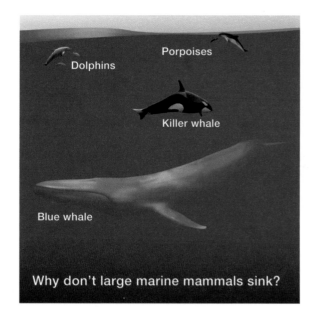

Why don't large marine mammals sink?

Chapter 6
Earth's Surface and Heat

How does Earth stay warm in cold, empty space? Most of Earth's heat energy comes from the Sun by the process of radiation. Energy from the Sun enters Earth's atmosphere and some gets trapped. This trapped energy warms the planet. In this chapter you will learn that ocean currents, wind, and weather are all related to heat energy at Earth's surface.

Key Questions

1. *Why is Earth's atmosphere important?*

2. *Why do palm trees grow in Scotland?*

3. *What causes wind?*

6.1 Earth Is Just Right

Earth is "just right" because its temperature is not too hot or too cold (Figure 6.1). Metals like lead melt on the hot surface of Venus, but not on Earth. Some gases freeze solid on Pluto, but not on Earth. Earth's temperature is especially nurturing for living things. This section is about how Earth's temperature stays "just right."

Temperature

Water for life
The temperature range on Earth's surface is just right for water to be a liquid. Liquid water is extremely important for living things. For example, an adult human body is 60% to 75% water. You need water to keep your blood, brain, and lungs working properly!

Earth's temperature range
Earth's surface temperature stays within a narrow range—it is not too hot or too cold. The average temperature of Earth's surface is about 15°C. This temperature is maintained because Earth has an atmosphere which traps some of the Sun's energy. Without an atmosphere, Earth's surface temperature would be about -18°C.

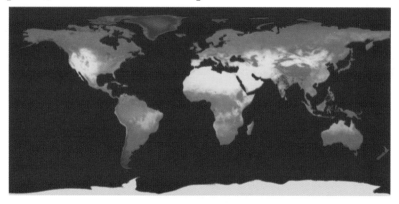

Land Surface Temperature (°C)

-25   -15   -5   5   15   25   35   45

July 2003. Image based on data from
NASA's Moderate Resolution Imaging Spectroradiometer (MODIS) Sensor. Credit: NASA

	Surface temperature (°C)
Mercury	-170 to 390
Venus	450 to 480
Earth	-88 to 48
Mars	-89 to -31
Jupiter	-108
Saturn	-139
Uranus	-197
Neptune	-201
Pluto	-223

Figure 6.1: *The surface temperatures for planets in our solar system.*

STUDY SKILLS

How to "read" diagrams

How do you read a diagram?

(1) Study the diagram to determine what information it is showing you.

(2) Read the caption and title.

(3) **Question:** Refer to the diagram at the left. In your estimation, what was the most common land surface temperature for July 2003?

Energy and motion

The Sun's energy Almost all of the heat energy on Earth's surface comes from the Sun. Hot spots like volcanoes and hot springs add some heat, but not as much as the Sun. At the same time that the Sun adds heat to Earth's surface, heat is being lost to space. The balance between the Sun's heat and heat lost into space is what determines Earth's surface temperature.

Earth's motion The motion of Earth also helps to balance its surface temperature. Read on to find out how two of these motions, rotation and revolution, affect the temperature of every place on Earth.

Rotation **Rotation** is the turning motion of a planet as it spins. It takes one day for Earth to make one complete spin. For half of a day, your side of Earth faces the Sun and experiences daytime. For the other half of the day, your side of Earth faces away from the Sun and experiences nighttime. The trick of spinning a basketball on your finger is a good example of rotation (Figure 6.2).

Revolution **Revolution** is the motion of a planet around its star, like a race car that moves around and around a circular track (Figure 6.2). One complete trip around the track would be one revolution. It takes about 365.25 days for Earth to make one revolution or one trip around the Sun. Later in this chapter we'll learn how the revolution of Earth is related to the seasons.

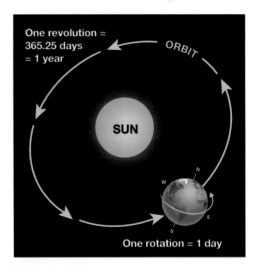

One revolution = 365.25 days = 1 year

ORBIT

SUN

One rotation = 1 day

Figure 6.2: *Earth rotates on its axis and revolves around the Sun.*

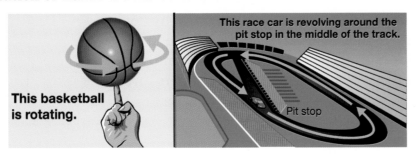

This basketball is rotating.

This race car is revolving around the pit stop in the middle of the track.

Pit stop

Temperature and Earth's rotation

Mercury is too hot and too cold!
It may seem strange to compare a planet to a grilled burger, but what happens if you put a burger on a hot grill and forget to turn it? The bottom will be burned to a crisp, and the top will be undercooked. The planet Mercury is like that. One day on Mercury lasts for about 58 Earth days! The long day causes the temperature on the Sun-facing side of Mercury to reach about 400°C. Something made out of the metal lead would melt at this temperature! At the same time, the dark nighttime side plunges to -170° Celsius. That's so cold that the liquid in a thermometer would freeze.

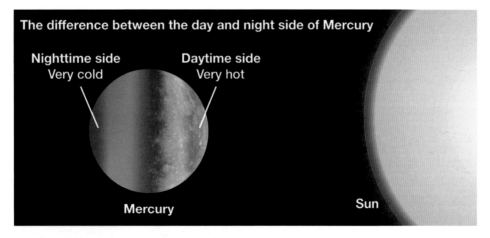

The difference between the day and night side of Mercury

Nighttime side
Very cold

Daytime side
Very hot

Mercury

Sun

The Earth is just right—not too hot or too cold!
Even though Earth is farther away from the Sun than Mercury, our night side never gets as cold as Mercury's night side. Why not? Think about burgers again. A good chef turns the burger so it browns nicely on both sides. Similarly, the Earth turns rapidly enough so that there isn't enough time for our night temperature to sink too low. In the same way, there isn't enough time for Earth's day temperature to rise extremely high.

Greenhouse Gases

A greenhouse is a glass building where plants can be grown in a warm, moist environment. Scientists use the term "greenhouse gases" to describe certain gases in Earth's atmosphere. Like the glass in a greenhouse, greenhouse gases can slow down Earth's natural heat-loss processes. These gases are useful because they keep Earth warm. However, the amount of these gases is increasing in our atmosphere. Due to the increase, less heat energy will be able to leave Earth. Scientists are concerned that the resulting rise in Earth's average surface temperature might alter climates and other aspects of our environment.

Revolution and Earth's seasons

Why does Earth have seasons? The diagram below shows Earth at four different places in its revolution around the Sun. Why is it warmer in summer and cooler in winter in the northern hemisphere? In other words, why do seasons occur?

Earth is tilted One guess might be that Earth is closer to the Sun during summer. But this isn't the correct answer! Earth has seasons because it is tilted on its axis. During our summer, the northern hemisphere receives sunlight that is more direct than it is in the winter, and in summer there are more hours of daylight. This means we have warmer temperatures in summer than we do in winter.

Earth's axis

Earth rotates about an imaginary axis that goes through its center. This axis is drawn on Earth images in the diagram at the left. The diagram shows that Earth is tilted at 23.5° as it revolves around the Sun.

The axis connects the north and south poles. The north end of the axis points toward the North Star throughout the year.

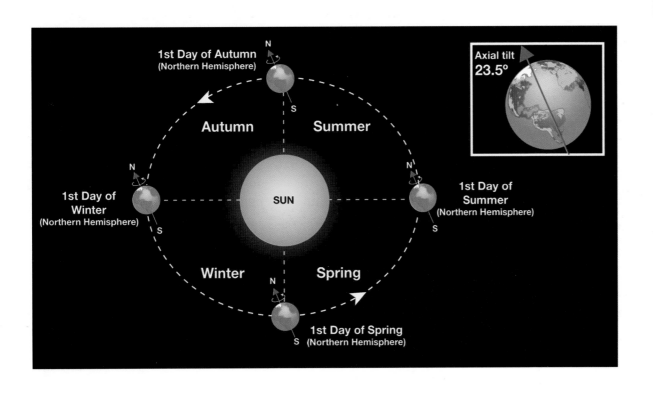

SOLVE IT!

Make your own sketch of the diagram at the left. Based on today's date, indicate on your diagram where Earth is on its path around the Sun.

6.1 Section Review

1. Describe two way that make Earth's climate "just right" for life on Earth.

2. What is the source of most of Earth's heat energy?

3. Some of Earth's heat energy is lost to space. Why is this important?

4. Define the term *rotation*. How long is one rotation of Earth?

5. Define the term *revolution*. How long is one revolution of Earth around the Sun?

6. Earth's surface does not get too hot or too cold compared to Mercury's surface. What difference between the two planets makes this possible?

7. What role do greenhouse gases play in keeping Earth warm?

8. Why does Earth have seasons?

9. Refer to the diagram on the previous page. During winter in the northern hemisphere, is the southern hemisphere tilted toward or away from the Sun?

10. How many degrees is Earth's axis tilted?

11. There are more hours of sunlight and more direct sunlight during summer. How does winter compare to summer in terms of hours of sunlight?

12. Research: You will need to do research on the Internet or at the library to answer these questions.

   a. What are the main greenhouse gases?

   b. Where do these gases come from?

   c. Which planet—Venus or Earth— exhibits a stronger greenhouse effect? Why?

MY JOURNAL

Water is everywhere!

1. Look indoors and outdoors and list everything you see that contains water. Remember to include food, drinks, things in nature, and even YOU!

2. Make a second list of every activity, job, or process you do throughout a usual day where water is used.

Compare your journal lists with your classmates. Are your lists complete?

CHALLENGE

Why is January a *winter* month in the northern hemisphere but a summer month in the southern hemisphere?

6.2 Ocean Currents

Cooks sometimes wrap warm food in a piece of aluminum foil to keep it warm. Aluminum foil helps spread the heat energy around the food. Our atmosphere and oceans act like foil because they spread heat around our planet. In this section, you will learn how heat is spread around by ocean currents.

Oceans

Water covers most of Earth's surface
Oceans are massive bodies of seawater that cover much of Earth's surface. Land only covers about one-quarter of Earth's surface. The rest is covered with water, especially ocean water. About 97% of Earth's water is contained in oceans.

Oceans spread heat energy
If Earth was the same temperature everywhere, the winds and ocean currents would be very weak. In Chapter 4 you learned that heat could spread from one place to another as a moving group of warm atoms. Oceans spread heat too. Oceans spread enormous amounts of energy from the hot equator toward the cold north and south poles. Earth has five major oceans (Figure 6.3). Can you name them? One of them was just named in the year 2000!

Figure 6.3: *Earth's five major oceans. The Southern Ocean was recently named as a separate ocean in 2000 by the International Hydrographic Organization (IHO). The IHO includes representatives from 68 countries that border the world's oceans.*

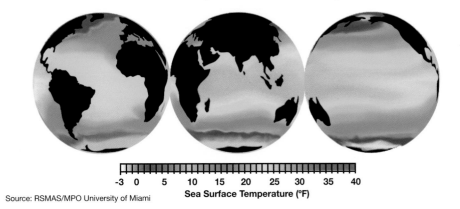

Source: RSMAS/MPO University of Miami

-3 0   5   10   15   20   25   30   35   40

Sea Surface Temperature (°F)

What causes surface ocean currents?

Wind creates currents

Energy from the Sun creates permanent belts of wind that blow over large parts of Earth. When wind moves over an ocean, it pushes water along its path. The moving water forms patterns called **surface ocean currents**. One well-known surface ocean current is called the Gulf Stream (Figure 6.4). The Gulf Stream moves northward from Mexico all the way to the British Isles!

Water expansion also drives surface currents

Ocean surface currents are also driven by a process called expansion. *Expansion* occurs when something increases in size. The climate at the equator (Figure 6.5) is hot all year long and warms the ocean surface. This makes the surface water expand so that the water level is a little higher at the equator. The force of gravity causes the expanded surface water to slide toward the north and south poles. This effect helps to drive the surface ocean currents. The diagram below shows why water expands when it is heated.

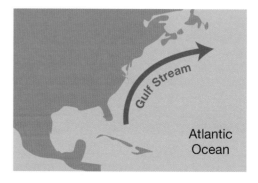

Figure 6.4: *The Gulf Stream is a surface ocean current.*

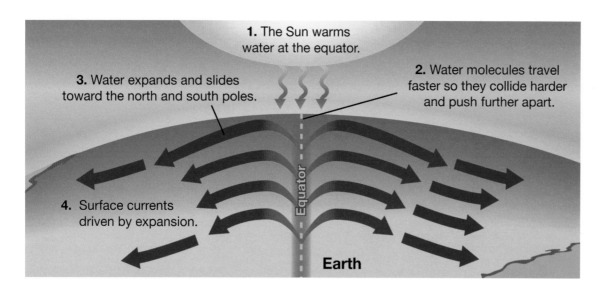

1. The Sun warms water at the equator.

3. Water expands and slides toward the north and south poles.

2. Water molecules travel faster so they collide harder and push further apart.

4. Surface currents driven by expansion.

Earth

Figure 6.5: *The equator is an imaginary line that forms a circle around Earth, dividing it into the northern and southern hemispheres.*

Ocean gyres

Rotation of Earth Surface ocean currents do not simply flow in a straight line away from the equator. The rotation of Earth causes the flow to curve to the right above the equator, and to the left below the equator. This natural phenomenon is called the *Coriolis effect*. Because of this effect, surface ocean currents can flow in a circular pattern called a **gyre**. Each ocean basin contains a gyre. Gyres north of the equator—like the North Atlantic Gyre below—turn in a clockwise direction. Gyres south of the equator turn in a counter-clockwise direction. It takes about three years for water to complete the path of the North Atlantic Gyre. This rate was determined by tracking bathtub toys that had spilled into the Atlantic Ocean (Figure 6.6)!

Heat energy Surface ocean currents move an enormous amount of heat energy away from the equator. Find New York and England on the map below. You can see that England is farther north of the equator than New York. Find the Gulf Stream part of the North Atlantic Gyre. The Gulf Stream carries so much heat energy that England is as warm as New York! Moving this amount of heat energy is incredible. With all our modern technology, we can't come close to producing this much heat energy.

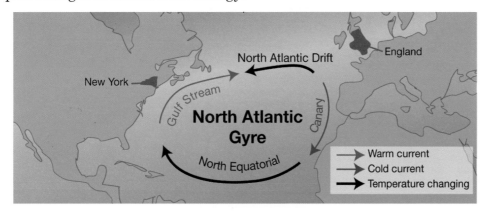

 **VOCABULARY**

gyre - a circular motion, such as a circular ocean current.

Tracking Ocean Currents

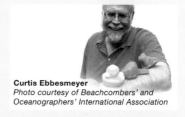

Curtis Ebbesmeyer
Photo courtesy of Beachcombers' and Oceanographers' International Association

Sometimes, ships spill interesting things into the ocean. Since 1991, Oregon scientist Curtis Ebbesmeyer has tracked spilled objects to learn about surface ocean currents. He has tracked 60,000 sneakers spilled in the North Pacific. He followed 29,000 bathtub toys, and over 4.5 million plastic bricks spilled off the coast of Britain. He records and maps where these objects wash ashore. His data can be used to find out how fast currents travel and to make predictions. If there is an oil spill, it can be cleaned up more quickly using knowledge of the paths of surface ocean currents.

Figure 6.6: *Tracking ocean currents.*

Deep ocean currents

What are deep ocean currents? **Deep ocean currents** move within the ocean and are slower than the surface currents. Another name for deep ocean currents is *thermohaline currents*. *Thermo* means temperature and *haline* means salt. Deep ocean currents can't be driven by the wind. They are driven by differences in temperature and saltiness, which is why they are called thermohaline currents.

Two things happen at the equator As surface ocean currents flow near the equator, the Sun warms the water and the water expands. This means that the surface water becomes less dense. At the same time, these warm currents lose water due to evaporation. **Evaporation** occurs when a liquid, like water, changes into a gas. As water evaporates from these currents they becomes saltier and denser.

A giant conveyor belt of water As long as salty currents are warm, their expansion keeps them near the ocean's surface. But as they flow toward the poles, these currents cool down and the expansion effect is lost. The cooler, saltier water sinks toward the ocean floor—like an underwater waterfall. Deep ocean current water eventually returns toward the surface forming a huge, slow "conveyor belt" of moving water. It takes 1000 years for water to travel the path shown below. The surface water of the North Atlantic Gyre is on a much quicker circulation pattern taking only three years.

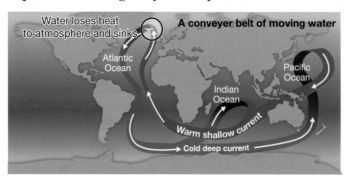

 VOCABULARY

deep ocean currents - density- and temperature-driven currents that move slowly within the ocean; also called thermohaline currents.

evaporation - occurs when a liquid changes to a gas.

 STUDY SKILLS

Learning new words

A good way to learn new words is to break down the word into parts.

Thermohaline has two parts:

Thermo- = temperature

-haline = salt

6.2 Section Review

1. The Sun is important in creating wind and ocean currents. Is this statement true or false? Explain your answer.

2. What role do ocean currents play in weather patterns? (Hint: Why is the weather in England similar to the weather in New York?)

3. What is the Coriolis effect? How does it affect paths of surface ocean currents?

4. Name the five major oceans. How much of Earth's surface is covered by ocean water?

5. Define surface ocean currents. From what two processes are they created?

6. Describe the process of expansion.

7. What is a gyre?

8. In what direction do gyres move in the southern hemispheres?

9. The surface ocean currents move heat energy away from where?

10. What is another name for deep ocean currents? What two factors drive them?

11. If a mass of ocean water is cold and salty, what will it do? Where on Earth's surface is this event common?

12. If a mass of ocean water is heated by the Sun and some water evaporates, what happens? Where on Earth's surface is this event common?

13. Research the answers these questions.
    a. In Early American history, how was mail service *expedited* (made quicker) between Europe and America once ocean currents were observed and studied?
    b. Where is the Sargasso Sea and what is interesting about it?

Palm Trees in Scotland?

Palm trees are common in Southern California, Florida, and other tropical locations—but could there be palm trees in a country as far north of the equator as Scotland? Scotland is a very small country located in the northern third of Great Britain's islands. Do some research to find out if there are palm trees in Scotland, and if so, explain how this could happen.

6.3 Wind and Weather

The combination of wind, water, and temperature creates Earth's weather patterns. The Sun is the major source of energy for weather. **Weather** is a term that describes the condition of the atmosphere in terms of temperature, wind, and atmospheric pressure. What is the weather like today in your town?

Wind

What is wind?   **Wind** is the flow of air that occurs as a result of unequal pressure in the atmosphere. Wind flows from an area of high pressure to an area of low pressure.

Heating and cooling   The Sun warms Earth's surface. Air near the warmed ground expands and becomes less dense. The less-dense air rises. Surrounding air is drawn in to take the place of the air that rose from the ground. Eventually the warm, less-dense air from the surface cools. The same chain of events that made the air rise now works in reverse and the air sinks back to the ground.

Unequal pressure   When warm air rises from Earth's surface, an area of low pressure is created. This lower-pressure area draws in air from surrounding higher-pressure areas. Eventually the warm air that rose from the surface cools and becomes denser. This dense, cool air sinks back to the surface causing an area of high pressure. This new high pressure may become the source of more wind.

Thermals   A small upward flow of warm air is called a **thermal**. Gliding birds like hawks often ride a thermal as they hunt for food. Pilots of sailplanes (which lack an engine) fly by riding the same thermals that gliding birds do (Figure 6.7). In fact, the pilots look for gliding birds to find these invisible air currents. Thermals are usually not stable and come and go over a short period of time.

VOCABULARY

weather - the condition of the atmosphere as it is affected by wind, water, temperature, and atmospheric pressure.

wind - air that flows, often because of heating and cooling of air or unequal air pressure.

thermal - a small heat-driven air current.

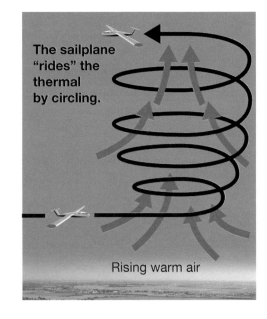

The sailplane "rides" the thermal by circling.

Rising warm air

Figure 6.7: *A thermal is a rising column of warm air. Gliding birds and sailplanes "ride" thermals.*

Convection in the atmosphere

Small convection currents   Thermals can be described as small convection currents in the atmosphere. Heated air near a surface becomes less dense than the colder air above it. The heated air rises, forcing the colder air to move aside and sink toward the ground. Then this colder air is warmed by the surface, and it rises. A thermal is created. As you learned on the previous page and in Chapter 4, hawks often ride these convection currents (Figure 6.8).

Global convection currents   Thermals form on a local level. Convection currents form on a global scale. These form as a result of the temperature difference between the equator and the poles. Warm, less-dense air at the equator tends to rise and flow toward the poles. Cooler, denser air from the poles sinks and flows back toward the equator.

Convection cells   The giant circles of air from the equator to the poles are complicated by Earth's rotation. Because of the rotation, the warm air from the equator doesn't make it all the way to the poles. The combination of global convection and Earth's rotation sets up a series of wind patterns called **convection cells** in each hemisphere. The turning Earth also changes the direction of airflow causing the path of the wind to be curved as it moves from high to low pressure.

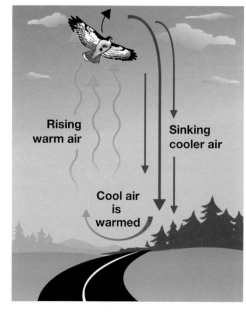

Figure 6.8: *A thermal is the result of convection.*

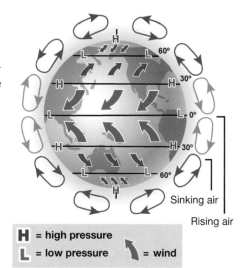

ⓐ **VOCABULARY**

convection cells - large wind patterns in Earth's atmosphere caused by convection.

Air and water vapor

Water vapor Water in gas form is called **water vapor**. During a rainstorm, puddles often form on sidewalks and streets. The puddles eventually "disappear." Where does the liquid water go? The liquid water changes to a gas and mixes with the air (Figure 6.9).

How much water vapor can air hold? Since air often contains water vapor it is helpful to compare an air mass to a sponge. Warm air is like a big sponge that can contain a lot of water vapor. Cold air is like a small sponge that can contain less water vapor. Air that contains the maximum amount of water is *saturated*. Like a soggy sponge, saturated air can't hold anymore water vapor. If more water vapor is added to saturated air, the water vapor will turn back into liquid and form droplets.

Relative humidity *Relative humidity* is a measure of how much water vapor an air mass contains relative to the total amount of water vapor it could contain at a certain temperature. Let's say a warm air mass contains twenty-five percent of the total amount of water vapor it could contain. If this warm air mass cools, its volume will get smaller. However, the air mass will have the same amount of water vapor. Therefore, the relative humidity value increases.

Figure 6.9: *When a puddle dries, the water becomes water vapor in the atmosphere.*

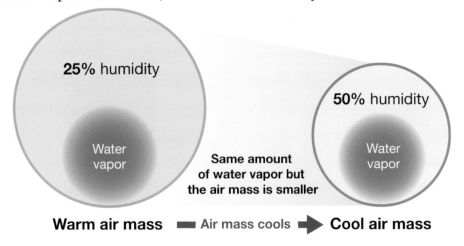

25% humidity

Water vapor

Same amount of water vapor but the air mass is smaller

50% humidity

Water vapor

Warm air mass ▬ Air mass cools ➡ **Cool air mass**

Rain

How does rain form?
Rain is the result of a cooling air mass. As the temperature of the air mass decreases, it gets smaller. At some temperature, the air mass humidity is 100% and it is *saturated* with water vapor. If the air mass cools even more, the water vapor will form water droplets. Tiny droplets form a cloud or fog. Larger droplets fall as rain. Cooling an air mass is like wringing out a wet sponge.

After rain
Suppose an air mass passes over warm ground after it has rained a lot of water. The air mass now contains only a little water vapor. As the temperature of the air mass increases, it gets bigger but the amount of water vapor it has stays the same. Therefore, the humidity of the air mass is extremely low.

From the ocean over a mountain
Warm, moist air crosses over the Pacific Ocean and reaches the coast. At first the air mass flows up the western side of a mountain which has a lot of trees and plants. Cool temperatures at the top of the mountain cause the mass to decrease in size so that water vapor becomes first a cloud and then rain droplets. The resulting cool, dry air mass sinks down the eastern side of the mountain into warm temperatures. The land that this dry air passes over will have a dry climate.

SOLVE IT!

A cool (10°C) air mass contains 80% of the water it could contain. The air mass warms to 30°C.

1. Does the volume of the air mass decrease or increase when the temperature goes up?

2. Does the relative humidity of the air mass increase or decrease when the temperature goes up? (Assume that the amount of water in the air mass stays the same.)

Hint: draw a diagram similar to the one on page 126 to help you answer these questions.

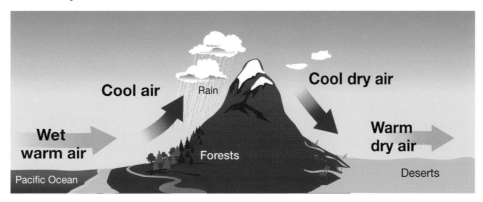

Weather

What is weather? *Weather* is caused by the effects of wind, water, temperature, and atmospheric pressure. The weather in a certain location is another way of describing what the atmosphere is doing at a certain time.

Weather transports heat energy The oceans are the most important source of water vapor in the atmosphere. Huge amounts of water vapor formed by evaporation near the equator carry tremendous amounts of heat energy. The water vapor forms clouds and releases heat energy wherever it changes back into rain (liquid water). In this way, wind systems carry moisture and work with surface ocean currents to move large amounts of heat energy all over Earth.

Weather vs. climate What is the difference between weather and climate? Both terms describe the temperature, precipitation, and wind that we feel. The main difference is time. Weather can change daily. **Climate** describes the long-term record of temperature, precipitation (rain or snow), and wind for a region. Climate changes slowly and is nearly the same from one year to the next. What is the climate like where you live? What is today's weather report? How are your answers to these questions similar and different?

What is a meteorologist? When you hear the word *meteorologist*, do you think of a television weather reporter? Many radio and television weathercasters are professional meteorologists, but others are reporters who are passing on information provided by the National Weather Service or private weather forecasters. A **meteorologist** is a person with specialized education who uses scientific principles to explain, understand, observe, or forecast Earth's weather. A meteorologist has a bachelor's degree (or higher) from a college or university. Many meteorologists have degrees in physics, chemistry, mathematics, and other fields.

ⓐ VOCABULARY

climate - the long-term record of temperature, precipitation, and wind for a region.

meteorologist - an individual who uses scientific principles to forecast the weather.

Surviving a desert climate

Did you know that the desert is home to more different types of animals than any other place except the rainforest? How can animals survive in such a hot climate?

Photo by George Harrison, USFWS

Jackrabbits have big ears. When the rabbit sits in the shade, the blood running under the surface of the ears is cooled, lowering the animal's body temperature. Use the library or Internet to learn how other animals are able to survive in this climate.

6.3 Section Review

1. Define wind. Draw a diagram that illustrates how wind is created.

2. What are small-scale and large-scale wind currents called?

3. Do convection currents connect the poles all the way to the equator?

4. What is water vapor?

5. Which holds more water vapor, a warm air mass or a cold air mass?

6. When the air is filled to capacity with water vapor, it is said to be _____.

7. What does it mean for the relative humidity of an air mass to be 70%?

8. If the temperature of an air mass increased by 20°C, would the relative humidity increase or decrease? Explain your answer.

9. An air mass cools to the point where it becomes saturated. What might happen next?

10. Draw a diagram of what happens when an air mass moves from the ocean over a mountain.

11. What is the most important source of water vapor in the atmosphere?

12. What is the main difference between weather and climate?

13. What is a meteorologist?

14. Research: What is a rainshadow desert? Where is one located in the United States?

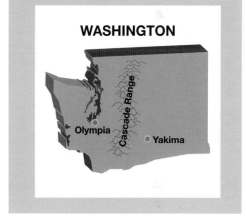

Look at the illustration below. Which city would receive more rain per year—Olympia or Yakima? Explain your answer. Go to the Internet and find out what the average rainfall actually is for each of these cities.

WASHINGTON

Cascade Range

Olympia

Yakima

▶RESEARCH◀ CONNECTION Weather Forecasting: The Heart of Meteorology

Neither rain nor sleet nor cold shall keep a mail carrier from doing his job (or you from walking the dog). The same can be said of your local meteorologist. Every day meteorologists broadcast weather reports. Millions of people plan what they will wear, what they will do after work or on the weekend, and if they will carry their umbrellas based on those reports.

But only a very few meteorologists in the United States wear a microphone or appear on camera at work. Most meteorologists work for the National Weather Service (NWS), a government agency that is part of the National Oceanic and Atmospheric Administration (NOAA).

NOAA was formed in 1970, and its mission is to predict changes in the atmosphere and ocean environments. This task includes predicting the weather.

Meteorologists observe and study Earth's atmosphere and its phenomena. Many work to forecast the weather and changing climate conditions, while others do scientific research. They try to understand how atmosphere affects environment. They study the constant changes in our atmosphere. They create computer models to predict how storms will form, when rivers will flood, and what areas will suffer droughts. Their work can go far beyond telling an audience whether it will be sunny or cloudy tomorrow.

Meteorologist at work

Julie Dian is a meteorologist who works at the National Weather Service Ohio River Forecast Center in Wilmington, Ohio. One of her responsibilities is to compare readings of temperature, winds, atmospheric pressure, precipitation

patterns, and other variables. She draws conclusions and makes predictions about local weather with this data.

Dian and other meteorologists use many tools of their trade. They gather information in many different ways.

- More than 11,000 volunteers from all over the United States and beyond provide daily reports. They phone their reports to warning and forecast centers.
- Satellites collect data and record images. The TV images you see of hurricanes in the Gulf of Mexico or Caribbean Sea, for instance, are provided by cameras on satellites high above Earth.
- Ground-based radar scans for precipitation and clouds.
- Weather balloons are launched to gather data.

Up, up, and away

Wind direction, air pressure, temperature, and humidity of air masses high in the sky all affect our weather down on the ground. Weather balloons can monitor these conditions.

Weather balloons are released at least twice a day from a structure (like the one at right) at the National Weather Service office in Wilmington. Additional balloons are released more often during severe weather.

The balloons are filled with helium. When they are inflated on the ground, they are about 2 meters across. As they rise, they grow to a diameter of about 6 meters. This is because the air pressure is lower at higher altitudes, so the gas inside the balloon expands.

One type of balloon carries a *radiosonde*, which is a miniature radio transmitter with instruments on it. The balloon rises 27,400 meters (90,000 feet) or higher. All along the way, the radiosonde measures data such as temperature, air pressure, and humidity and transmits the measurements to a ground receiver or satellite.

Dian uses a theodolite to track balloons that have been launched from her center. A *theodolite* is a surveyor's instrument for measuring angles and, in this case, for following the altitude and movement of the balloon. In this photo, Dian shows a student the radio theodolite at the NWS office. In her left hand she holds an unopened weather balloon. The theodolite in the photo shows the wind speed at different altitudes. Some theodolites contain telescopes, others have radio receivers.

Methods for predicting

There are several different ways to predict the weather. All of the information collected—from volunteers, radar, satellites, and weather balloons—is used in different models. Some of the older methods use historical information to predict future weather events. The most complex of these involves finding very similar conditions at some point in the past. Then the weather is predicted based on what happened in the "same" situation back then.

Today, computers have made forecasting much more successful. Numerical weather prediction, or NWP, is used to create computer models of the atmosphere. With NWP, many variables are considered. Air temperatures at different altitudes, wind speeds, humidity, high and low pressure areas—all this is fed into a computer. The computer creates a complex model of the atmosphere and provides the most accurate forecasts available.

Questions:

1. What is the mission of the National Oceanic and Atmospheric Administration?
2. What causes weather balloons to grow in diameter from 2 to 6 meters?
3. Why are today's weather forecasts more accurate than in the past?

CHAPTER ACTIVITY: Circumnavigating the Globe

The map on this page shows the world surface currents. Cold currents are marked in blue and warm currents are marked in red. You will use this map to plot a sailboat route for *circumnavigating* the globe from the coast of Massachusetts to the coast of California. This means you can't just go around North America. You need to go around the world!

Materials

Bathymetric map and colored markers or pencils (red, blue, and black)

What you will do

1. With a partner, study the map on this page. Find the coast of Massachusetts. Then, find the coast of California.

2. Large surface currents are mostly driven by winds. With your partner, you need to decide what currents to use so that your sail takes you from Massachusetts to California. Before you get started on "sailing around the world" come up with a name for your sailboat.

3. As you choose currents, draw them on your bathymetric map. Use a red to indicate a warm current, blue to indicate a cold current, and black to indicate other currents. Also use your black pencil or marker to label each current you draw.

Applying your knowledge

a. Do the warm currents flow towards or away from the equator? Do the cold currents flow towards or away from the equator?

b. On which side of the ocean basins are warm currents found? On which side of the ocean basins are cold currents found?

c. List any uninterrupted currents (they flow around the globe without being blocked by land)?

d. How many currents did you need to use to sail from Massachusetts to California? How does your route compare with the routes used by other teams?

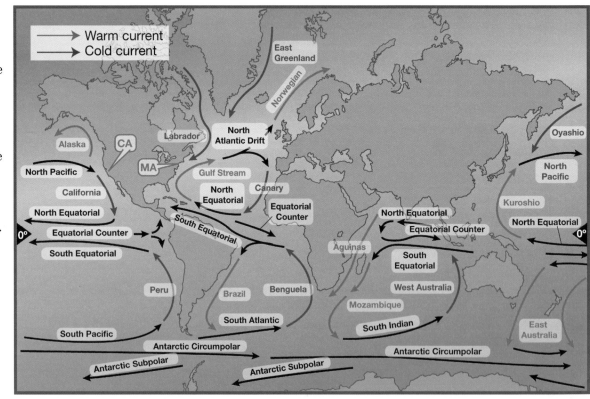

Chapter 6 Assessment

Vocabulary

Select the correct term to complete the sentences.

surface ocean current	rotation	thermals
evaporation	convection cells	deep ocean cur-
water vapor	revolution	rents
climate	weather	meteorologist
gyre	wind	

Section 6.1

1. Earth spinning once on its axis is a _____.

2. One Earth _____ represents a year.

Section 6.2

3. The Gulf Stream is an example of a _____.

4. In the ocean, _____ causes tropical waters to become more salty.

5. A current that moves within the ocean is called a _____. Another name for this kind of current is thermohaline current.

6. A circular ocean current is called a _____.

Section 6.3

7. _____ is water in gas form.

8. The long-term record of temperature, precipitation, and wind for an area is known as _____.

9. Air that flows, often because of unequal heating, is called _____.

10. Gliding birds use small heat-driven airflows called _____ to hunt for food.

11. _____ describes changes in temperature, precipitation, and wind for an area over a few days.

12. _____ are large wind loops that are heated and rise at the equator and cool and sink at higher latitudes.

13. A _____ uses scientific principles to forecast Earth's weather.

Concepts

Section 6.1

1. Why is it important that Earth have an atmosphere?

2. Could water exist as a liquid on Earth if it did not have an atmosphere?

3. According to this land surface temperature image (from the first page of Section 6.1), what large area of the United States had the highest temperatures in July 2003?

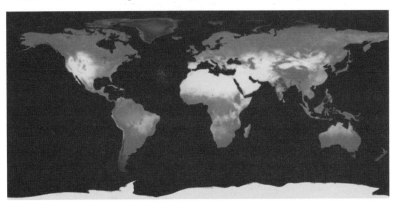

Land Surface Temperature (°C)

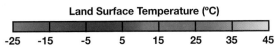

-25 -15 -5 5 15 25 35 45

July 2003. Image based on data from
NASA's Moderate Resolution Imaging Spectroradiometer (MODIS) Sensor. Credit: NASA

4. Earth's main source of heat energy is the Sun. Why doesn't Earth get too hot? List two reasons in your answer.

5. What are greenhouse gases?

6. Draw a diagram of Earth revolving around the Sun. Be sure to show Earth's axial tilt. Indicate on your diagram when it will be summer in the southern hemisphere.

Section 6.2

7. Name two ways that heat is moved around Earth.

8. Earth's oceans:

    a. Name Earth's five oceans.

    b. How much of Earth's surface is covered by oceans.

    c. How much of Earth's water is in the oceans?

9. Why does water expand at the equator?

10. What two factors cause the Gulf Stream to move away from the equator?

11. Which motion of Earth causes surface ocean currents to flow in a circular pattern: the rotation of Earth or the revolution of Earth?

12. Why are deep ocean currents also called thermohaline currents?

Section 6.3

13. What two factors cause wind?

14. A weather map shows a high pressure area located over Town A and a low pressure area located over Town B. Which direction will the wind blow? From Town A to Town B or from Town B to Town A?

15. Why is the equator a low air pressure area? Does air rise or sink at the equator?

16. What is a convection cell?

17. A weather report states that the relative humidity is forty percent. What does this value mean?

18. An air mass is described as being saturated. This means that the air mass contains _____ percent of the amount of water vapor it can hold.

    a. 100

    b. 1000

    c. 0

    d. 10

19. What is the relative humidity of an air mass that has just produced rain? High or low?

20. For each of the following statements write whether it describes the weather or the climate for an area:

    a. The temperature today is 40°C.

    b. In the northeastern United States, it often snows in the winter.

    c. It is supposed to rain tomorrow.

    d. Hurricanes commonly occur in tropical regions like the Caribbean and Florida.

    e. Where would you like to live: in a place where there are polar bears (the tundra) or in a place where you can see toucans (the tropical rainforest)?

    f. The desert southwest has very low humidity while the southeastern United States tends to have high humidity.

    g. Today's relative humidity was 80%.

    h. The average yearly temperature for Nome, Alaska is lower than the average yearly temperature for Paris, Texas.

Math and Writing Skills

Section 6.1

1. What is the total range in surface temperature on Earth according to Figure 6.1?

   a. 188 degrees Celsius

   b. 136 degrees Celsius

   c. 40 degrees Celsius

2. What was the range of temperature for Earth's surface for July 2003 based on the Land Surface Temperature graph?

3. In Section 6.1, you learned how long it takes for Earth to revolve around the Sun. Based on what you learned and doing conversion calculations, fill in the table below (one day = 24 hours).

Time for one revolution around the Sun	
Number of years	
Number of days	
Number of hours	

Section 6.2

4. One of the deep ocean currents is called the Antarctic Circumpolar Current. It is so called because it circles Antarctica. It aids in the circulation of deep and middle-range waters between the Atlantic, Indian, and Pacific Oceans. The average speed is about 10 cm/s. How many kilometers would this represent for a year's time?

5. Curtis Ebbesmeyer studies ocean currents by tracking different objects—like bathtub toys and sneakers—that have spilled into the ocean off of ships. In January of 1992, he tracked 28,800 rubber duckies and other floating toys in the mid-Pacific Ocean. Between the years of 1993 and 2004, 111 of these floating toys were found in Sitka, Alaska. They had been 2,200 miles adrift.

   a. If the floating toys traveled at 7 miles per day. How long would it take to travel 700 miles?

   b. It took the floating toys 3 years to complete the gyre in the Pacific—called the Subtropical Gyre—and the speed they traveled at was approximately 7 miles per day, then about how many miles does this gyre represent?

Section 6.3

6. In what general direction does wind blow between the latitudes of 30 degrees and 60 degrees north?

7. An air mass can hold at total of 20 grams of water vapor per kilogram of air. Right now the air mass has 5 grams of water vapor per kilogram of air. What is the relative humidity of this air mass?

8. In the air mass described in question 7, the water vapor increased to 20 grams of water vapor per kilogram of air. What is the relative humidity now?

Chapter Project—Mobiles and Water Tricks

Project 1: A seasons mobile

Make a mobile that represents Earth's four major positions in relation to the Sun. Make an axis through each Earth, draw the equator, the Tropics of Cancer and Capricorn. Use the diagram at the end of Section 6.1 to help you design your mobile.

Project 2: A water trick

See if you can setup two jars inverted on one another such that the liquid in one jar does not mix with the liquid in the other. *Important hints:* Ask an adult to help you. Work in a tray to catch any spills. Use two same-sized baby food jars that have been cleaned. Fill them to the rims with water. Make choices about the temperature and saltiness of the water in each jar. Add red food coloring to jar A and blue food coloring to jar B. Place an index card over the mouth of the jar B. Using both hands to hold the card to the rim of jar B, invert it on top of jar A. Gently pull out the card. Do the two volumes of water mix or stay separated?

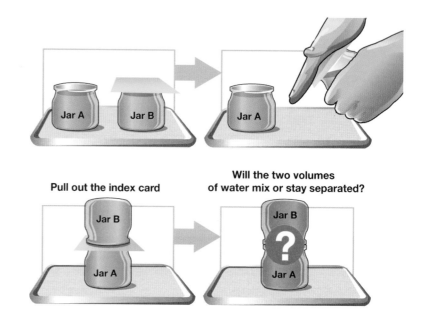

Pull out the index card

Will the two volumes of water mix or stay separated?

Chapter 7
Heat Inside Earth

People often travel to tropical areas to get warm in the winter time. What would you think if you saw an advertisement that said, "Warm up this winter in the hot center of Earth"? The center of Earth is hot, but could you actually get to the center of Earth and take a vacation there? On the next page, you will read about a science-fiction story that was based on this idea. However, in the chapter, as you learn what Earth looks like inside, you will also learn that traveling to the center of Earth is not possible!

Key Questions

1. *Is it possible to travel to Earth's core through a volcano?*

2. *What is Earth's core made of?*

3. *How is a continent like a boat?*

7.1 Sensing the Interior of Earth

No one has seen the center of our planet because it's impossibly deep. The distance from Earth's surface to its center is about 6,400 kilometers. The deepest we have drilled into Earth is about 13 kilometers—not even close! For a long time our knowledge of the center of Earth could be drawn only from studying its surface. In this section, you will learn how we study Earth's interior and what it looks like.

Ideas from the past

Science fiction Jules Verne wrote popular science-fiction books in the mid-1800s (Figure 7.1). Verne was popular among readers because he researched his topics and wrote stories that could have been true. In 1864, he wrote *A Journey to the Center of the Earth*. The main characters were three adventurers who explored a hollow Earth and lived to tell their tale. Along the way, they:

- entered Earth through an opening in a volcano in Iceland;
- climbed down through many strange chambers;
- crossed an ocean at the center of Earth; and
- escaped to the surface by riding a volcanic eruption.

Today scientists know that this adventure story is purely fictional and could never happen. But, how do they know this? What has changed in our view of the interior of Earth since the 1800s?

Special vibrations Scientists began to study special vibrations that travel through Earth shortly after Verne's book was written. These vibrations, called **seismic waves**, have revealed the structure of Earth's interior. Seismic waves are caused by events like earthquakes and human-made blasts. The waves pass along the surface and through Earth. A **seismologist** is a scientist who detects and interprets these vibrations at different locations on Earth's surface.

VOCABULARY

seismic waves - vibrations that travel through Earth and are caused by events like earthquakes or human-made blasts.

seismologist - a scientist who detects and interprets seismic waves.

Figure 7.1: *Jules Verne wrote popular science-fiction books—like* A Journey to the Center of the Earth— *in the mid-1800s.*

Wave motion

A push moves along a line

Imagine a line of students waiting for a bus. A student at the end of the line falls forward and bumps into the student in front of him before righting himself again. This causes that student to bump into the next student. The bumped student bumps another student and so on along the line. Each student in the line falls forward, bumps the next student, then rights himself. Eventually, the student at the head of the line feels the push that began at the end of the line.

Forward-and-backward motion

The "push" or **disturbance** that traveled down the line of students is an example of forward-and-backward wave motion. The student at the end of the line was still at the end of the line when the student at the front of the line felt the push. The disturbance traveled down the line while the students kept their places.

A domino "wave"

A line of dominoes also illustrates how a disturbance can travel. The first domino is pushed and soon the last domino falls over, even though it is far from the first one! However, a line of dominoes falls in one direction without any forward-and-backward motion.

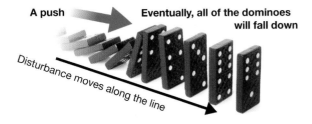

Up-and-down and side-to-side motion

Other kinds of wave motion are up-and-down and side-to-side motion (Figure 7.2). You are probably familiar with the up-and-down motion of water waves in a pool. You can demonstrate side-to-side wave motion by wiggling a rope.

disturbance - a movement that begins in one location and sets things in motion farther away.

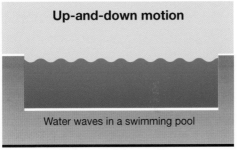

Figure 7.2: *Up-and-down and side-to-side motion.*

What kinds of disturbances can create water waves? Make a list of these disturbances and draw sketches to illustrate your list.

Kinds of seismic waves

P-waves and S-waves
There are several kinds of seismic waves. Two that are important for studying Earth's interior are primary and secondary waves. These waves are usually called by their first letter, P-waves and S-waves. **P-waves** travel faster than S-waves and move with a forward-and-backward motion. Slower **S-waves** travel with a side-to-side motion. S-waves do not pass through liquids, unlike P-waves which pass through solids, liquids, and gases.

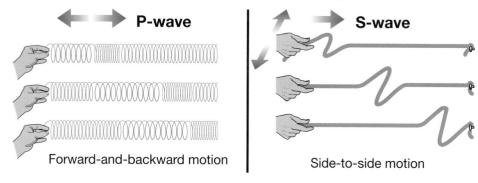

P-wave

Forward-and-backward motion

S-wave

Side-to-side motion

Waves tell us about Earth's interior
As P-waves and S-waves travel through Earth, they might be bent, bounced, sped up, or slowed down depending on the nature of the material they encounter. By studying what happens to the waves on their path through Earth, scientists are able to make detailed maps of Earth's interior.

A clue from S-waves
Here is a simple example of how scientists use seismic waves. Scientists observed that when S-waves are produced on one side of Earth due to an earthquake, there is a large area on the other side where the waves can't be detected (Figure 7.3). They called this area the *S-shadow*. Something was blocking the S-waves as they tried to pass through! Scientists know that secondary waves do not pass through liquid. With this fact and these observations, they realized that the outer core of Earth must be liquid.

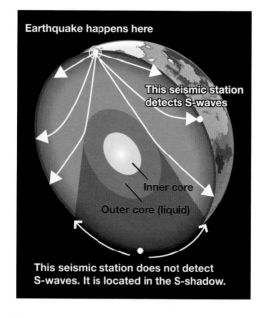

Earthquake happens here

This seismic station detects S-waves

Inner core

Outer core (liquid)

This seismic station does not detect S-waves. It is located in the S-shadow.

Figure 7.3: *In the graphic above, S-waves deflect off the liquid outer core of Earth. Since S-waves cannot pass through the outer core, an S-shadow is created on the side of Earth opposite the earthquake.*

7.1 Section Review

1. What is Earth's radius in kilometers? What is Earth's radius in miles (1 kilometer = 0.62 miles)?

2. Answer these questions about the vibrations that travel through Earth:

   a. What are these vibrations called?

   b. What causes them?

   c. What have these vibrations revealed about Earth's interior?

3. What is a seismologist?

4. During wave motion, what moves from one place to another?

5. What are the two general types of wave motion described in this section?

6. List the two most important seismic waves used for studying Earth's interior. Give three facts about each type of wave.

7. After an earthquake, P-waves travel at an average speed of 5 kilometers per second and S-waves travel at an average speed of 3 kilometers per second. A seismic station is located 30 kilometers from where the earthquake occurred (Figure 7.4).

   a. How many seconds would it take for the P-waves to reach the seismic station?

   b. How many seconds would it take for the S-waves to reach the station?

8. What can happen to seismic waves as they travel through Earth?

9. What are S-shadows? You may use a diagram to help you answer this question.

10. What do S-shadows tell us about the interior of Earth?

MY JOURNAL

Is it possible to travel to Earth's core through a volcano?

Write a paragraph that answers this question based on what you knew about Earth *before* you read Section 7.1.

Then, write a paragraph that answers this question based on what you know about Earth *now that you have finished* reading Section 7.1.

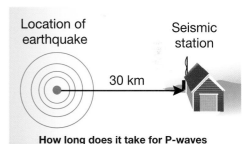

How long does it take for P-waves and S-waves to reach the seismic station?

Figure 7.4: *An earthquake occurs 30 kilometers away from a seismic station. How long does it take for P-waves and S-waves to reach the station?*

7.2 Earth's Interior

Simple diagrams of Earth's interior show it as having three layers—an outer crust, a mantle, and a core. Modern science has revealed much more detail in these layers. The graphic below shows some of this detail.

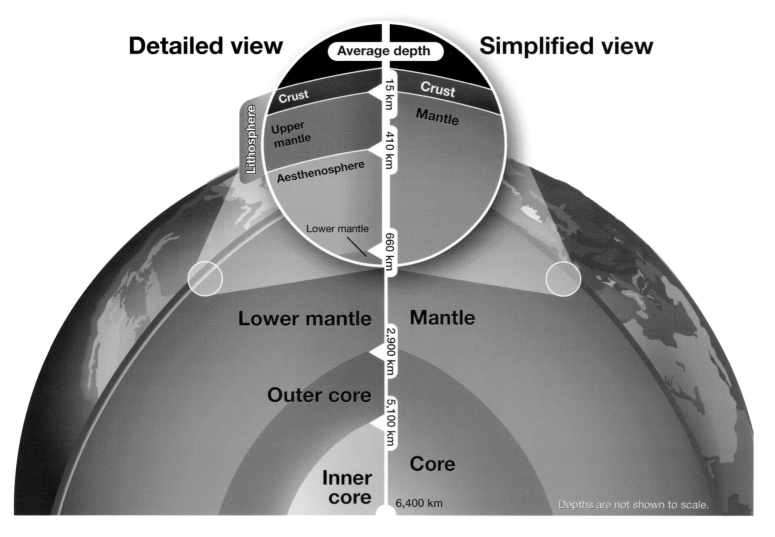

Detailed view

Average depth

Simplified view

Lithosphere

Crust

Crust

Upper mantle

Mantle

Aesthenosphere

15 km

Lower mantle

410 km

660 km

Lower mantle

Mantle

2,900 km

Outer core

5,100 km

Inner core

Core

6,400 km

Depths are not shown to scale.

The crust and the mantle

What is Earth's crust?

The **crust** is the outermost surface of Earth. Oceanic crust lies under the oceans and is thin. Its average thickness is about 5 kilometers. Continental crust forms continents and is thicker. Its average thickness is 30 kilometers (Figure 7.5). Because rock in the crust is cool, the crust is brittle (cracks and breaks easily). Shallow earthquakes occur in the crust.

What is Earth's mantle?

In the simplified view of Earth, the **mantle** is the layer between the crust and the core. The simplified mantle includes the upper and lower mantle of the detailed view, and is about 2,900 kilometers thick. Mantle material is warm and soft enough to flow. The less-dense crust floats on the mantle!

Lithosphere

The **lithosphere** includes the crust and a thin part of the mantle. This thin, outer-most mantle is called the *upper mantle*. The plates that move about Earth's surface are pieces of lithosphere.

Aesthenosphere

The aesthenosphere lies just under the lithosphere and is the outermost part of the lower mantle. The aesthenosphere is a slushy zone of hot rock with a small amount of melted rock. This part of the lower mantle is important because the lithospheric plates slide on it. The aesthenosphere is 100 or more kilometers thick under oceans, and much less under continents.

Lower mantle

In the simplified view of Earth, the mantle includes everything below the crust and above the core. The detailed view of Earth separates the mantle into the upper and lower mantle. The lower mantle includes the aesthenosphere. The lower mantle is the largest part of Earth's interior. Although the lower mantle is made of rock, it is warm. Because it is warm, it is *plastic*. Plastic here means that the lower mantle flows slowly rather than breaking.

VOCABULARY

crust - the outermost surface of Earth.

mantle - the warm, flowing, solid layer of Earth between the crust and the core.

lithosphere - a layer of Earth that includes the crust and upper mantle.

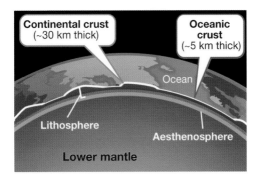

Figure 7.5: *The continental crust is about 30 kilometers thick. The oceanic crust is about 5 kilometers thick.*

The core

What is Earth's core? The **core** is the name for the center of Earth. In the simplified, traditional view of Earth, the core is a single central ball. The detailed view divides the core into two layers, the inner and outer core. The material that makes up the core is denser than the material in the mantle. The core is also an extremely hot place! Earth's temperature increases from the crust to the core.

Outer core Seismic S-waves show that the outer core is liquid. The outer core is made mostly of iron, and is so hot the iron is melted. Powerful electric currents are formed as the liquid outer core moves. These electric currents create Earth's magnetic field. This magnetic field protects the planet from harmful solar radiation (Figure 7.6). It also protects the atmosphere. Life on Earth would be in danger if the outer core cooled and stopped moving.

Inner core The inner core is also made mostly of iron, but it is solid. The inner core is also hot enough to melt iron, so why is it solid? Melting depends on pressure as well as temperature. The pressure at the inner core is so enormous that iron, and the rest of the inner core, remains a solid.

Summary Information about the layers of Earth is summarized below.

core - the center of Earth; it is divided into the inner core and the outer core.

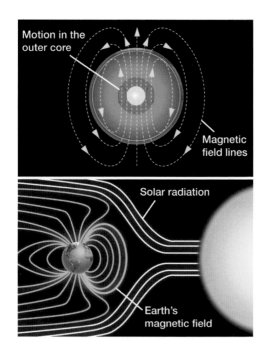

Figure 7.6: *Earth's magnetic field is created by powerful electric currents formed by the motion of liquid iron in Earth's outer core. Earth's magnetic field protects the planet from harmful radiation from the Sun.*

Layers of Earth		Average depth (km)	Relative temperature (°C)		Description
Lithosphere {	Crust	15	0	Temperature increases with depth	The uppermost layer
	Upper mantle	410	870		
	Aesthenosphere	660			The surface of the lower mantle on which lithospheric plates slide.
	Lower mantle	2900	3700		Largest part of Earth's interior
Core {	Outer core	5100	4300		Liquid
	Inner core	6400	7200		Solid (hotter than the surface of the Sun)

7.2 Section Review

1. Simplified diagrams of Earth's interior show three layers. What are these layers?

2. Use Figure 7.7 to help you answer the following questions.
   a. What layers compose Earth's core?
   b. The upper mantle and crust make up which layer of Earth's interior?
   c. What is the name of the thickest layer of Earth's interior?

3. How thick is the outer core in kilometers?

4. Which is thicker—oceanic crust or continental crust?

5. Is the crust brittle? Why is this? Do earthquakes occur in the crust?

6. The plates that move about Earth's surface are pieces of the
   _____.

7. What is the aesthenosphere and why is it important?

8. What material makes up most of the outer core? Is it solid or liquid? Why?

9. What material makes up most of the inner core? Is it solid or liquid? Why?

10. What very important process happens in the outer core? Why is it important?

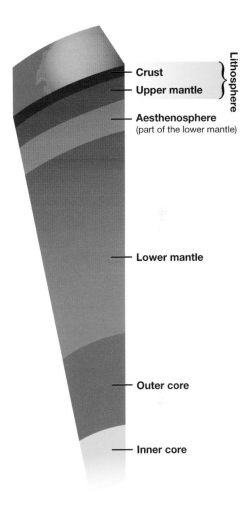

Figure 7.7: *A detailed view of the layers of Earth's interior.*

7.3 Density and Buoyancy Inside Earth

Scientists believe that Earth formed from the gas and dust that surrounded our young sun. At first, Earth's surface was made of the same materials as its center. At some point, the material melted and became fluid.

Earth's materials sorted by density

Earth's layers You learned in Chapter 5 that less dense objects will float in more dense fluids. Once Earth became fluid, materials began to sort out by their densities. Less buoyant, denser materials settled toward the center. More buoyant and less dense materials rose toward the surface. Today aluminum and silicon are common within Earth's crust. These elements have low densities. The inner and outer cores are composed mostly of dense iron (Figure 7.8).

Earth's crust floats on the mantle Earth's crust is made of different types of rock that are less dense than the mantle. Oceanic crust is made of *basalt* and is slightly denser than continental crust. Continental crust is made of mostly *andesite* and *granite* (Figure 7.9). Oceanic crust is thinner than continental crust, but both kinds of crust float on the mantle.

Rocks float on rocks! We tend to think that rocks are all the same. It's hard to imagine rocks floating on other rocks, but this is what happens inside Earth! The cold brittle rocks of the crust float on the hot, soft, and denser rock below.

	Density (g/cm^3)
aluminum	2.7
silicon	2.3
iron	7.9
water	1.0

Figure 7.8: *Density values for substances that make up Earth.*

Figure 7.9: *The oceanic crust is made mostly of basalt. The continental crust is made mostly of andesite and granite.*

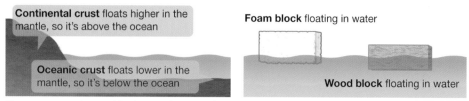

Because oceanic crust is denser than continental crust, it floats lower in Earth's mantle. Blocks of foam and wood floating in water demonstrate this phenomenon.

Floating continents

How is a continent like a boat? Imagine stacking blocks on a toy boat floating in a pool. As you add blocks, the stack gets higher and heavier. The extra weight presses more of the boat into the water to support the stack. The finished stack stands taller than the original boat, but the boat is also deeper in the water.

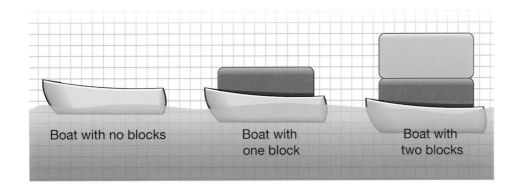

Boat with no blocks   Boat with one block   Boat with two blocks

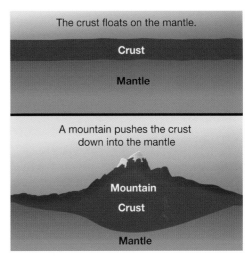

Figure 7.10: *How a mountain affects the crust.*

Mountains on continents Earth's crust floats on the mantle just like the boat. A mountain on land is just like the stack of blocks (Figure 7.10). Like the boat, the crust with a mountain sticks down into the mantle. The average thickness of continental crust is 30 kilometers, but the combination of a mountain and its bulge underneath may make the crust as thick as 70 kilometers.

Glaciers on continents During an ice age, the weight of glacial ice presses down the crust just like a mountain. After the ice age ends and the glacier melts, the crust springs back up again (Figure 7.11). Scientists studying shorelines have detected these up-and-down movements.

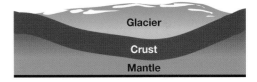

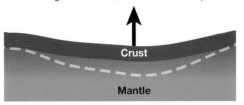

Figure 7.11: *How a glacier affects the crust. The effects have been exaggerated to show the changes.*

Convection

Convection in the lower mantle

Most of the remaining heat from the formation of our planet lies in the core. The hot core heats the lower mantle where the two layers come together. Can you predict what happens next? Heating the lower mantle causes the material to expand. The mass doesn't change, but the volume increases. This makes the heated material less dense. You know that less dense objects will float in more dense fluids. The result is a plume of hot lower mantle material rising up from near the core toward the lithosphere.

As the convection current nears the lithosphere, it turns and runs along underneath. Eventually the convection current loses its heat and sinks back toward the core. You will recognize this as a convection cell (Figure 7.12). Convection in the lower mantle is identical to convection in a heated room and in our atmosphere. In the next chapter on plate tectonics, you will see how lower mantle convection drives the lithospheric plates across Earth's surface.

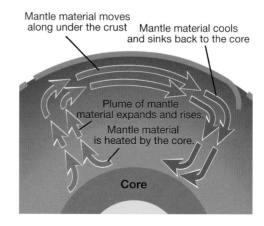

Figure 7.12: *How convection in the mantle occurs.*

Seismic tomography

In the early days of seismology, scientists detected seismic waves with mechanical detectors. All studies of arriving waves were done with paper and pencil. Today the tools are much better. Electronic detectors provide much more information about seismic waves. But the real improvement is in the use of computers and the invention of *seismic tomography* by Dr. Adam Dziewonski of Harvard University. Seismic tomography uses seismic waves collected from all over the world to create a three-dimensional image of Earth's interior (Figure 7.13). This process is similar to using many x-ray sensors to create a CAT scan of someone's head. CAT stands for computer-assisted tomography. A computer combines the signals from these x-ray detectors to produce a three-dimensional image of the inside of the patient's head.

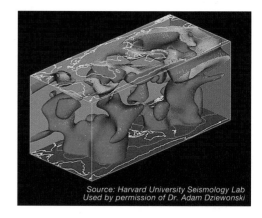

Figure 7.13: *The red blobs in the graphic are warmer, less dense convection currents of mantle rising toward Earth's surface from the core.*

7.3 Section Review

1. Explain how the young Earth separated into layers. Use the term *density* in your answer.

2. Draw a simplified diagram of Earth's interior.

   a. Indicate on the diagram where you would find aluminum and silicon.

   b. Then, indicate on the diagram where you would most likely find iron.

   c. Using the density values in Figure 7.8, explain why water floats on Earth's surface.

   d. How do you think the density of the mantle compares to the densities of the crust and the core? Explain your answer.

3. What kind of rock makes up the ocean floor?

4. What kind of rock makes up the continents?

5. Can rocks float? Explain.

6. What might happen to a mountain that would cause the crust to float higher in the mantle?

7. What might happen to a glacier that would cause the crust to float higher in the mantle?

8. What process drives the lithospheric plates across the surface of Earth? Draw a diagram of this process.

9. What is seismic tomography?

10. How is a CAT scan like seismic tomography?

 **STUDY SKILLS**

You have learned many new terms in Units 1 and 2. To help you better understand and remember these terms, make a flash card for each vocabulary word using index cards.

A flash card has the term on one side and the definition on the other side. It looks like this:

Front:

Mantle

Back:

The warm, flowing, solid layer of Earth between the crust and the core.

Mantle

Flash cards are useful because they are small enough to take anywhere. Study one or two flash cards whenever you have a break during the day.

If you have read all of Unit 1 and Unit 2, you have learned more than 60 new vocabulary terms!

Good job!

Drilling to Earth's Core

How do you get to the heart of the matter on this planet? It's deep down there, nearly 4,000 miles (about 6,500 kilometers) beneath your feet. If we could somehow reach Earth's core, from there every direction would be "up."

We may never reach that center core, but scientists are always getting closer. For the first time, people have drilled into the lower section of Earth's crust. Just getting through the planet's outer layer was a huge job: eight 0weeks of drilling a hole in the ocean floor.

Scientists will not stop there. They hope to break into the upper mantle, the layer just beneath the crust, some time in the coming years. That is one of the goals of the Integrated Ocean Drilling Program (IODP).

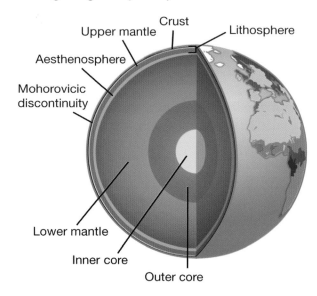

Crust
Upper mantle
Lithosphere
Aesthenosphere
Mohorovicic discontinuity
Lower mantle
Inner core
Outer core

Scientists are looking for a boundary they call the "Moho," short for the Mohorovicic discontinuity. This boundary between Earth's crust and the upper mantle below is named for Andrija Mohorovicic, the Croatian seismologist who first identified it in 1909.

The planet's outer crust is thin and hard. The mantle lies just below the crust, and it is hot and soft and a more flexible layer. The three layers of the mantle (the upper mantle, the aesthenosphere, and the lower mantle) make up nearly 80 percent of Earth's total volume. Beneath the mantle is the liquid outer core and the solid inner core.

Digging for clues

By drilling deep into the crust, scientists hope to learn more about how it forms. They also hope to learn more about the movement of the upper mantle.

Why drill in the oceans? The simple reason is that the oceanic crust is thinner, about 5 kilometers (3 miles) thick in the ocean trenches. The continental crust is about 30 kilometers thick (about 18 or 19 miles).

If the drill can reach the Moho, we may learn how the mantle and the crust interact, or, more importantly, how the crust forms. All of this information will help scientists understand the differences between the mantle and the crust.

Ocean drilling platform

The complex inner Earth

Drilling has allowed scientists to learn more about Earth's structure. It shows how complex the structure is and how Earth evolved. The IODP scientists for the first time have collected data from the lower crust. Mantle material, however, has yet to be recovered.

Finding the Moho isn't easy because it isn't at the same depth everywhere. The latest IODP hole—that took almost 8 weeks to drill—went about 4,644 feet (1,415 meters) below the floor of the Atlantic Ocean.

Drilling into the rock

Even at that depth, the Moho was not reached. Still, the rock that was drilled out taught us new things about the complexity of the planet's structure.

Another glimpse deep down

Another way we learn about Earth's interior is from earthquakes. An earthquake's seismic waves travel through the layers of the mantle and through the core.

The study of seismic waves has already convinced scientists that Earth's core is rotating faster than its surface. This was confirmed by comparing the travel times of waves passing through the core.

Researchers did this by comparing two earthquakes that had happened in almost the exact same place but on different dates. Then they compared the time it took each quake's shockwaves to pass through the core. Some parts of the core are denser than others, which can speed up or slow the shock waves as they pass through the core.

Scientists studied two almost identical earthquakes that happened at the same place near South America. If the core was moving at the same speed as the surface, the time it took for the seismic waves to be recorded would be the same for each earthquake. But the times and shapes of the waves were different. This meant that the seismic waves passed through a different part of the core in each earthquake.

Based on this, scientists believe Earth's core is spinning faster than the planet's surface. It actually "laps" the surface about every 400 years!

Why does this matter? Differences in the core's rotation may affect the whole planet's rotation. Understanding Earth's past and present will influence how we move forward into the future. By looking inside it, we may see much farther outside Earth as we evolve along with it.

Questions:

1. What is the IODP and what is one of its goals?
2. Has the IODP succeeded in reaching its goal? Why or why not?
3. What is the Moho?
4. Which layer of Earth makes up nearly 80 percent of its total volume?
5. What has convinced researchers that Earth's core is spinning faster than the planet's surface?

CHAPTER ACTIVITY Modeling Wave Motion Through Different Materials

In this activity, you will be observing wave motion, the movement of primary and secondary waves, and the change in behavior of a wave as it passes from one material to another. As you have learned, seismic waves have given humans a great amount of information about our Earth. You have also learned that there is more than one kind of seismic wave and that even though all of them produce wave motions, the individual disturbances along the wave move very differently through the planet. Let's look and see if we can demonstrate how this energy travels.

Materials

*   Large springs (both metal and plastic)
*   Electrical tape
*   Meter stick
*   Water
*   Shallow rectangular bin for water
*   Small stone

What you will do

1. Modeling wave motion: Fill the bin with an inch or two of water. Drop the stone into the water and watch the waves. Try this several times and then answer questions a-c. You have just modeled wave motion!
2. With a partner take the metal spring and stretch it about 3 meters and lay it on a flat surface such as the floor or a long table.
3. To demonstrate P-wave motion, one person will hold the spring at one end. The other person will move their hand holding the spring forward and backward. Answer question d.
4. To demonstrate S-wave motion, one person will hold the spring on one end firmly and the other person will move his or hand quickly side-to-side. Answer question e.

5. Now take the plastic spring and tape one end to one end of the metal spring. The two springs represent two different materials. This demonstration will show what happens when wave energy passes through a boundary of two different materials, like different layers in Earth. Generate both P- and S-waves as you did before using the metal spring. Watch as the wave motion travels through to the plastic spring. Answer question f.

What happens when a wave travels from one material to another?

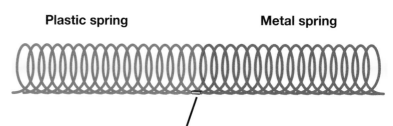

Plastic spring   Metal spring

Tape the springs together

Applying your knowledge

a. Draw or describe how the waves looked in the water.
b. Did the waves in the water tend to move over the surface or down through the water to the bottom of the bin?
c. How is this different from how P- and S-waves move?
d. Describe or draw what happens with the P-wave motion.
e. Describe or draw what happens with the S wave motion.
f. Describe what happens at the boundary of the two springs.
g. A P-wave from an earthquake goes through the mantle and then through the core of Earth. Based on what you have observed in this lab, what would you expect about the path of this wave?

Chapter 7 Assessment

Vocabulary

Select the correct term to complete the sentences.

seismologist	crust	seismic waves
lithosphere	core	P-waves
mantle	S-waves	disturbance

Section 7.1

1. _____ are seismic waves that do not pass through liquids.

2. A scientist that detects and interprets seismic waves at different locations on Earth is called a _____.

3. Vibrations that travel through Earth are called _____.

4. _____ are seismic waves that move in a forward-and-backward motion.

5. During wave motion, a _____ moves from one place to another.

Section 7.2

6. The largest part of Earth's interior that is made of rock, but is flexible, is the _____.

7. The _____ is the inner iron-containing layer of Earth.

8. Made of the crust and upper mantle, the _____ makes up the plates that move about Earth's surface.

9. The outermost surface of Earth is called the _____.

Concepts

Section 7.1

1. Jules Verne described Earth and its interior in his book *A Journey to the Center of the Earth*. Was he a scientist? Why or why not?

2. People cannot travel to the center of Earth in person. How then do scientists study what Earth looks like inside?

3. You can create an up-and-down wave by wiggling a jump rope. What travels from one place to another during the wave motion? What stays in place?

4. For each of these statements write either P-wave or S-wave:
   a. Travels through all material.
   b. Does not travel through liquids
   c. Forward-and-backward motion
   d. Side-to-side motion
   e. Slower
   f. Faster

Section 7.2

5. How is Earth's crust different from the mantle? List three ways.

6. The _____ is the slippery surface on which the lithospheric plates move around Earth's surface.

7. What causes Earth's magnetic field? Why is Earth's magnetic field important?

8. The inner core is really hot but solid. Why isn't the inner core a liquid like the outer core?

Section 7.3

9. With all the layers that make up Earth, which layer is the densest and which is the least dense? Why?

10. List the differences between the continental crust and the oceanic crust.

11. How would studying a shoreline help a scientist figure out that there had been up and down movement of the crust?

12. What do you think would happen if there was no convection in Earth's mantle?

13. The up-and-down movement of the crust due to the weight of overlying objects, such as mountains or melting of glaciers is a result of _____.

   (a) convection in the mantle   (c) magnetic fields

   (b) buoyancy of the crust   (d) mantle plumes
   floating on the mantle

14. The rock of the ocean floor, basalt, is slightly _____ than granite, the rock of the continents.

   (a) denser   (c) more magnetic

   (b) less dense   (d) more flexible

Math and Writing Skills

Section 7.1

1. In the box below is a list of four events that happen in *A Journey to the Center of the Earth*. Write a paragraph that explains whether each is a realistic event or not.

> In *A Journey to the Center of the Earth*, the main characters were three adventurers who explored a hollow Earth and lived to tell their tale. Along the way, they:
>
> - entered Earth through an opening in a volcano in Iceland;
> - climbed down through many strange chambers;
> - crossed an ocean at the center of Earth; and
> - escaped to the surface by riding a volcanic eruption.

2. Reading about the way scientists learned about the outer core being liquid, do you have a personal experience where you learned something new in an indirect way? Explain your experience in a paragraph.

3. After an earthquake, P-waves travel at an average speed of 5 kilometers per second and S-waves travel at an average speed of 3 kilometers per second. A seismic station is located 15 kilometers from where the earthquake occurred. How many seconds would it take:

   a. the P-waves to reach the station?

   b. the S-waves to reach the station?

Section 7.2

4. What is the radius of Earth in kilometers? What is the diameter of Earth in kilometers?

5. Scientists have only been able to drill into the lower part of Earth's crust. What percentage of the radius have scientists drilled into?

    (a) 100%   (c) less than 1%

    (b) 50%   (d) 25%

6. The continental crust averages about 30 kilometers thick. You learned that the continental crust is thickest at mountains. Where would it be thinnest?

7. Where would the oceanic crust (which averages about 5 kilometers thick) be thinnest?

8. How thick is the lower mantle?

Section 7.3

9. Why does water float on Earth's surface? Refer to the table below to help you answer this question.

	Density (g/cm^3)
aluminum	2.7
silicon	2.3
iron	7.9
water	1.0

10. Imagine you are a lithospheric plate on Earth's surface. Describe yourself. Explain how you move around on Earth.

Chapter Project—Earth Model Flash Cards

1. Make a 3-dimensional model of the detailed view of Earth's interior (see Figure 7.7). Include all the layers and label them. For your materials, you will need to be creative. Some ideas—use modelling clay or place layers of colored sand in a transparent container.

2. In Section 5.1, you learned a good study skill—making flash cards to help you learn concepts and vocabulary. Make flash cards of the vocabulary you have learned so far in chapters 1 through 7. Add colorful diagrams to your flash cards!

WHERE DO YOU FIND VOLCANOES?

CASCADE TRENCH

SAN ANDREAS FAULT

Appalachian Mountains

TRY THIS AT HOME

Find five rocks near your house. Wash off any soil that is on the rocks. Study them and describe each rock in a short paragraph. What colors do you see? Do you see layers or crystals? Compare your rocks. Are they the same kind or different?

What do your rocks tell you about where you live? Bring your rocks to school and see if they match any of the rocks in your classroom rock set.

Chapter 8
Plate Tectonics

In this chapter, you will learn about one of the most important discoveries of the 20th century—plate tectonics. You have already learned about Earth's surface and that it is covered with a lithosphere that is broken into pieces called "plates." Plate tectonics is the study of the movement of these plates. It is a relatively new field of study. Scientists have only arrived at our current understanding of plate tectonics over the past 40 years. This is a very short time in science years!

Key Questions

1. *How is the surface of Earth like a giant jigsaw puzzle?*

2. *Why are magnetic patterns important?*

3. *How do rocks change?*

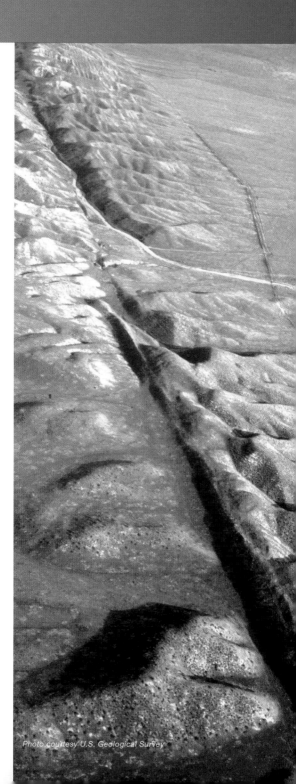

Photo courtesy U.S. Geological Survey

8.1 Alfred Wegener's Supercontinent

While looking at a map of the world, have you ever noticed that the continents look like pieces of a puzzle? If they are moved closer together across the Atlantic Ocean, they would fit neatly to form a giant landmass (Figure 8.1). In this section, you will learn about Alfred Wegener and his idea that a "supercontinent" once existed on Earth.

Movement of continents

Continental drift
Alfred Wegener was a German climatologist and arctic explorer who suggested the concept of continental drift. **Continental drift** is the idea that the continents move around on Earth's surface.

Wegener's hypothesis
In the early 1900s, Wegener hypothesized that the continents were once connected. Today, after a lot of scientific research and collected evidence, we know that Wegener was right.

Pangaea — a supercontinent
In 1915, Wegener published his ideas in a book, *Origins of the Continents and Oceans*. Wegener thought that the continents we know today had once been part of an earlier *supercontinent*. He called this great landmass **Pangaea** (Greek for "all land"). According to continental drift, Pangaea broke apart and the pieces moved to their present places, becoming today's continents.

What is plate tectonics?
In Chapter 1, you were introduced to plate tectonics, the study of lithospheric plates. You learned that the surface of Earth is broken into many pieces like a giant jigsaw puzzle. **Plate tectonics** describes how these pieces move on Earth's surface. By the time you finish this chapter, you will know more about this theory than any scientist knew only forty years ago. Wow! Additionally, you will learn that the development of this theory is an excellent example of how the scientific process works. Now, let's return to Wegener and his idea of continental drift.

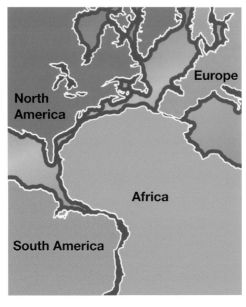

Figure 8.1: *The continents on either side of the Atlantic Ocean fit together like puzzle pieces.*

continental drift - the idea that continents move around on Earth's surface.

Pangaea - an ancient, huge landmass composed of earlier forms of today's continents; an ancient supercontinent.

plate tectonics - a theory explaining how the pieces of Earth's surface (the plates) move.

Evidence for continental drift

Matching coal beds, mountains, and fossils

Wegener was not the only scientist to suggest that continents moved. But his theory stood out because of the evidence that he gathered to support his idea of continental drift. Wegener's evidence is presented in the graphic below and listed at the right in the sidebar.

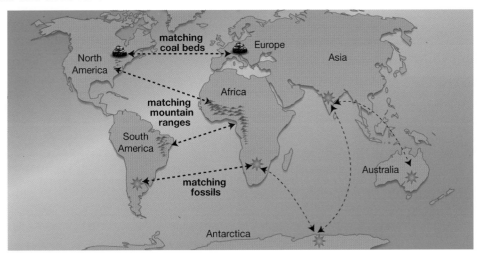

A good hypothesis

Wegener's belief that the continents had been connected in the past was a good idea. It was a *scientific hypothesis based on observations.*

Continental drift was rejected

Continental drift was a good hypothesis that was rejected by other scientists. A key part of Wegener's hypothesis was that some unknown force had caused the continents to slide over, or push through, the rocky bottoms of the oceans. Yet, neither he nor anyone else could identify the source of the force needed to move continents. Continental drift helped explain issues in geology—like why South America and Africa seem to fit together. However, continental drift could not be accepted by scientists because there was no evidence to explain how continents could move.

Wegener's evidence for continental drift

Coal beds stretch across the eastern United States and continue across southern Europe.

Matching plant fossils in South America, Africa, India, Australia, and Antarctica.

Matching reptile fossils have been found in South America and Africa.

Matching early mammal fossils found in South America, and Africa.

Fossils in South America and Africa are found in rocks of identical age and type.

Matching mountain ranges in North America, Africa, and South America.

Evidence of glaciers is present in regions with warm, dry climates. This indicates that continents that are close to the equator today were once closer to the South Pole in the distant past.

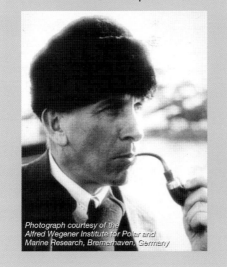

Photograph courtesy of the Alfred Wegener Institute for Polar and Marine Research, Bremerhaven, Germany

8.1 Section Review

1. Who was Alfred Wegener?

2. Alfred Wegener thought that all continents were once connected. Explain one observation that led to this belief.

3. Why did scientists reject Wegener's idea of continental drift?

4. In this section, you read that the development of the theory of plate tectonics is a good example of the scientific process.

   a. How did Wegener follow the scientific process?

   b. When scientists rejected continental drift, were they using the scientific process? Why or why not?

5. Answer these challenge questions.

   a. Name the seven modern continents.

   b. Make a table that lists the modern continents and describes the animal fossils that are found on each, according to the graphic below (Figure 8.2).

   c. A long time ago, glaciers covered parts of some the continents. Why aren't glaciers on these continents today?

Cynognathus ("Dog jaw")
Primitive mammal

Glossopteris (Glossa means "tongue" in Greek; this plant had tongue-shaped leaves)
Seed fern

Lystrosaurus ("Shovel lizard")
Primitive mammal

Mesosaurus ("Middle lizard")
Freshwater reptile

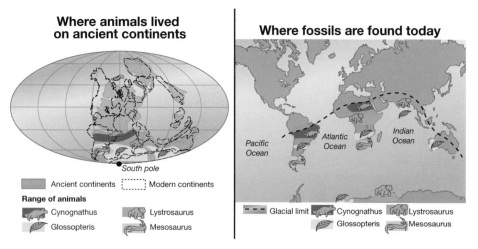

Figure 8.2: *Fossils that are found on modern continents. In the ancient past, the modern continents were connected as a supercontinent.*

8.2 Sea-floor Spreading

In Wegener's time, the world's ocean floors were largely unexplored. Mapping the sea floor provided more important evidence for the theory of plate tectonics.

Undersea mountains discovered

A map of the ocean floor During World War II, the United States Navy needed to locate enemy submarines hiding on the bottom of shallow seas. Therefore, large areas of the ocean floor were mapped for the first time. American geophysicist and Naval officer Harry Hess did some of the mapping. His work helped develop the theory of plate tectonics.

Mid-ocean ridges The naval maps showed huge mountain ranges that formed a continuous chain down the centers of the ocean floors. These mountain ranges are called **mid-ocean ridges**. Hess was intrigued by their shape and location. He wondered if it was possible that new ocean floor was created at the mid-ocean ridges. If new ocean floor formed at the ridges, then continents on either side would get pushed apart during the process (Figure 8.3).

Harry Hess' idea
As new sea floor is made at mid-ocean ridges, the continents are pushed away.

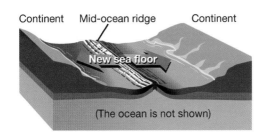

Continent   Mid-ocean ridge   Continent

New sea floor

(The ocean is not shown)

Figure 8.3: *Harry Hess wondered if it was possible that new ocean floor was created at the mid-ocean ridges.*

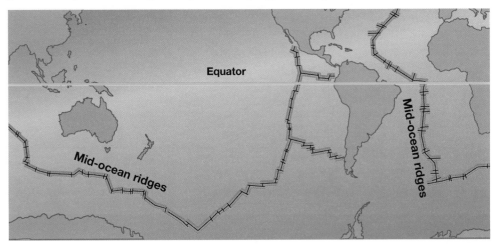

Equator

Mid-ocean ridges

Mid-ocean ridges

The sea-floor spreading hypothesis

A hypothesis is born Hess believed that Wegener was partly right. The continents *had* separated from a supercontinent, but not by plowing through the sea floor. Instead, continents moved along as a part of the growing sea floor! Hess called his hypothesis **sea-floor spreading**. Although his idea seemed to fit with existing observations, Hess realized that he didn't have enough supporting evidence for such a breathtaking idea. Because his theory was speculative, he called it "geo-poetry."

A good idea needs more evidence Sea-floor spreading was an attractive idea. But for many years scientists had viewed the continents as fixed in place. They felt that their shapes were due to causes that did not involve moving. Sea-floor spreading would need strong support before it would be more than geo-poetry.

Rapid scientific progress A time of tremendously rapid scientific progress followed Hess' sea-floor spreading hypothesis. Many scientists added to each other's work and found the strong evidence needed to explain sea-floor spreading.

Magnetic patterns and the age of rocks The key was the discovery that there are patterns (called "magnetic patterns") in the rocks on either side of the mid-ocean ridges (Figure 8.4). Scientists were able to read these patterns. They determined that on either side of a mid-ocean ridge, the oldest rocks were furthest from the ridge. They also found that the pattern on one side of a ridge matched the pattern on the other side. These patterns showed that Hess' geo-poetry was correct. New ocean floor is formed at mid-ocean ridges and the new floor moves away from the ridge as time passes.

sea-floor spreading - a hypothesis that new sea floor is created at mid-ocean ridges and that in the process the continents are pushed apart from each other.

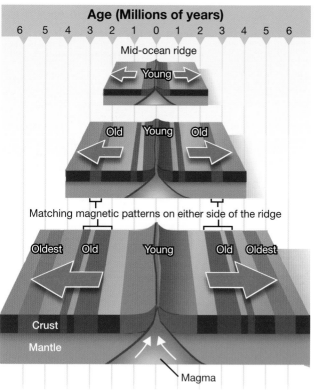

Figure 8.4: *Matching magnetic patterns and the age of rocks on either side of mid-ocean ridges provide strong evidence for sea-floor spreading.*

Moving pieces of the lithosphere

After a breakthrough After the breakthrough discovery of magnetic patterns was understood, there was great scientific interest in the idea of sea-floor spreading. Scientists realized that large pieces of Earth's surface moved about like rafts on a river.

Today we know these "rafts" are pieces of lithosphere called **lithospheric plates** that move over the aesthenosphere (review the interior of Earth in Chapter 7). Plate tectonics is the study of these lithospheric plates.

There are two kinds of lithospheric plates: **oceanic plates** and **continental plates**. Oceanic plates form the floor of the ocean. They are thin and made of dense basalt. Continental plates are thick and made of less-dense granite. Often a lithospheric plate is a mix of both kinds of plates.

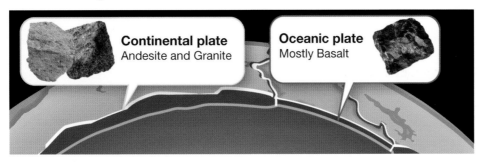

Continental plate
Andesite and Granite

Oceanic plate
Mostly Basalt

Plate tectonics answers other questions Science is a process that builds on itself. Early discoveries provide a better understanding that leads to more discoveries. The evidence that Alfred Wegener collected to support an ancient supercontinent is valid today. And our understanding of plate tectonics has allowed us to answer other questions such as:

- Why are volcanoes and earthquakes located where they are?
- Where can we find oil, gas, gold, and other important resources?

ⓐ VOCABULARY

lithospheric plates - large pieces of Earth's lithosphere that move over the aesthenosphere.

oceanic plates - thin, dense lithospheric plates that are made of basalt and form the ocean floor.

continental plates - thick, less-dense lithospheric plates that are made of granite and form the continents.

MY JOURNAL

How is plate tectonics related to earthquakes and volcanoes?

Write an answer based on what you know. Then, check your answer by doing research to answer this question. Use research resources in your classroom and school library.

What drives lithospheric plates?

Convection cells Convection cells in Earth's lower mantle drive the lithospheric plates on the surface. Here again we see the effect of heat on materials. The rocks of the lower mantle are not brittle like the rocks of the lithosphere. They are hot enough so that they flow very slowly. The core heats the rock material of the lower mantle. As it is heated, it expands and becomes less dense.

The lower mantle rock material rises toward Earth's surface and may divide the lithosphere above and form a mid-ocean ridge. The pieces of separated lithospheric plate will move away from each other on either side of the new mid-ocean ridge.

Subduction The far edge of a lithospheric plate is much older than the edge close to the mid-ocean ridge that formed it. Over time, the far edge cools and becomes denser (Figure 8.5). Eventually, it may sink below another lithospheric plate and enter the lower mantle. This sinking process is called **subduction**. As the now-cool subducting plate enters the lower mantle, it cools the nearby lower mantle material in turn. Cooling makes the nearby material denser and it sinks deeper into the lower mantle. This sinking completes the lower mantle convection cell.

(ā) VOCABULARY

subduction - a process that involves a lithospheric plate sinking into the mantle.

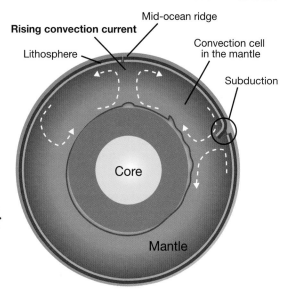

Mid-ocean ridge
Rising convection current
Lithosphere
Convection cell in the mantle
Subduction
Core
Mantle

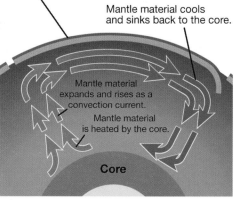

The lithospheric plate rides like a passenger on the mantle material underneath.

Mantle material cools and sinks back to the core.

Mantle material expands and rises as a convection current.

Mantle material is heated by the core.

Core

Hot, expanded, less dense, more buoyant
Cool, contracted, denser, less buoyant

Figure 8.5: *A convection cell in the lower mantle.*

Hot spots and island chains

Mid-ocean ridges form when rising hot mantle rocks separate the plate above it. Sometimes a single hot rising plume, called a **mantle plume**, causes a volcanic eruption in the plate above it. If the eruption is strong and lasts long enough, the volcanic eruption may form an island on the plate. Plates move more quickly than the underlying mantle plumes. After the island forms, the movement of the plate carries it away from the mantle plume. Without the heat from the mantle plume underneath, the volcano that formed the island becomes dormant. In the meantime, a new volcano begins to form on the part of the plate that is now over the mantle plume.

This process repeats over and over and forms a string of islands. The first island formed in the string is made of old dormant volcanoes, while the most recent island in the string probably has active volcanoes. Scientists determine the direction and speed of plate movement by measuring these island chains. The Hawaiian Islands are a good example of an island chain formed by a mantle plume hot spot.

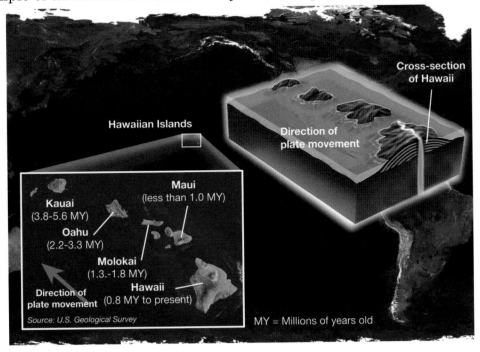

VOCABULARY

mantle plume - heated lower mantle rock that rises toward the lithosphere because it is less dense than surrounding mantle rock.

SOLVE IT!

Are you faster than the speed of a moving plate on Earth's surface?

The speed of a moving plate ranges from one to ten centimeters each year. On average, that's about as fast as your fingernails grow! So, even if you are walking slowly, you are moving very quickly compared to a plate moving on Earth's surface. Plates move so slowly that scientists measure their movement in millions of years.

If a lithospheric plate moved 5 centimeters per year for 1,000 years, how far would it have traveled during this time?

8.2 Section Review

1. Explain why magnetic patterns are important evidence for plate tectonics?

2. How were mid-ocean ridges discovered?

3. What was Harry Hess' hypothesis regarding the ocean floor and how it was made?

4. What two discoveries supported Hess' hypothesis?

5. What is the study of lithospheric plates called?

6. Over what surface do lithospheric plates move?

   a. lower mantle   b. outer core
   c. inner core   d. aesthenosphere

7. Name the two types of lithospheric plates and describe them.

8. What are some questions that are answered by plate tectonics?

9. What is the source of energy that drives the movement of the lithospheric plates?

10. Do lithospheric plates move quickly or slowly? Explain your answer.

11. Describe the process of subduction in your own words. What causes subduction to happen?

12. Name an example of an island chain formed by a mantle plume hot spot. Describe/draw the process of how it forms.

13. Research question: The Mid-Atlantic Ridge (see page 16) goes through the country of Iceland. What effect is it having on this country?

14. Research question: It is thought that when Pangaea broke apart, it first split into two large landmasses, each of which were given names. What are the names? What do these names mean?

MY JOURNAL

Create a table to compare and contrast continental drift and plate tectonics. Include the answers to the following questions.

Which is a hypothesis and which is a theory?

What is the difference between these two ideas when explaining why Africa and South America seem to fit together like two puzzle pieces?

CHALLENGE

Drummond Matthews and Fred Vine, British geologists from Cambridge University, England, are credited with recognizing the significance of magnetic patterns.

Research these magnetic patterns so that you understand what they are and how they are caused. Make a poster to display your findings.

Although the contributions of Matthews and Vine are considered huge among all earth scientists, they never received any special recognition for their work.

8.3 Plate Boundaries

In this section, you will learn how movement at the boundaries of lithospheric plates affects Earth's surface.

Moving plates

Three types of boundaries

Imagine a single plate, moving in one direction on Earth's surface (Figure 8.6). One edge of the plate—the trailing edge—moves away from things. This edge is called a **divergent boundary**. The opposite edge—called the leading edge— bumps into anything in the way. This edge is called a **convergent boundary**. The sides of our imaginary plate do not collide with or move away from another plate. These sides slide by other plates. An edge of a lithospheric plate that slides by another plate is called a **transform fault boundary**.

How plates move relative to each other

Earth's surface is covered with lithospheric plates. Unlike our single imaginary plate, the boundaries of real plates touch each other. Plates move apart at divergent boundaries, collide at convergent boundaries, and slide by each other at transform fault boundaries.

a) VOCABULARY

divergent boundary - a lithospheric plate boundary where two plates move apart.

convergent boundary - a lithospheric plate boundary where two plates come together.

transform fault boundary - a lithospheric plate boundary where two plates slide by each other.

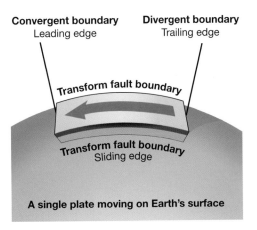

Convergent boundary / Leading edge. Divergent boundary / Trailing edge. Transform fault boundary. Transform fault boundary / Sliding edge. **A single plate moving on Earth's surface**

Plate boundaries

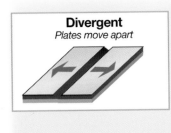
Divergent Plates move apart

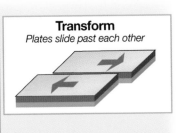
Convergent Plates come together

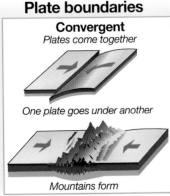
One plate goes under another — Mountains form

Transform Plates slide past each other

Figure 8.6: *Divergent, convergent, and transform fault boundaries.*

Divergent boundaries

New sea-floor at mid-ocean ridges

Divergent boundaries are found in the ocean as mid-ocean ridges. A divergent boundary is the line between two plates where they are moving apart. This type of boundary is found over the rising plume of a mantle convection cell. The convection cell causes the two plates to move away from each other. As they move, melted rock fills the space created by their motion. The melted rock hardens and becomes new ocean floor. This process is how new Earth surface is created!

Rift valleys

Divergent boundaries can also be found on continents as *rift valleys*. When a rift valley forms on land, it may eventually split the landmass wide enough so that the sea flows into the valley. When this happens, the rift valley becomes a mid-ocean ridge. The East African Rift Valley is an example of rifting in progress. This rift is marked by a series of long lakes that start near the southern end of the Red Sea and move southward toward Mozambique.

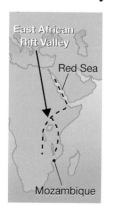

East African Rift Valley
Red Sea
Mozambique

Divergent Plate Boundaries

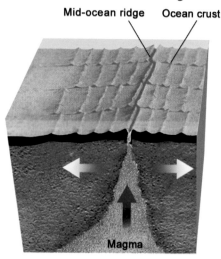

Mid-ocean ridge   Ocean crust

Magma

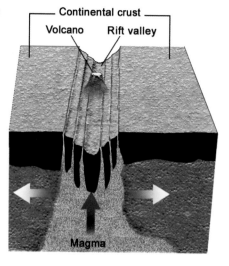

Continental crust
Volcano   Rift valley

Magma

MY JOURNAL

Using clues to make discoveries

At the ocean floor, special lava formations called *pillow lava* are clues to the location of ancient mid-ocean ridges.

The pillow lava forms when basalt lava flows out under water. The water cools the surface of the lava, forming a crust. This crust stops the flow of lava for a moment. Then the crust cracks and a new jet of lava flows out. This process causes the lava to form what looks like a pile of pillows. Ancient mid-ocean ridges can be located near pillow lava formations.

Pillow lava

Source: OAR/National Undersea Research Program (NURP)

Write a paragraph describing a recent experience where you used a clue to discover something about a place or an object.

Convergent boundaries

Trenches When oceanic plates collide, one subducts under the other. This forms a valley in the ocean floor called a **trench**.

Why does one plate subduct under another? A denser plate subducts under a less dense one. Older plates are cooler plates, and therefore denser than younger plates. So we can say that older plates tend to subduct under younger plates.

Convergent plate boundary

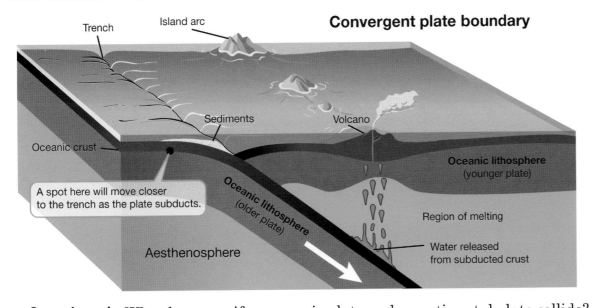

Oceanic and continental plate subduction What happens if an oceanic plate and a continental plate collide? Continental plates are largely made of andesite and granite. Andesite and granite are much less dense than the basalt of oceanic plates. Which plate would subduct? You're on the right track if you realized that the oceanic plate must subduct under the continental plate. A continental plate is simply too buoyant to subduct under an oceanic plate. A good example of this is the Nazca Plate off the coast of South America. The Nazca Plate is subducting under the South American Plate (Figure 8.7).

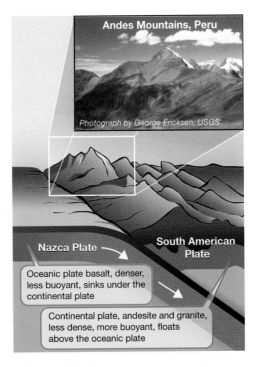

Figure 8.7: *The collision of the Nazca and South American Plates has deformed and pushed up the land to form the high peaks of the Andes Mountains. This photograph is of the Pachapaqui mining area in Peru.*

Mountains and convergent boundaries

What happens when two continents collide?

What happens if an oceanic plate with a continent on it subducts under a continental plate? Eventually the subducting plate brings its continent right up against the continental plate!

What happens then? The forces in the lower mantle that drive the movements of the lithospheric plates are too great to be changed by this collision. The continents cannot be sucked into the trench because their granite rocks are too buoyant to be subducted. Therefore, the two continents collide!

What happens when two continents collide?

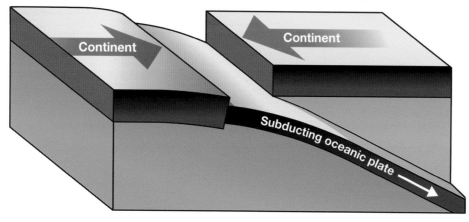

Colliding continents form mountains

Vast mountain ranges are formed when continents collide. Millions of years ago, India was a separate continent and not attached to South Asia. The Indo-Australian oceanic plate carried the landmass of India toward China as it subducted under the Eurasian continental plate. Today the Himalayan Mountains are the result of this collision (Figure 8.8). What's more, the impact of the collision continues today—it's a slow process and the Himalayan Mountains are still growing!

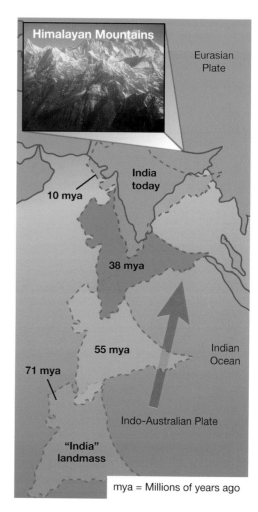

Figure 8.8: *The Himalayan Mountains are the result of the slow but powerful collision between India on the Indo-Australian Plate and the China on the Eurasian Plate.*

Transform fault boundaries

Finding boundaries Once scientists began to understand lithospheric plate boundaries, finding divergent and convergent boundaries was easy. Mid-ocean ridges and continental rift valleys are divergent boundaries. Trenches and mountain ranges mark convergent boundaries. Finding transform fault boundaries is more difficult. Transform faults leave few clues to indicate their presence.

Zones of activity One reason for the difficulty in locating transform faults is that they are not single straight lines of movement. Transform faults are usually branched and often change location with time. It's helpful to think of transform faults as a zone of motion rather than a line that separates two plates.

Zig-zags are clues Sometimes the action of a transform fault will form a small valley along the line of movement. Often there will be ponds along the line. A good clue for locating transform faults is *offsetting*. If a feature like a creek or a highway crosses a transform fault, the movement of the fault will break, or offset, the feature. When seen from above, the feature will appear to make a zig-zag (Figure 8.9).

Earthquakes are another clue The best way to detect transform faults is by the earthquakes they cause. Movement along a transform fault causes the vast majority of earthquakes. For example, the San Andreas Fault is a well-known fault that causes earthquakes in California (Figure 8.10). The San Andreas Fault is the boundary between two lithospheric plates—the Pacific Plate and the North American Plate.

Using plate tectonics to understand other events Before plate tectonics was understood, scientists knew where earthquakes commonly occurred, but they didn't know why. This is another example of how understanding plate tectonics leads to other new understandings. You will learn more about earthquakes and transform faults in the next chapter.

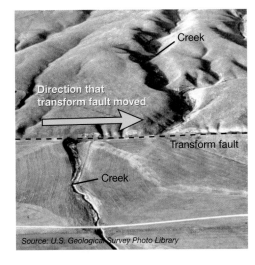

Source: U.S. Geological Survey Photo Library

Figure 8.9: *The creek is offset to the right as viewed from bottom to top in the photo.*

Photo courtesy of Dr. John B. Reid

Figure 8.10: *This line of students stretches across part of the San Andreas Fault in California.*

Earth's lithospheric plates

This map shows the largest lithospheric plates that cover Earth. There are many small plates, but some of these have been combined with the larger ones to simplify the map.

Study the map. Can you identify the labeled plate boundaries? Use the arrows on the map to help you. Remember that the three types of plate boundaries are divergent, convergent, and transform. Then, see if you can answer the question.

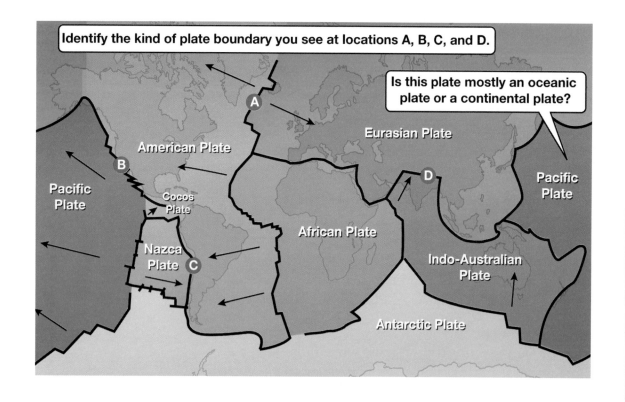

Identify the kind of plate boundary you see at locations A, B, C, and D.

Is this plate mostly an oceanic plate or a continental plate?

- A
- B
- C
- D
- American Plate
- Pacific Plate
- Cocos Plate
- Nazca Plate
- Eurasian Plate
- African Plate
- Indo-Australian Plate
- Antarctic Plate
- Pacific Plate

From Pangaea to Today

245 mya

180 mya

North America
Europe
Asia
South America
Africa
India
Australia
Antarctica

Earth today

North America
Europe
Asia
Africa
India
South America
Australia
Antarctica

About 245 million years ago (mya), all land on Earth was part of the supercontinent called Pangaea. About 180 mya, this huge landmass began to split apart into many sections. Seven of the largest sections form our continents. It is important to note that Pangaea was not the original landmass formation. Before Pangaea, there were other earlier formations of the oceans and continents and over a very long period of time, forces brought them together to form Pangaea.

8.3 Section Review

1. What are the three types of plate boundaries and what does each do in relation to other plate boundaries?

2. What kind of boundary is a mid-ocean ridge?

3. What is pillow lava and where is it found?

4. What is a place (on land) where divergent boundaries can be found? Give an example of a divergent boundary on land.

5. What happens when ocean plates come together? What landform does this event create?

6. What features of a plate determine whether a plate will subduct under another plate? Pick the two correct features:

a. How much ocean water is on top of the plate	b. The age of the plate
c. Whether the plate is made of basalt or granite	d. How fast the plate is traveling
e. Whether the plate is in the northern or southern hemisphere	f. Whether the plate is traveling east or west

7. Which is more buoyant—a continental plate or oceanic plate? Which would subduct if the two were to collide with each other?

8. What happens when two continental plates collide? Give an example of continents colliding today.

9. Why are transform faults harder to find than divergent and convergent boundaries?

10. What are three clues to finding transform faults?

CHALLENGE

1. The oldest parts of Earth are found on the continents and not in the oceans. Why do you think this is?

2. Earth is 4.6 billion years old but the oldest sea floor is only 200 million years old. Why do you think this is?

3. Where might you find the oldest rocks on Earth?

4. How likely are we to find any rocks that are as old as Earth itself?

MY JOURNAL

Careers in Earth Science

Have you ever thought about being an earth scientist?

Find out what kinds of careers are available to people who study earth science and geology.

For example, a *geodynamacist* studies how lithospheric plates move and change shape.

Write a description of one earth science career that interests you.

8.4 Metamorphic Rocks

Metamorphism means to change the form of something. A **metamorphic rock** is a rock formed from another kind of rock due to heat and pressure. A metamorphic rock might have originally been a rock made from sediments that formed at the bottom of a lake—a *sedimentary rock*. Or it might have been a rock formed from material that flowed from a volcano—an *igneous rock*.

Heat and pressure at subduction zones

Many metamorphic rocks are formed at convergent boundaries where there is pressure and heat. A subduction zone is a place where metamorphic rocks are formed. Also, metamorphic rocks can be formed by heat alone. For example, when magma comes in contact with another type of rock, the high heat may form metamorphic rock near the point of contact. This is called *contact metamorphism*.

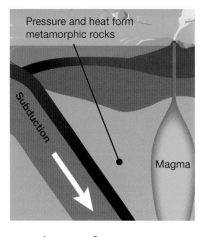

Pressure and heat form metamorphic rocks

Subduction

Magma

Heat and pressure when continents collide

Heat and pressure result when colliding continents form mountains at a convergent boundary. Therefore, mountains are locations where you can find metamorphic rocks. In Chapter 7 you learned that continents are thicker than ocean floor, and that continents can push down into the warm lower mantle. Therefore the mantle provides heat for metamorphic rock formation.

Metamorphism example

Limestone is a sedimentary rock that forms on the ocean bottom from the shells of tiny one-celled animals and other material. When this ocean bottom is squeezed at a subduction zone, the limestone is metamorphosed into marble (Figure 8.11). Italy lies near a convergent boundary. Italy is also the source of some of the world's finest marble.

Limestone

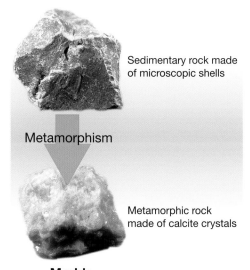

Sedimentary rock made of microscopic shells

Metamorphism

Metamorphic rock made of calcite crystals

Marble

These rock images are from the "Minerals in Your World" project, a cooperative effort between the USGS and the Mineral Information Institute.

Figure 8.11: *Limestone is a sedimentary rock made of shells. At subduction zones, it is metamorphosed into marble.*

8.4 Section Review

1. What does the term *metamorphism* mean?

2. What two things can cause metamorphic rock formation?

3. What is contact metamorphism?

4. Look at the rock images in Figure 8.12. Which image is most likely to be a metamorphic rock? Explain your answer.

5. Metamorphic rocks are commonly formed at what kind of plate boundary?

6. In which location would you be most likely to find a metamorphic rock?

   a. The beach

   b. A forest

   c. On a mountain

   d. At the bottom of a stream

   e. Near a volcano

7. At what type of plate boundary can limestone be metamorphosed into marble?

8. Challenge question: The introduction of this section discusses three types of rocks. For the following questions, state whether the description describes a metamorphic, sedimentary, or igneous rock. You will learn more about these rocks in later chapters.

   a. A rock formed from particles of sand and soil.

   b. A rock formed after a volcano erupts.

   c. This kind of rock is likely to be formed at a subduction zone.

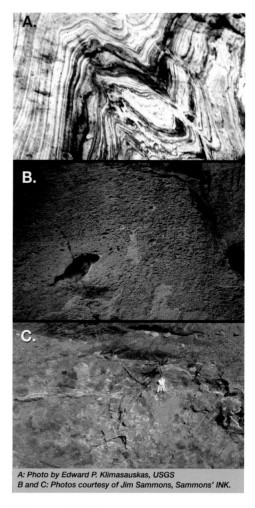

A: Photo by Edward P. Klimasauskas, USGS
B and C: Photos courtesy of Jim Sammons, Sammons' INK.

Figure 8.12: *Which one of these images is of a metamorphic rock?*

ARCHAEOLOGY CONNECTION Fossils of the Ice Age

Sticky. Tacky. Gooey. What do you think of when you hear those words? Bubble gum? Marshmallow? Glue? Tar? Could any of those materials have preserved fossils for thousands of years? Indeed, sticky tar formed from seeping crude oil in what is now California helped to preserve one of the world's richest fossil sites.

Fossils are the preserved remains of animals or plants. Some fossils can include animal tracks and prints. Natural remains are usually recycled back into the earth. The creation of a fossil is a special and rare event because those remains must be buried and preserved quickly.

Imagine finding fossils from an ice age. There have been several long ice ages on Earth. The most recent lasted from 1.6 million years ago to 10,000 years ago. Over an ice age Earth is cooler and covered by huge sheets of ice. During the last ice age, glaciers covered large sections of North America and Europe. You might have fossils right in your backyard.

La Brea tar pits

The La Brea tar pits are located in Los Angeles, California. For thousands of years, Native Americans used the tar, or more accurately, asphalt, as glue and waterproof caulking. Colonists used it for roofing. In the early 1900s, researchers from the University of California at Berkeley identified ice age fossils at the site.

During the ice age, rainwater covered the tar pits. Animals and plants became trapped in the tar and died. The La Brea tar pits contain a large number of mammal remains including saber-toothed cats, mammoths, dire wolves, and short-faced bears. Scientists believe large animals or prey became trapped in the tar. Meat-eating predators then followed the prey into the tar also becoming trapped. Predators hunting prey explains the large number of remains found; La Brea has over 3 million fossils and the oldest are nearly 38,000 years old. This site has provided fossils of over 500 mammal, bird, insect, and plant species.

Smilodon californicus

Do you know your state flower? Your state bird? How about your state fossil! Not every state has one, but in Alaska and Nebraska, for instance, the state fossil is the woolly mammoth. Montana and New Jersey share the duck-billed dinosaur. California adopted the saber-toothed cat, *Smilodon californicus*, in January 1974.

The word Smilodon means "knife tooth." The Smilodon had 7-inch-long saber-like canine teeth. It was about 4 or 5 feet long, about 3 feet tall, and weighed over 400 pounds. It was not as large as today's lion, but weighed more. It did not run fast, but could pounce upon its prey. Smilodon is the second most common mammal found at La Brea.

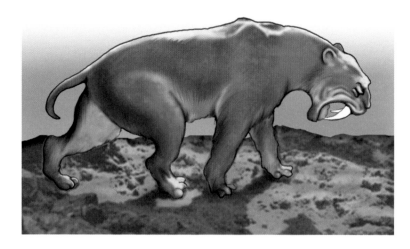

Smilodon californicus

Other ice age fossils

In Australia, scientists discovered remains of the largest marsupial that ever lived. A marsupial is a mammal that carries its young in a pouch. *Diprotodon optatum* weighed over 6,000 pounds, humongous compared with today's largest marsupial, the red kangaroo, at about 187 pounds.

Diprotodon opatum
The largest marsupial that ever lived

In South Dakota, the world's largest collection of Columbian mammoths is housed at Mammoth Site in Hot Springs. Fossils were found by chance in 1974 during excavations for a housing development. More than 26,000 years ago, these animals walked into a pond and were trapped. Over 50 woolly and Columbian mammoths have been found here. The Columbian mammoth weighed 16,000-20,000 pounds and ate about 700 pounds of vegetation daily.

In Los Angeles, subway construction unearthed over 2,000 fossils. The Metropolitan Transportation Authority digs with caution and works closely with the Natural History Museum of Los Angeles County to protect fossils. Fossils include ground sloths, mammoths, horses, camels, and mastodons. Fossils of the mormon tea plant have helped scientists understand the climate of Los Angeles in the ice age. The plant grows now in the Mojave Desert, so scientists believe ice age Los Angeles had hotter summers and cooler winters similar to the modern-day desert.

So you want to study fossils?

Paleontology could be your life's calling. It is the study of life using fossils from past geological times. Paleontologists study extinct animals and plants in order to understand ancient life and explain how life has changed. Preparing for a career in paleontology includes studying biology, geology, and computers. A keen eye and the desire to find hidden treasures are also helpful.

Paleontologist at work

Photo courtesy of the National Park Service

Questions:

1. What is an ice age and when did the most recent ice age occur?
2. What is a fossil and why are fossils relatively rare?
3. Why are the tar pits of Rancho La Brea so rich with fossils?
4. Name several ice age fossils and where they have been found.

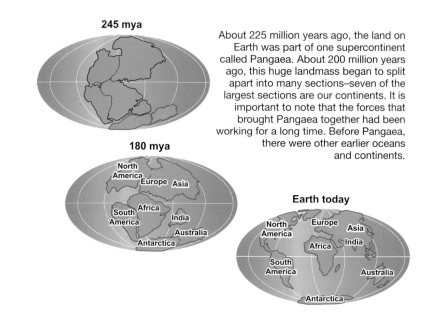

CHAPTER ACTIVITY Make a Plate Tectonics Book

In this chapter, you learned about plate tectonics—about how Earth has large blocks of lithospheric plates moving about, interacting with one another. You learned that some blocks move toward each other and make mountains and others get subducted below a less dense lithospheric plate. In the oceans, plates are moving apart from each other, creating new floor. In places like the Pacific Rim, there are many earthquakes which means transform fault boundaries are there. Earth is an amazing place!

Materials

Pieces of paper (copy paper, construction paper, or newsprint), staples and a stapler, glue, colored pencils and markers, pens, scissors, old magazines, and any other material you need to make your book

What you will do

1. Get into a group of three or four people to make the book.
2. With your group, decide on a title for your book. Here are a couple of ideas: *Plate Tectonics* or *How South America and Africa Moved Apart.*
3. Your book will recount part of the plate tectonics story. Use the graphic on this page and others in Chapter 8 to help you outline your story.

If you would like, you can come up with mythical creatures that lived on the ancient continents before they reached their current positions—just as long as you explain in some way how the continents got to where they are today. Use lots of pictures. Maybe someone in your group is an artist.

Your book will need a cover and back, a title, and a list of the authors. You may want to give credit to the artist or maybe there were a few artists in the group. The book size is optional. An oversized book can be very attractive to younger children. Use whatever resources you can find, but ask your teacher to check your information for accuracy. Maybe the book will be in the form of a poem or a pop-up book. There are many creative ways to tell a story—have fun!

245 mya

180 mya

Earth today

About 225 million years ago, the land on Earth was part of one supercontinent called Pangaea. About 200 million years ago, this huge landmass began to split apart into many sections–seven of the largest sections are our continents. It is important to note that the forces that brought Pangaea together had been working for a long time. Before Pangaea, there were other earlier oceans and continents.

Applying your knowledge

a. What was the title of your group's book?
b. Imagine your book will be in a library or sold in a book store. Write a short summary of the book so that a reader will know what it is about.
c. What did you like most about making the book with your group?
d. Share your plate tectonics story in class or read it to a group of younger students. Describe your experience at sharing your book with others.

Chapter 8 Assessment

Vocabulary

Select the correct term to complete the sentences.

Pangaea	oceanic plates	mid-ocean ridges
mantle plume	trench	lithospheric plates
subduction	plate tectonics	sea-floor spreading
continental plates	continental drift	transform fault boundary
metamorphic rock	divergent boundary	convergent boundary

Section 8.1

1. _____, meaning "all land," is the name for the great landmass that existed millions of years ago.

2. The idea that the continents move around on Earth's surface is called _____.

3. The study of Earth's lithospheric plates is called _____.

Section 8.2

4. The _____ are thick and made of granite.

5. The sinking process that completes the lower mantle convection cell is _____.

6. _____ move over the aesthenosphere.

7. New ocean floor is created at the locations of these undersea features called _____.

8. Hess proposed the idea of _____.

9. _____ are thin and made of basalt.

10. A _____ rises to the surface and may create a volcanic center.

Section 8.3 and Section 8.4

11. Mountains form along a _____.

12. Mid-ocean ridges indicate the presence of this type of boundary: _____.

13. The occurrence of earthquakes and offsetting are clues that a location is near a _____.

14. A _____, or valley in the ocean floor, is created when one lithospheric plate subducts under another.

15. A sedimentary rock that experiences intense heat and pressure will become a _____.

Concepts

Section 8.1

1. According to the hypothesis of continental drift, how would a world map have changed over the last 250 million years?

2. How do fossils support the idea of continental drift?

3. Earth's surface is often described as a giant jigsaw puzzle. What are the pieces of the puzzle?

4. Wegener collected a lot of evidence to support his idea of continental drift. Was his evidence enough to prove continental drift was correct? Why or why not?

Section 8.2

5. Describe how Harry Hess thought the continents moved apart. What did Hess call his set of ideas?

6. The Mid-Atlantic Ridge is a mid-ocean ridge in the Atlantic Ocean. Is the Atlantic ocean getting larger or smaller?

7. The graphic below shows the magnetic pattern on one side of a mid-ocean ridge. Make a sketch of the magnetic pattern that would appear on the other side of the ridge.

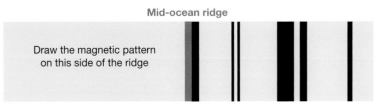

Mid-ocean ridge

Draw the magnetic pattern on this side of the ridge

8. Where would you find the oldest rocks on the sea floor? Where would you find the youngest rocks?

9. In your own words, describe how an island chain forms.

Section 8.3 and Section 8.4

10. List the three types of plate boundaries. What famous feature in California represents one of these boundaries?

11. What kinds of geologic features form when two continental plates come together?

12. Under what conditions are metamorphic rocks formed?

Math and Writing Skills

Section 8.1

1. How can evidence of a glacier be in a place that has a warm, dry climate?

Section 8.2

2. To calculate the speed of plate motion, divide the distance the plate moves by the time it takes to move that distance (speed = distance ÷ time). Give your answer in kilometers per one million years (km/one million years). (Usually these values are stated in centimeters/year or millimeters/ year.)

   a. It takes 10 million years for the Pacific Plate to slide 600 kilometers past the North American Plate. How fast is the Pacific Plate moving?

   b. There are two islands on opposite sides of a mid-ocean ridge. During the last 8 million years, the distance between the islands has increased by 200 kilometers. What is the rate at which the two plates are diverging?

Section 8.3 and Section 8.4

3. Draw diagrams of the three types of plate boundaries.

4. Give an example of a metamorphic rock that changes from sedimentary to metamorphic. How does this rock form?

Chapter Project—Sea-Floor Spreading Model

Materials: Shoe box lid, piece of copy paper cut lengthwise (in half), red and black markers, scissors.

1. Cut a slit in the shoe box so that the paper can fit in widthwise.

2. Put the pieces of paper in the slit from the underside of the shoebox lid. Allow about 2 cm of paper to show through the slit.

~ 1 inch

Keep creating stripes until you're almost finished with the paper.

3. One piece of paper will be folded back to the left of the slit and one will be folded to the right of the slit.

4. Use your red marker to color the paper that is showing (on both sides of the slit). Optional: Write the year you were born on this stripe.

5. Now pull another inch or so of paper through the slit. The amount pulled through doesn't matter as much as the fact that both sides need to pull through the same amount.

6. Now color this new strip of white paper in black marker. Optional: Write the year after you were born on this stripe.

7. Continue to pull the paper through the slit and coloring the strips (in alternate colors), until you almost run out of paper. You have now created a model for sea-floor spreading. Optional: Keep writing the year on each stripe. This shows that the older stripes end up further away from the ridge and the youngest are closest to the ridge.

8. Questions: (a) Where can you find the landform represented by the box top and paper? and (b) How do these magnetic patterns on the sea-floor support plate tectonics.

Chapter 9
Earthquakes

Earth is not a solid ball. Rather, as you have learned, it has different layers. And Earth's surface is so interesting because the outer shell of Earth—the lithosphere—is broken up into pieces. As you learned in Chapter 8, these pieces—the lithospheric plates—move! Scientists have learned that a great deal of geologic action takes place at the boundaries of these plates. How do scientists know where the plate boundaries are? The quickest and easiest way to find plate boundaries is to plot earthquakes on a map. This chapter is all about earthquakes!

Key Questions

1. *How is an earthquake like a stuck door?*

2. *How are seismic waves like race cars?*

3. *What is the Richter magnitude of the largest earthquake ever recorded?*

9.1 What Is an Earthquake?

Have you ever tried to open a stuck door? You pull and pull and then... Bang! The door flies open with a sound that would wake a statue! This particular experience is similar to how an earthquake happens in Earth's interior. Read on!

Stick-slip motion

Three conditions needed for stick-slip motion
The scenario described above illustrates *stick-slip motion* (Figure 9.1), the same motion that causes earthquakes. Three conditions are needed for stick-slip motion:

1. Two objects that are touching each other where at least one of the objects can move.

2. A force, or forces, that will cause the movement.

3. Friction strong enough to temporarily keep the movement from starting. Recall that friction is a resistance to slip that occurs when two objects rub against each other (Figure 9.2).

An everyday example
Can you identify these three things in the stuck-door example? The two objects are the door and its frame. The force that will cause movement is you pulling on the door. The friction that made the door stick was probably due to changing moisture in the house. Moisture in a wooden door makes it swell so that it jams in the door frame. You have to pull hard to overcome the friction, so that when the door opens, you hear a loud noise as some of the energy stored is released.

Earthquakes and stick-slip motion
An *earthquake* is a form of stick-slip motion. The movement of lithospheric plates over Earth's surface causes earthquakes at plate boundaries and even within plates. However, transform fault boundaries are especially likely to cause earthquakes. Review the different types of plate boundaries in Section 8.3.

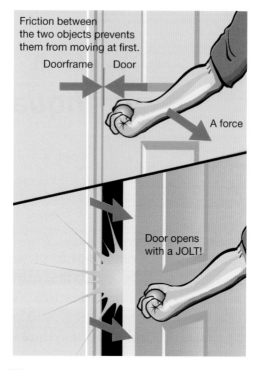

Figure 9.1: *A stuck door is an example of stick-slip motion.*

Figure 9.2: *There is more friction between a sneaker and a gym floor than between a sock and the gym floor.*

What causes earthquakes?

Plates stick together, then break Lithospheric plates on Earth's surface slide past each other. As this happens, the plates stick together at the brittle crust near the surface of Earth. However, the *plastic* (plastic here means "able to change shape without breaking," like modeling clay) upper mantle continues to flow underneath. With the crust stuck and the upper mantle moving, the rocks at plate boundaries stretch or compress. As a result, *potential energy* (stored energy) builds in the plate. Just like the stick-slip motion of the stuck door, when the potential energy exceeds the strength of the rock—BANG!—the rock breaks.

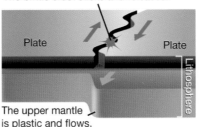

Stick-slip motion
The brittle crust sticks and releases.

Plate   Plate

Lithosphere

The upper mantle is plastic and flows.

ⓐ VOCABULARY

earthquake - the movement of Earth's crust resulting from the building up of stored energy between two stuck lithospheric plates.

focus - the point below Earth's surface where a rock breaks and causes an earthquake.

fault - a region on Earth's surface that is split into two pieces.

epicenter - a point on Earth's surface right above the focus of an earthquake.

Parts of an earthquake An **earthquake** is the movement of Earth's crust resulting from the release of built-up potential energy between two stuck lithospheric plates. The point below the surface where the rock breaks is called the earthquake **focus**. As soon as the rock breaks, there is movement along the broken surface causing a split in the surface called a **fault**. The energy of the movement is spread by *seismic waves*. The seismic waves from an earthquake are usually strongest at the **epicenter**, the point on the surface right above the focus (Figure 9.3).

Shallow and deep quakes Earthquakes that result from movement in the crust are called *shallow focus earthquakes* because their focus is less than 50 kilometers below the surface. There are also other kinds of earthquakes. *Deep focus earthquakes* occur at subduction zones when a subducting plate breaks. The focus of a breaking plate may be as deep as 700 kilometers below the surface.

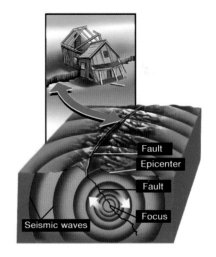

Fault
Epicenter
Fault
Focus
Seismic waves

Figure 9.3: *The focus, epicenter, and seismic waves of an earthquake occurring at an active fault.*

Slickensides, evidence of plate boundaries

What are slickensides? The photo at the near right shows the effect of rock moving against rock along a fault in the Coronado Heights section of San Francisco. The polished surface is called *slickensides*. At one time, the slickensides were below Earth's surface with another mass of rock pressing against it. The other mass has since weathered away.

Figure 9.4: *The edge that is sticking out indicates that the slickensides moved away from you.*

Motion of the slickensides Figure 9.4 is a close-up of the slickensides looking to the right. Look at the edge that is sticking out. This edge indicates that the direction that the slickensides moved in the past was away from you. The rock mass that weathered away would have been to the right of the slickensides. The graphic below at the left gives you a bird's eye view of how these plates moved.

Looking at a transform fault boundary

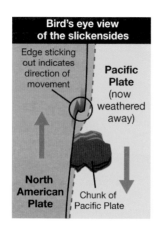

Figure 9.5 is another close-up of the same slickensides, but looking to the left. From this view we can see part of the rock mass that moved against the slickensides rock mass. The blue pen marks the fault that separates the two rock masses. The rock mass to the left of the fault was part of the Pacific Plate. The slickensides rock mass to the right of the fault was part of the North American Plate. This is the location of a transform fault boundary!

Figure 9.5: *A transform fault boundary between the Pacific Plate to the left and the North American Plate to the right (marked by the photographer's blue pen).*

The nature of plates

Boundaries within boundaries

Throughout Earth's history, lithospheric plates have been torn apart, added to, and joined with other plates. As a result of this reshaping, there are old plate boundaries inside of the plate boundaries we see today. These old boundaries are now faults inside the plates. The New Madrid Fault, for example, is a fault zone within the North American Plate. This zone is an "old" plate boundary that can break when the North American crust flexes as a result of plate tectonic activity. This can result in a major earthquake, such as the New Madrid event in 1895.

The New Madrid Fault Zone

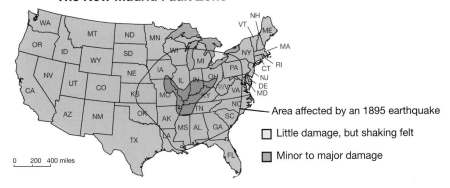

Area affected by an 1895 earthquake

☐ Little damage, but shaking felt

■ Minor to major damage

0 200 400 miles

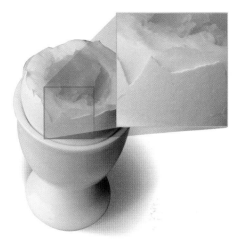

Figure 9.6: *Are lithospheric plates on Earth like pieces of eggshell on a hard-boiled egg?*

Plates as grocery carts

A cracked shell on a hard-boiled egg is similar to lithospheric plates on Earth's surface (Figure 9.6). However, a line of grocery carts is a better analogy of a lithospheric plate because it demonstrates movement of the plate. (Figure 9.7). You've seen people pushing long lines of grocery carts around supermarket parking lots. The line of carts moves along as a single unit, but there are small "wiggles" between each cart. In the same way, a plate moves across Earth's surface as a single unit. However, a part of the plate may "wiggle" at one of its old faults inside the more recent plate boundaries. This kind of movement is what causes earthquakes in the interior sections of plates, far away from plate boundaries.

A single cart can move independently within the line

A line of carts moves together in one direction

Figure 9.7: *A moving line of grocery carts is like a moving lithospheric plate.*

Lithospheric plates have many sections

Plates have sections
Transform fault boundaries are much longer than the longest area affected by any earthquake. This tells us that although a plate may be moving as a single unit, its boundaries act as though they were made of many sections like the line of carts.

A plate is like a long line of grocery carts
When one end of the shopping cart line is pushed, the carts on the other end of the line remain still for a moment. It takes some time for the first cart to push the second, the second to push the next, and so on, until the last cart starts to move. Since a plate is thousands of kilometers across, it can take a long time for movement on one end of the plate to affect the section furthest away.

The San Andreas Fault
For example, parts of the San Andreas Fault can be stuck together and other parts may creep along at any given time (Figure 9.8). Each section of a plate may move a little earlier or later than another. An earthquake happens each time a plate section moves, but only in the section that moved.

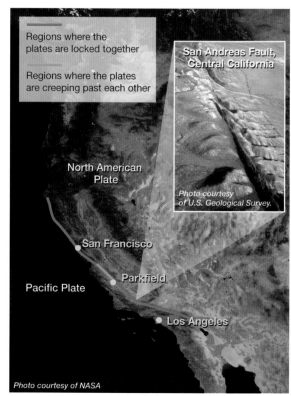

Figure 9.8: *The San Andreas Fault in California. The graphic illustrates that some parts of the fault are locked together and some parts creep along at any given time.*

A cross-section of the San Andreas Fault Zone

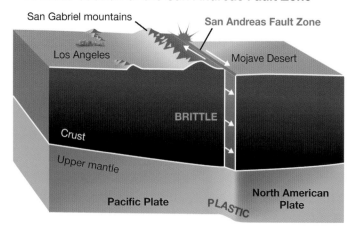

When do earthquakes happen?

Earthquakes release energy

The release of built-up potential energy causes earthquakes. In this sense, an earthquake is a stress reliever for a lithospheric plate! However, once a quake occurs, potential energy builds up again.

Earthquake frequency and strength

Imagine two sections along the same transform fault boundary. Both sections should move at the same rate (like a single line of grocery carts). Let's say the first section has frequent earthquakes (a few times a year). Potential energy cannot build up when earthquakes happen frequently. Therefore, not much energy is released when an earthquake occurs. Earthquakes are mild in the first section. Now, let's say the second section has earthquakes only once every 20 years. In the time between earthquakes, a great deal of potential energy builds. Therefore, earthquakes in this section are more violent when they occur.

One earthquake may trigger others

Imagine that it has been a long time since an earthquake has released the potential energy in both sections. Then, an earthquake occurs in the first section, reducing its potential energy. The movement of the first section may increase the stress and built-up potential energy in the second section. This added stress may be enough to trigger a new earthquake in the second section.

What happens during an earthquake?

A strong burst of shaking occurs during an earthquake. The second longest ever recorded earthquake occurred in 1964 in Alaska and lasted for four minutes (Figure 9.9). *Foreshocks* are small bursts of shaking that may precede a large earthquake. Foreshocks can occur days before the earthquake hits, or just minutes before. *Aftershocks* are small tremors that follow an earthquake, lasting for hours or even days after the earthquake. The time between foreshocks gets shorter just before an earthquake. Similarly, aftershocks occur further apart as time passes after an earthquake.

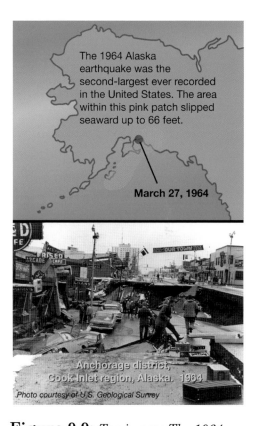

The 1964 Alaska earthquake was the second-largest ever recorded in the United States. The area within this pink patch slipped seaward up to 66 feet.

March 27, 1964

Anchorage district, Cook Inlet region, Alaska. 1964
Photo courtesy of U.S. Geological Survey

Figure 9.9: *Top image: The 1964 Alaska earthquake was the longest ever recorded and the largest ever recorded in the United States. The red dot shows the epicenter of the earthquake. The pink region indicates the area affected by the quake. Bottom image: Part of a street and sidewalk dropped 11 feet below the original level due to the 1964 Alaska earthquake!*

9.1 Section Review

1. What is the name of the kind of motion that causes an earthquake?

   a. Give an everyday example of this kind of motion.

   b. What three conditions are needed for this motion?

2. Lithospheric plates have two parts. Name the parts and describe how they are different from each other.

3. What causes lithospheric plates to build up pressure and finally "give" along transform faults?

4. What is the difference between the focus and the epicenter of an earthquake?

5. How is a lithospheric plate like a long line of moving grocery carts?

6. The polished surfaces of rock which are a result of rock moving against rock along a fault are known as _____.

7. Most earthquakes occur at plate boundaries. However, some occur inside plate boundaries in the interior of a lithospheric plate. Give the explanation for this from the reading.

8. Is the movement of a plate uniform or uneven along its boundary? Explain your answer.

9. Where are earthquakes generally more violent: (a) along a boundary where tension is released frequently, or (b) along a boundary where tension builds up over a greater period of time?

10. From the reading, state how can one earthquake cause another earthquake?

11. Put these events in order and then describe each: aftershock, foreshock, and earthquake.

In this section you learned about the Coronado Heights slickensides in San Francisco, California. Research slickensides to learn of other locations where you could find these geologic formations.

Who named the San Andreas Fault?

Trivia is information that doesn't matter very much but it can be interesting. For example, it may be more important to know that the San Andreas Fault is a transform plate boundary rather than to know who named this fault.

Make a list of 10 trivia facts about earthquakes and/or plate tectonics. You will need to do some research to find trivia about these topics.

9.2 Seismic Waves

An earthquake rapidly converts a large amount of built-up potential energy into the energy of motion. This energy of motion is spread by seismic waves. These waves start underground at the earthquake focus and radiate in all directions. In this section, you will learn more about these special waves.

Body and surface waves

Body waves   Seismic waves that travel through Earth's interior are called **body waves**. The two main kinds of body waves are P-waves and S-waves (Figure 9.10). You read about these waves in Chapter 7.

Review of P-waves and S-waves   P-waves (primary waves) are faster. These waves push and pull on rock as they travel. The rock moves in the same direction that the wave moves. After an earthquake, P-waves arrive first at any location. S-waves (secondary waves) travel more slowly and arrive after the P-waves. S-waves cause the rock to move in a side-to-side motion. The side-to-side motion is across (perpendicular to) the direction of the traveling wave. Although an S-wave is slower than a P-wave, both are many times faster than the speed of sound.

How materials affect seismic waves   The speed of P- and S-waves is affected by the properties of the rock they pass through. They travel faster in cool material and slower in hot material. Seismic waves may bend or be reflected when they contact different materials. Liquid—like the liquid outer core of Earth—acts as a barrier to S-waves. P-waves pass through liquid.

Surface waves   Waves on the surface, or body waves that reach the surface, are called **surface waves**. Surface waves are slower than the slowest body wave, but they are the waves that cause the most damage. Surface waves can move up and down, almost like waves on the ocean. They can also move from side to side, often causing buildings to collapse.

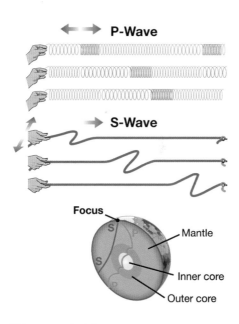

ⓐ VOCABULARY

body waves - seismic waves that travel through the interior of Earth.

surface waves - body waves that reach and travel along Earth's surface.

Figure 9.10: *P-waves and S-waves are types of body waves.*

Measuring seismic waves

Recording seismic waves

People who record and interpret seismic waves are called *seismologists*. Seismic waves are recorded and measured by an instrument called a **seismograph**. Seismographs show the kinds of waves that occur, their strength, and the time that they arrive at the instrument. Seismographs are located all around the world at seismic stations on land, and in special locations in the oceans.

The order of seismic waves

In the image below, seismic waves of the Loma Prieta earthquake are recorded on paper wrapped around a large drum. Figure 9.11 shows that seismic waves can also be recorded by computers.

Seismograph with a recording of the Loma Prieta, California earthquake, October 17, 1989.

Photo courtesy of U.S. Geological Survey.

Looking inside Earth

Seismologists study the interior of our planet by observing the way seismic waves travel through Earth. This process is similar to using X rays to create a CAT scan of the interior of a human body.

Zeroing in on Earth's features

Seismographs can be set up to provide detail about a small area. For example, multiple seismographs have been used to study a particular fault (like the San Andreas Fault), the deep lower mantle convection currents, and other features of Earth's interior.

seismograph - an instrument that measures and records seismic waves.

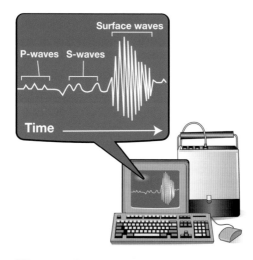

Figure 9.11: *After an earthquake occurs, the first seismic waves recorded will be P-waves. S-waves are recorded next, followed by the surface waves. P-waves travel faster than S-waves, and both travel faster than surface waves. This means that P-waves arrive at a seismic station before S-waves, and both arrive before surface waves. The data recorded about an earthquake is used to help locate the epicenter of the quake.*

Locating an earthquake epicenter

An analogy All cars start at the starting line on a race track. After a while, the fastest car gets ahead of the slowest car. In a quarter-mile race, the track is so short that fast and slow cars are often just fractions of a second apart. In a long race, like the Indianapolis 500, the cars might be minutes apart. The time difference between slow and fast cars is related to the length of the race track (Figure 9.12).

Seismic waves are like cars in a race Like fast and slow race cars, P- and S-waves have different speeds. Seismologists use the difference in the arrival time of these waves to calculate the distance to the epicenter from the seismic station.

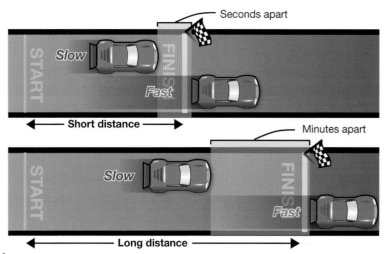

Figure 9.12: *The time difference between slow and fast cars is related to the length of the race track.*

Review Whenever an earthquake occurs, seismologists want to determine the location of the epicenter. Recall that an earthquake starts underground at a focus. The epicenter is the location on Earth's surface above the focus (review Figure 9.3). Seismic waves radiate from the focus after the earthquake.

Three seismic stations are needed Seismic stations can accurately determine the times of body wave arrival. However, a single station cannot determine the exact direction from which the waves arrived. At least three stations are needed to complete the locating process. First, one station draws a circle around its location on a map. The epicenter distance sets the size of the circle. The edge of this circle represents all of the possible locations of the earthquake from that station. Next, the other two stations add their circles to the same map. The second circle will cross the first circle at two points. When the third circle is added, all three circles will cross at only one point, the location of the epicenter (Figure 9.13).

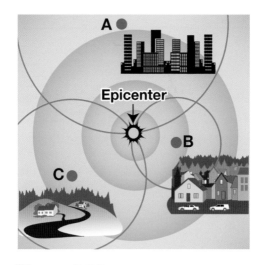

Figure 9.13: *An epicenter is identified using data collected from seismographic stations in three different locations.*

How to determine the distance to an epicenter

Today, seismologists use computers to determine the distance to an epicenter. However, locating an epicenter can also be done with paper and a pencil. Follow these steps and you will be able to determine the location of an epicenter.

Station name	Arrival time difference between P- and S-waves	Distance to epicenter
1	10 seconds	80 km
2	50 seconds	420 km
3	30 seconds	250 km

Figure 9.14: *Sample data for finding an epicenter.*

1. Identify three seismic stations and locate them on a map.
2. Determine the time difference between the arrival of the S-waves and the P-waves at each station. See Figure 9.14 for sample data.
3. Use the seismic time-distance graph below to convert the time differences into distances to the epicenter.

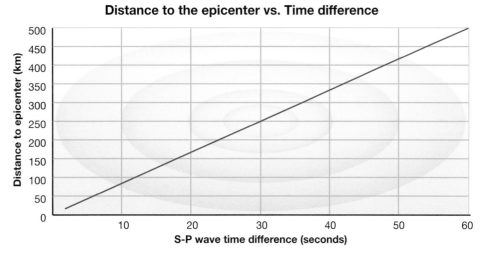

Distance to the epicenter vs. Time difference

4. Use the distance scale on your map to set a geometric compass so that the space between the point and pencil on the compass is proportional to the distances that you found in Step 3.
5. Draw a circle around each seismic station location.

Find the point where all three circles cross (Figure 9.15). Sometimes the crossed circles make a small triangle, not a single point. The center of the triangle is the epicenter.

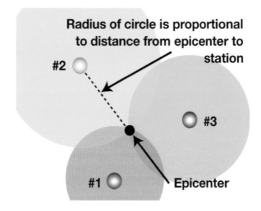

Figure 9.15: *The epicenter is located at the point where the circles around three seismic stations cross. The radius of each circle is the distance to the epicenter.*

9.2 Section Review

1. What is the difference between these two kinds of seismic waves: body waves and surface waves?

2. This seismic wave is the fastest type of body wave. This wave pushes and pulls rock in the direction the wave travels. This is called a _____ wave.

3. This seismic wave is slower than a P-wave, but still faster than the speed of sound. It moves rock in a side-to-side motion that is perpendicular to the direction of the moving wave. This is called a _____ wave.

4. Which type of seismic waves—body or surface—tend to cause the most damage during an earthquake?

5. As a seismic wave travels through Earth, it encounters different materials. List what can happen to a seismic wave as it moves from one material to another.

6. What information is gained about an earthquake from using a seismograph?

7. How would a seismologist use seismographs to study a small part of a fault zone?

8. What is measured to determine the location of an epicenter?

9. At least how many data stations are needed to find the epicenter of an earthquake?

10. S-waves from a quake arrive at a seismic station 40 seconds after the arrival of P-waves. How far away is the epicenter?

11. The distance scale on a map is 1 centimeter = 10 kilometers. The distance from a seismic station to the epicenter of an earthquake is 50 kilometers. To locate the epicenter, what would be the radius of the circle that is drawn around this station on a map?

STUDY SKILLS

Get to know your waves

You have learned about different seismic waves: surface waves, and body waves (P- and S-waves). How are you going to remember the differences? Here's an idea.

1. **List:** For each type of wave, make a list of words and phrases that describe the wave.

2. **Make a study tool:** Combine the three lists into a table, poster, diagram, concept map, or in another creative way.

3. **Show and tell:** Show your waves study tool to classmates, family, and friends and tell them about it!

MY JOURNAL

How are seismic waves like race cars?

In your own words, write a paragraph that answers this question. Use illustrations to explain your answer.

9.3 Measuring Earthquakes

There are two related measurements taken during and after an earthquake—the energy released and the damage caused. Low magnitude earthquakes are less likely to cause as much damage as high magnitude earthquakes. But, if a high magnitude earthquake occurred in a desert, there would be less damage than if a low magnitude earthquake occurred in a heavily populated city. In this section, you will learn how earthquakes are measured and compared.

Measuring the magnitude of an earthquake

The Richter scale

The **Richter scale** rates earthquakes according to the size of the seismic waves recorded on a seismograph. The seismic wave energy increases ten times for each Richter number change. The Richter scale assumes that the

Damage caused by the 1960 Chile earthquake

Photo courtesy of the National Geophysical Data Center

measurements were taken near the earthquake epicenter. The largest earthquake recorded occurred in Chile in 1960. It was off the Richter scale; seismologists estimated this quake to be 9.5.

The Moment Magnitude scale

Both the Richter scale and the **Moment Magnitude scale** rate the energy of an earthquake. The Moment Magnitude scale rates the total energy released by an earthquake. This scale can be used at locations that are close to and far away from an epicenter. The numbers on this scale combine energy ratings and descriptions of rock movements. The Richter and Moment Magnitude scales are about the same up to a rating of 5. However, when earthquakes are larger, seismologists tend to use the more descriptive Moment Magnitude scale.

The Richter scale		
Level	**Magnitude**	**Effects**
Micro	Less than 2.0	Barely felt
Very minor	2.0 - 2.9	Recorded but not felt by most people
Minor	3.0 - 3.9	Little damage but felt by people
Light	4.0 - 4.9	No serious damage, objects shake
Moderate	5.0 - 5.9	Major damage to poorly-designed buildings
Strong	6.0 - 6.9	Serious damage over a 100-mile area or less
Major	7.0 - 7.9	Serious damage over a larger area
Great	8.0 - 8.9	Serious damage over several hundred miles
Rare great	9.0 or greater	Serious damage over several thousand miles

Figure 9.16: *The Richter scale with a description of the effects at each magnitude.*

Measuring the damage caused by an earthquake

The Mercalli Intensity scale The **Mercalli Intensity scale** has 12 descriptive categories. Each category is a rating of the damage suffered by buildings, the ground, and people. Because earthquake damage can be different from place to place, a single earthquake may have different Mercalli numbers in different locations (Figure 9.17).

Table 9.1: Mercalli Intensity Scale.

Mercalli Intensity	Characteristic Effects	Approximate Richter Magnitude
I. Instrumental	Not felt	1
II. Just perceptible	Felt by only a few people, especially on upper floors of tall buildings	1.5
III. Slight	Felt by people lying down, seated on a hard surface, or in the upper stories of tall buildings	2
IV. Perceptible	Felt indoors by many, by few outside	3
V. Rather strong	Generally felt by everyone; sleeping people may be awakened	4
VI. Strong	Trees sway, chandeliers swing, bells ring, some damage from falling objects	5
VII. Very strong	General alarm; walls and plaster crack	5.5
VIII. Destructive	Felt in moving vehicles; chimneys collapse; poorly constructed buildings seriously damaged	6
IX. Ruinous	Some houses collapse; pipes break	6.5
X. Disastrous	Obvious ground cracks; railroad tracks bent; some landslides on steep hillsides	7
XI. Very disastrous	Few buildings survive; bridges damaged or destroyed; all services interrupted (electrical, water, sewage, railroad); severe landslides	7.5
XII. Catastrophic	Total destruction; objects thrown into the air; river courses and topography altered	8

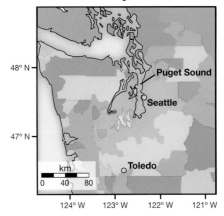

Sample intensity map for an earthquake in Washington state

INTENSITY	I	II–III	IV	V	VI	VII	VIII	IX	X+
Shaking	Not felt	Weak	Light	Moderate	Strong	Very strong	Severe	Violent	Extreme
Damage	None	None	None	Very light	Light	Moderate	Moderate/Heavy	Heavy	Very Heavy

Figure 9.17: *A sample intensity map for a single earthquake in Washington state. From the map, you can see that the earthquake was a category IX on the Mercallli Intensity scale in a very small area. Most of the surrounding areas experienced less shaking and damage.*

Where do earthquakes occur?

Boundaries of plates

When earthquake locations are plotted for many years, a map like the one below (at the lower left) can be created. Earthquakes commonly occur at the boundaries of lithospheric plates. Earthquakes occur less commonly at faults that are inside plate boundaries. Note that in Figure 9.18, the earthquakes along the converging plates do not form a neat line. This is because plate boundaries tend to be *zones* of seismic activity. In particular, faults at transform fault boundaries, like the San Andreas Fault in Figure 9.19, have many branches. These fault branches form an *earthquake zone*.

Earthquakes along a transform fault boundary

The California coast lies along the San Andreas Fault (Figure 9.19). This famous fault passes right through San Francisco and part of Los Angeles. These metropolitan areas have a combined population of over ten million people. San Francisco has experienced several severe earthquakes and many smaller ones. The earthquake of 1906, together with the fires that it caused, destroyed much of the city. The damage caused by the earthquake was probably 8 or 9 on the Mercalli scale. Future earthquakes must be expected here because the fault that lies under the city is still active.

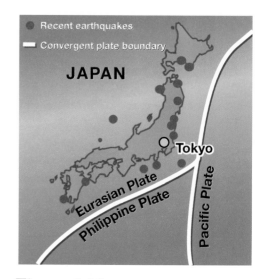

Figure 9.18: *These moderate earthquakes in Japan are associated with subduction occurring at plate boundaries.*

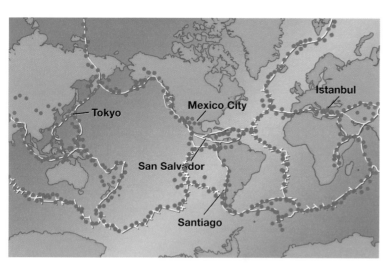

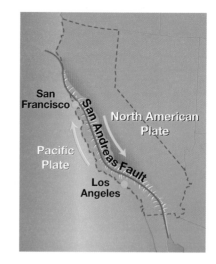

Figure 9.19: *The California coast lies along the San Andreas Fault.*

9.3 Section Review

1. What two measurements are taken during and after an earthquake?

2. Compare and contrast the three earthquake measuring scales discussed in this section.

3. How many times stronger is a 3.0 magnitude earthquake compared to a 2.0 magnitude earthquake on the Richter scale?

4. A friend tells you that he once experienced an earthquake. He said that he witnessed books and other objects falling off his bookcase.

   a. What was the magnitude of this earthquake on the Mercalli Intensity scale?

   b. What was the most likely magnitude of this earthquake on the Richter scale?

5. The largest earthquake ever recorded occurred in Chile which is on the west coast of South America. Why are earthquakes to be expected in Chile? Explain your answer.

6. Why is it possible for a single earthquake to have different Mercalli Intensity scale ratings in different locations?

7. Why don't earthquakes follow plate boundary lines exactly?

8. In the text, you read that future earthquakes will probably occur near the San Andreas Fault because the fault is still "active." What do you think it means to say a fault is "active?"

Earthquakes inside plate boundaries

Here are two descriptions of earthquakes that occurred inside plate boundaries. Pick one and find out more information about the quake. Imagine you are an investigative reporter. Write a paragraph about each quake. Read your paragraph to the class as if you were reporting on the quake after it has happened.

(1) The New Madrid Fault is a 250-mile long fault located in the Midwest. Very strong earthquakes in 1811 and 1812 destroyed most of the town of New Madrid, Missouri.

(2) You probably don't think of New England as an earthquake area. But in 1755, a strong earthquake struck colonial Boston and destroyed many homes. The damage was greatest north of Boston and the earthquake was felt as far north as Montreal, Canada.

2004 Indian Ocean Earthquake and Tsunami

The top satellite picture of Kalutara, Sri Lanka was taken about an hour after the first tsunami wave hit on December 26, 2004. Water is rushing back out to sea after inundating the land. The lower picture shows what the same area looked like under normal conditions in January 2004.

Tilly Smith probably never imagined what she learned in geography class would help save lives. When the Indian Ocean tsunami hit on December 26, 2004, Tilly and her family were vacationing at Miakho Beach in Phuket, Thailand. Tilly, 10 years old, noticed something strange happening on the beach. The water at the beach suddenly went away. In the distance, she could see boats bouncing wildly and the water bubbling. The ocean water returned quickly and kept coming onto shore. Tilly screamed for her family to leave the beach right away. Her parents warned others. Due to her knowledge of tsunami early warning signs, the girl from England saved other tourists on the beach that day.

What is a tsunami?

Tilly had just learned that underwater earthquakes could cause tsunamis. *Tsunami* is a Japanese word meaning "harbor wave." Underwater earthquakes, landslides, and volcanoes may cause tsunamis. Not every earthquake leads to a tsunami. Yet, large ocean earthquakes that move the sea floor up and down cause many tsunamis.

The size of a tsunami depends on many factors. How large is the earthquake? Where does the earthquake occur? How much of the sea floor moves up and down? How deep is the ocean water where the earthquake occurs? In the deep ocean, tsunamis may be only several feet high. Often ships at sea never feel a tsunami. This is not the case as the tsunami travels toward shore and shallower water. The amount of water begins to build. Wave height increases as they approach land. Some waves may travel 800-1,000 kilometers per hour (500-600 miles per hour) and be as high as 15 to 30 meters (50 to 100 feet).

The Indian Ocean tsunami

The Indian Ocean tsunami may be one of the deadliest natural disasters in modern history. Officials believe over 275,000 people died. The final number of deaths may never be known. The US Geological Survey originally reported the earthquakes at a 9.0 magnitude. This is the strongest in the world since 1964 and the forth largest since 1900. Scientists used data from around the world to revise the earthquake to a 9.3 magnitude. This would make it the second largest earthquake since the 9.5 magnitude in Chile in 1960.

Earth's surface is made up of plates that are constantly in motion. Plates meet one another along plate boundaries. Pressure along these boundaries causes rock to break creating earthquakes.

During the Indian Ocean earthquake, 1,200 kilometers (750 miles) of the plate boundary slipped when the India Plate (part of the Indo-Australian Plate) slid under the

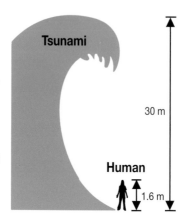

Tsunami

30 m

Human

1.6 m

Burma Plate (part of the Eurasian Plate). That is about 400 kilometers (250 miles) more than the distance between San Diego and San Francisco! The seabed rose over six feet causing huge tsunami waves.

Imagine a plastic squeeze bottle filled to the top with water. As you squeeze the container the water spills out over the top. The upward motion of the earthquake displaced an enormous amount of water similar to the squeeze bottle. This displacement of water created the tsunami that flooded the coastlines.

The Indian Ocean earthquake occurred off the west coast of Sumatra, an Indonesian island. Waves reached 20 to 30 meters (65 to 100 feet) high. The tsunami destroyed the shores of Indonesia, Sri Lanka, and Thailand. The tsunami even traveled as far as Africa, nearly 8,000 kilometers (5000 miles) from the center of the earthquake.

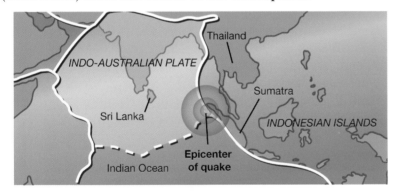

The tsunami waves did not start from one central location, but occurred along the entire 750 miles of fault line. That is why the waves affected so many areas of the world.

Indian Ocean tsunami warning system

Why did so many people die from the tsunami? Tsunamis are rare in the Indian Ocean and a warning system was not in place. The last major tsunami in the region was caused by the 1883 volcanic eruption of Krakatoa in Indonesia.

People were not aware of the signs of a tsunami—a strong earthquake in the area and a quick rise or fall in water levels by the coast.

Historically, tsunamis usually happen in the Pacific Ocean where many earthquakes occur. In the Pacific, there are two warning centers monitoring the area: the Alaska and the Pacific Tsunami Warning Centers. The Alaska Tsunami Warning Center includes the west coast of the United States and Canada. The Pacific Tsunami Warning Center covers Hawaii and all other Pacific areas. The centers monitor the size and location of earthquakes in the ocean. If a tsunami is possible, the center sends out a warning estimating when the tsunami will reach land. This allows coastal areas to have time to evacuate.

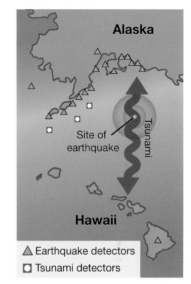

One month after the Indian Ocean tsunami, the United Nations recommended a warning system for the Indian Ocean. Plans are in place to have as many as 27 centers created, one for each Indian Ocean country. In May of 2005, Thailand opened a center linked to the Pacific Tsunami Warning Center. The goal is to have all systems in place by July 2006. There has been discussion about creating a global warning system that would include the Atlantic Ocean and the Caribbean.

Questions:

1. What causes a tsunami?
2. What are signs that a tsunami might be coming?
3. Why was there no tsunami warning system in the Indian Ocean?

CHAPTER ACTIVITY The Dragon and Toad Mystery

In this chapter, you learned about earthquakes and how scientists collect data using seismographs. In this activity, you will learn something about the history of using seismographs.

In about 132 A.D., a long time ago, a Chinese philosopher, Chang Heng, invented the earliest known seismoscope. The paragraph below describes Heng's seismograph.

Imagine a large, ceramic vessel or jar about six feet in diameter. On the outside of this vessel were eight dragon heads. These faced the eight main directions that you would find on a compass. Not attached to the vessel, but seated below each of the dragon heads were eight toads, with their mouths open in the direction of the dragon head it was below. In the mouth of the dragon was a ball. The idea was that when an earthquake happened, a dragon would release its ball and it would fall into the appropriate toad's mouth. The direction of the shaking would determine which ball was released. Heng would know if an earthquake happened and from what direction it came.

The mystery is this—the inside of this early seismoscope is unknown.

What you will do

1. Draw your interpretation of the outside of this vessel.
2. Spend some time thinking about mechanisms that might be found inside to make this instrument work. Once you have given it some thought and come up with an idea, draw/sketch your idea.
3. Below your sketch, write a step-by-step procedure of how this instrument works. Be sure to write clearly.

4. Exchange your instrument description and procedure with the instrument and procedure completed by someone else in your class.
5. You will present the description and procedure of one your classmates. This classmate will present your description and procedure to the class.
6. Your procedure on how to use it needs to be clear because that person is going to explain your instrument to the class and you will be explaining theirs based on the sketch and description. Remember, there are no right answers for this activity!

Applying your knowledge

a. Which instrument in the class would work best and why? Write a paragraph to answer this question.
b. How did your description and drawing compare to Chang Heng's seismograph? Learn more about Chang Heng's seismograph on the Internet—http://neic.usgs.gov/neis/seismology/part03.html. Write a paragraph comparing your seismograph to Heng's.
c. How do modern seismographs work? Research modern seismographs and write a paragraph about them.

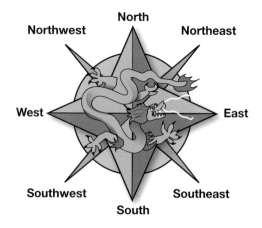

Chapter 9 Assessment

Vocabulary

Select the correct term to complete the sentences.

earthquake	fault	Richter scale
surface waves	seismograph	Moment Magnitude scale
body waves	epicenter	Mercalli Intensity scale
focus		

Section 9.1

1. The place on Earth's surface above where the rock breaks during an earthquake is the _____.

2. Stick-slip motion between lithospheric plates is what causes an _____.

3. The point below the epicenter is called the _____.

4. A _____ is a place where rocks break and there is movement.

Section 9.2

5. The type of seismic waves that travel at Earth's surface are called _____.

6. _____ are seismic waves that travel through the planet.

7. The instrument used to record seismic waves is a _____.

Section 9.3

8. Each number change on the _____ means a 10-fold increase in seismic wave energy.

9. Eyewitness accounts of earthquake damage are incorporated into this earthquake measurement scale: _____

10. The _____ rates the total energy of an earthquake.

Concepts

Section 9.1

1. What is friction?

2. Stick-slip motion can occur between any two objects. Give an example of stick-slip motion that you have experienced.

3. When two plates slide past each other, what happens to the crusts of these plates? What happens to the upper mantle parts of these plates?

4. The upper mantle is described as being *plastic*. Why is this a good term to describe the upper mantle?

5. What's the difference between shallow focus earthquakes and deep focus earthquakes?

6. What is a slickensides?

Section 9.2

7. Describe surface waves and how they affect an area that is experiencing an earthquake.

8. How are S- and P-waves used to find the distance from a seismic station to the epicenter of an earthquake?

9. What is the smallest number of seismic stations needed to determine the location of the epicenter of an earthquake?

Section 9.3

10. Why is a seismograph useful for measuring the magnitude of an earthquake on the Richter scale?

11. Is it possible that an earthquake could happen and you would not know it? Explain your answer.

12. What is the difference between the Moment Magnitude scale and the Richter scale?

13. After an earthquake, one person says that the intensity of the quake was VI on the Mercalli Intensity scale. Another person says that the intensity was III. Why might these individuals have had different experiences?

14. Where do most earthquakes occur? Explain your answer.

Math and Writing Skills

Section 9.1

1. In this chapter, you learned about the depth at which shallow and deep focus earthquakes originate in Earth. In what layers of Earth (from the detailed view of Earth in Chapter 7) do these types of earthquakes originate?

2. How wide was the area affected by the 1895 New Madrid earthquake? Refer to the New Madrid Fault Zone graphic in Section 9.1. Give your answer in miles. Then, convert this value to kilometers (1.6 km = 1 mile).

3. Since 1964, the longest earthquake ever recorded was the 1964 Alaskan earthquake. It lasted 4 minutes. The 2004 Indonesian earthquake broke the 1964 record. Find out the new record for the longest earthquake ever recorded. Write a short paragraph that describes three interesting facts you learned from your research.

Section 9.2

4. P-waves travel faster than S-waves and both of these seismic body waves travel faster than the speed of sound. Given the approximated values in this table, how much faster do P-waves travel than S-waves? How much faster do S-waves travel than sound (in air)? (Hint: Divide the smaller value into the larger value.)

Approximate Speed (km/s)	
P-wave	7
S-wave	3.6
Sound in air	0.34

5. The time difference between the arrival of a P-wave and an S-wave at a seismic station is 25 seconds. How far away is the epicenter?

6. The distance from the epicenter of a quake to a seismic station is 180 kilometers. If the distance scale on your map is 1 centimeters = 20 kilometers, what would be the radius of the circle that is drawn around this station on the map?

Section 9.3

7. If each Richter value represents seismic waves 10 times greater than the one before, than how much larger are the waves of an earthquake with a magnitude 6 versus a magnitude 3?

8. What is the Richter magnitude and Mercalli Intensity for an earthquake that causes enough shaking to wake you up, but not enough to cause damage?

Chapter Project—Demonstrating Liquefaction

First, gather the following items: brick, rubber mallet, water, sand, a plastic bin. Place the bin on a table. Fill the plastic bin 2/3 full with sand. Pour water into the bin to just below the surface of the sand. Hold the brick upright so that it represents a tall building. Wiggle it into the sand so that it stands up on its own. Using your mallet, tap the side of the bin repeatedly and gently. Watch what happens to the sand and brick.

This model demonstrates what can happen when an earthquake shakes an area that has been filled by humans, such as Boston's Back Bay or the China Basin in the southeast portion of San Francisco. There are several regions in the Bay Area of California that have been filled to create land. They are all susceptible to liquefaction.

Liquefaction occurs when the seismic waves travel through the ground, the sandy soil is suspended in the water as the water fills in all the spaces in between the soil particles. Now the soil acts like a liquid and losing the ability to support buildings. The soil and water engulf the buildings as they sink into the ground.

Chapter 10
Volcanoes

Our early ancestors created stories to explain volcanic eruptions. For example, it was thought that the volcanic island Vulcano off the coast of Italy was a smoke stack for Vulcan, the Roman god of fire and metalworking. Today, volcanic eruptions make the news when they occur. What do you know about volcanoes? How do you think they are connected to plate tectonics?

Key Questions

1. *What does the inside of a volcano look like?*

2. *Where do we find volcanoes on Earth?*

3. *What are the different kinds of volcanoes?*

10.1 What Is a Volcano?

Volcanoes are spectacular when they erupt but they can be dangerous! You have probably seen a volcanic eruption on television. Mount St. Helens in Washington is a famous volcano that erupted in 1980 (Figure 10.1). What is a volcano? A **volcano** is a site where melted rock and other materials from Earth's mantle are released.

Looking inside a volcano

The parts of a volcano During an eruption, melted rock called **magma** leaves the **magma chamber** and moves up the *conduit*. The magma leaves the conduit at the *vent*. Magma may leave the vent gently, or with violent force. Magma is called **lava** after it leaves the vent. Magma may leave the conduit by moving sideways along weaknesses between rock layers. This sideways movement of magma forms a *sill*. Magma may also move upward in a sheet to form a *dike*. If a sill or a dike breaks through to the surface, another vent will form.

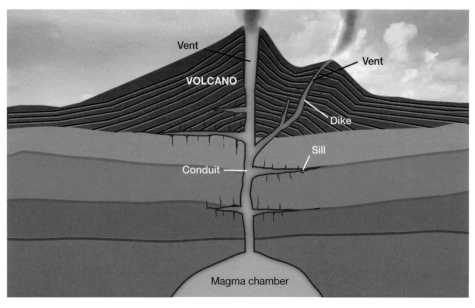

volcano - an erupting vent through which molten rock reaches Earth's surface, or a mountain built from the products of an eruption.

magma - underground melted rock.

magma chamber - a location where magma collects inside Earth.

lava - magma that has reached and cooled on Earth's surface.

Figure 10.1: *Mount St. Helens is a type of volcano called a* composite volcano *(also known as a* stratovolcano*).*

What happens after a volcano erupts?

Formation of a caldera
Eventually, all volcanic eruptions end. The magma drains back down the conduit. The vent winds up looking like a bowl. This bowl is called the **caldera** and may be very large.

Caldera

Photo courtesy U.S. Geological Survey

caldera - the bowl-shaped vent of a volcano after it has erupted.

resurgent dome - a mound in the vent of an erupted volcano.

lava lake - a lake that contains lava that has formed in a caldera.

Resurgent dome
If magma begins to return back up the conduit, a mound called a **resurgent dome** may form on the caldera floor. Another kind of volcano, a *cinder cone*, may also form in the caldera. You'll learn about cinder cones in Section 10.3.

Novarupta Dome
Katmai, Alaska

Resurgent dome

Photo courtesy of U.S. Geological Survey

Lava lake

Photo courtesy U.S. Geological Survey

Figure 10.2: *A lava lake.*

Lava lake
Water may fill the caldera forming a lake. It's also possible that the magma may not drain completely. In that case, the caldera will contain lava and become a **lava lake** (Figure 10.2).

The life of a volcano

Volcanoes have a lifetime Volcanoes are not permanent features on the surface of Earth. They have a lifetime that occurs in phases. Volcanoes are described according to the phase they are in. The three phases are active, dormant, and extinct.

Active volcanoes An **active volcano** is the most vigorous kind of volcano. Active volcanoes are erupting or have erupted recently, and are expected to erupt again in the near future. However, volcanic activity during the life of a volcano doesn't last forever. Eventually, the conditions that make a volcano active change and the volcano becomes dormant.

Dormant volcanoes A **dormant volcano** is a quiet volcano. "Dormant" means sleeping. Dormant volcanoes are not active now, but may become active again in the future. Most of the volcanoes along the northern Pacific coast of North America are dormant.

Extinct volcanoes An **extinct volcano** is at the end of its life and is no longer able to erupt. As the volcano erodes, a core of now-solid magma, called a volcanic neck, may be exposed.

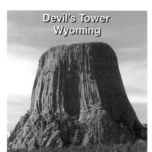
Devil's Tower Wyoming

A **volcanic neck** is the solid remains of magma that filled the conduit. Figure 10.3 is a photo of Ship Rock in New Mexico. The "ship" is a volcanic neck. Devil's Tower National Monument in Wyoming is another famous volcanic neck. You can see the remains of several dikes running out from the neck. Devil's Tower was featured in the 1977 Steven Spielberg movie *Close Encounters of the Third Kind*!

active volcano - a volcano that is erupting or that has erupted recently.

dormant volcano - a volcano that is not erupting now, but that may erupt in the future.

extinct volcano - a volcano that no longer erupts and is in the process of eroding.

volcanic neck - solid remains of magma that filled the conduit of an extinct volcano. The neck is exposed as the volcano erodes.

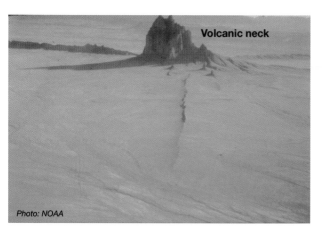
Volcanic neck

Photo: NOAA

Figure 10.3: *The volcanic neck of Ship Rock in New Mexico has been exposed by erosion.*

Making magma

Where does magma come from? Earth's crust is so cool that it's brittle. Nevertheless, hot, melted rock makes its way to Earth's surface and comes out of volcanoes as lava. What makes rock melt so that it becomes magma and then explodes out onto Earth's surface?

Temperature You know that heating ice, butter, and a lot of other solids will make them melt. At high enough temperatures, solid rock will melt too. However, the lithosphere is not hot enough to melt rock.

Pressure and water There are two other ways to make rock melt that are very important. One way is to reduce the pressure. The other way is to mix water with the hot rock. The conditions needed to melt rock are very special and they exist inside our planet. They are listed in Figure 10.4 and illustrated below.

Where does magma form? You will learn where magma is made in Section 10.3. For now, you can make predictions about where the conditions for making magma occur by answering the questions in the Challenge box.

Conditions that melt rock

Changes in pressure

Rock under high pressure melts at a higher temperature.

Rock under low pressure melts at a lower temperature.

Adding water to hot rock

Dry rock melts at a higher temperature.

Rock that contains water melts at a lower temperature.

Figure 10.4: *Conditions for making magma.*

Make predictions about where rocks melt! Pick your answers from this list: crust, core, mid-ocean ridge, subduction zone, and transform fault boundary.

1. Where would rocks experience decreasing temperature and lowering pressure?

2. Where would rocks experience lowering temperature and the addition of water?

What causes rock to melt?

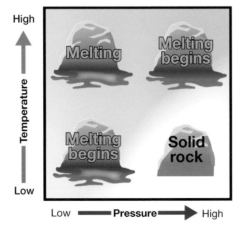

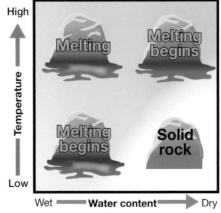

10.1 Section Review

1. What is the difference between magma and lava?

2. Imagine a volcano with only one vent. What change might cause a second vent to appear on the side of the volcano?

3. About 7,000 years ago, Mount Mazama erupted and the summit (top) of the volcano collapsed forming a depression that was then filled with rain and melted snow. The depression is now called Crater Lake. Mount Mazama is an extinct volcano. What is the best term to describe the depression that holds Crater Lake?

4. Which kind of volcano is being described? Write *active*, *dormant*, or *extinct* for each item below.
   a. No longer erupting
   b. Could be described as "sleeping"
   c. May erupt in the future but is not erupting at present or recently
   d. Erupting on a regular basis
   e. The volcano is eroding and a volcanic neck is exposed

5. What is the difference between a dormant volcano and an active volcano?

6. Based on your reading in this section, answer these questions:
   a. Under what conditions of temperature and pressure does a solid rock begin to melt?
   b. Under what conditions of temperature and water content does a solid rock begin to melt?

SOLVE IT!

Volcano Trivia

You will need to do research to answer each question.

1. Where does the word "volcano" come from?

2. What is the Roman god Vulcan known for?

3. How many active volcanoes are on Earth right now?

4. What is the most volcanic moon in our solar system?

5. What is the biggest volcano on Earth?

6. Come up with three more volcano trivia questions (and their answers) to ask your friends!

10.2 Where Do You Find Volcanoes?

Early humans could not travel easily and only knew of a few local volcanoes. They couldn't see a pattern among volcanoes and made up stories to explain why volcanoes occurred. As explorers started traveling the world, map makers noticed that many volcanoes were located along coastlines, but they didn't know why. Do you? In this section, you will learn about where Earth's volcanoes are found.

Volcanoes at plate boundaries

Where are most volcanoes located? Most volcanoes are located along plate boundaries. About half of the active surface volcanoes on Earth occur along the shores of the Pacific Ocean! This region is called the Ring of Fire.

The Ring of Fire The **Ring of Fire** coincides with regions where the oceanic crust of the Pacific Plate is subducting under other plates. Mount St. Helens is one of the volcanoes within the Ring of Fire (Figure 10.5).

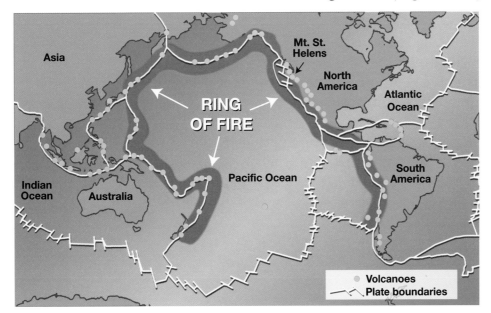

Elevation: 2,932 meters

Before 1980

Elevation: 2,535 meters

1984

Photos courtesy U.S. Geological Survey

Figure 10.5: *Mount St. Helens before and after its eruption. This volcano formed when the small Juan de Fuca Plate subducted under the North American Plate.*

Volcanoes at mid-ocean ridges

Pressure decreases at mid-ocean ridges

Mid-ocean ridges occur at diverging plate boundaries. Convection currents in the lower mantle pull the plates away from each other (Figure 10.6). As the plates move apart, lower mantle material is drawn toward Earth's surface. The rock of the lower mantle is hot, flexible, and solid. This rock is solid because of the great pressure of the layers above it. However, as the rock of the lower mantle rises, the pressure drops and the material melts.

Basalt and silica

The melted lower mantle material forms basalt magma. **Basalt** is a dark-colored rock that is not silica-rich. **Silica** makes magma thick and sticky. Basalt magma is runny because of its low silica content. *Quartz* is a mineral that you may be familiar with. Quartz is made of silica.

Quartz
A mineral made of silica

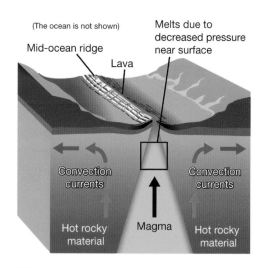

Photo courtesy U.S House Subcommittee on Energy and Natural Resources

Runny lava

If a lot of silica makes magma thick and sticky, then magma without much silica must be thin and runny! When runny basalt lava oozes out at a mid-ocean ridge, it immediately hits cold seawater. The seawater cools the lava, forming a crust. But soon the crust cracks and another jet of basalt magma squirts out. This cycle repeats over and over, forming lava that looks like a pile of pillows. You read about this distinctive lava called *pillow lava* in Section 8.3. The presence of pillow lava can be a clue for the location of ancient mid-ocean ridges.

Basalt lava

Photo courtesy U.S. Geological Survey

(The ocean is not shown)

Mid-ocean ridge

Lava

Melts due to decreased pressure near surface

Convection currents

Convection currents

Hot rocky material

Magma

Hot rocky material

Figure 10.6: *As the plates move apart at a mid-ocean ridge, the mantle material is drawn upward. The pressure decreases as this material rises. This causes mantle material to melt.*

Volcanic chains

Away from plate boundaries A **volcanic island** is not formed at a plate boundary. It forms as a result of narrow *mantle plumes* bringing material from deep within the lower mantle. The magma of both volcanic islands and mid-ocean ridges forms as hot, but solid rock moves closer to Earth's surface. As the hot rock rises, the pressure drops, and the rock melts, forming magma.

A volcanic island is born The melted lower mantle material forms runny basalt magma that is less dense than the surrounding rock. The basalt magma melts its way through the lithospheric plate above it. An underwater volcano forms when the magma breaks through the surface of the plate. If the eruption is strong enough, the magma will reach the surface of the sea, forming a volcanic island.

volcanic island - a volcano that forms away from a plate boundary on an oceanic plate.

hot spot - the top of an established mantle plume.

volcanic island chain - a series of volcanoes formed by a hot spot as a lithospheric plate moves over the hot spot.

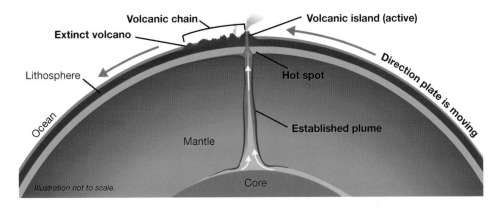

Volcanic chain · Extinct volcano · Volcanic island (active) · Lithosphere · Hot spot · Ocean · Established plume · Mantle · Direction plate is moving · Core · *Illustration not to scale.*

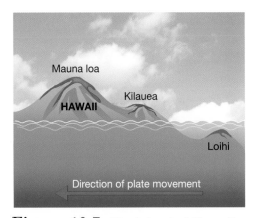

Mauna loa · Kilauea · HAWAII · Loihi · Direction of plate movement

Figure 10.7: *The island of Hawaii sits on top of a hot spot. The hot spot has formed the Mauna Loa and Kilauea volcanoes on the island. Currently, the hot spot is making the undersea volcano Loihi to the southeast of the island. When Loihi gets bigger and reaches the ocean surface, it will increase the size of Hawaii.*

Volcanic island chains The plate on which a volcanic island sits is moving, but the mantle plumes stay in one place. The top of an established mantle plume is called a **hot spot**. As the plate moves, it carries the volcanic island away from the hot spot that formed it. Without the hot spot to supply magma, the volcano becomes extinct. At the same time, the hot spot begins to form a new volcano beside the old one (Figure 10.7). In this way, a **volcanic island chain** is formed.

Using island chains to measure the motion of a plate

The Hawaiian Islands
The Hawaiian Islands are an example of a volcanic island chain. The biggest island, Hawaii, is over the hot spot now and has active volcanoes. Hawaii has been on top of this hot spot for the last 800,000 years (0.8 million years). The islands to the northwest of Hawaii are older and their volcanoes are either dormant or extinct.

Island chains and the speed of plates
By studying the direction, age, and length of a volcanic chain, scientists can determine the direction and speed that a plate is moving. The Hawaiian Chain shows us that the Pacific Plate is moving northwest at nearly nine centimeters per year.

Adding to a volcanic island
To the southeast of the Hawaiian Chain, the mantle plume under Hawaii is making a new volcano—Loihi. Loihi is an undersea volcano (Figure 10.7). When enough lava builds up so that Loihi is above sea level, it will extend the eastern border of Hawaii!

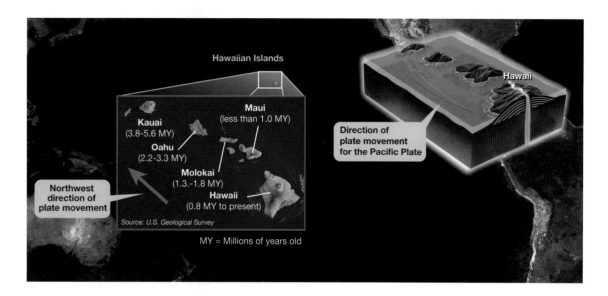

Hawaiian Islands

Maui
(less than 1.0 MY)

Kauai
(3.8-5.6 MY)

Oahu
(2.2-3.3 MY)

Molokai
(1.3.-1.8 MY)

Hawaii
(0.8 MY to present)

Northwest direction of plate movement

Direction of plate movement for the Pacific Plate

Hawaii

Source: U.S. Geological Survey

MY = Millions of years old

Island arcs are features near plate boundaries

An island chain occurs on a lithospheric plate. For example, the Hawaiian Chain is in the middle of the Pacific Plate located away from the plate's boundaries.

In contrast, an *island arc* is a string of volcanic islands that forms close to a plate boundary. The island of Japan and neighboring islands are an island arc at the subduction zone where three plates come together.

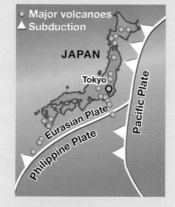

Major volcanoes
Subduction

JAPAN

Tokyo

Eurasian Plate

Philippine Plate

Pacific Plate

Eventually, plate movements at a subduction zone bring the islands and continents together. In this way, continents grow larger! Scientists can detect where island arcs have increased the size of the North American continent on both the west and east coasts.

Volcanoes at subduction zones

What happens when a plate subducts? A subducting plate bends and passes under a more buoyant, less dense plate. As the subducting plate sinks into the mantle, mud and water are carried along. As the plate sinks further, the water is released. Water combines with the hot mantle rock of the aesthenosphere (the part of the upper mantle just under the crust). The combination of water and hot mantle rock allows the rock to melt at a lower temperature. This magma is less dense than the surrounding rock so it rises. Eventually, the magma melts through the edge of the overlying plate forming a volcano (Figure 10.8).

Thick and sticky magma Through a complex process, the magma that forms volcanoes in this way is rich in silica. Silica-rich magma is light in color, thick, sticky, and less dense than basalt magma. When cooled, the silica-rich magma forms granite and other closely-related rocks.

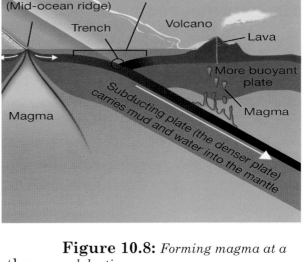

Figure 10.8: *Forming magma at a subduction zone.*

Granite domes of Yosemite National Park, California
Photo courtesy of Jim Sammons, Sammons' INK.

The famous granite domes of Yosemite National Park in California were formed as silica-rich magma rose through the edge of the overlying North American Plate at a subduction zone that no longer exists. When subduction stopped, the flow of magma stopped too (Figure 10.9). The magma below the surface cooled where it was. The surrounding land later eroded away, exposing the granite domes.

Granite is silica-rich Continents are made of granite (and andesite). Silica-rich granite is not as dense as the basalt of the ocean floor. This is why continental plates float high on the lower mantle. Because they float high, they stand above the oceans and provide us with dry land.

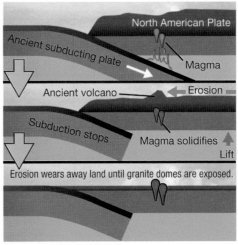

Figure 10.9: *Diagram of how the granite domes of Yosemite formed.*

10.2 Section Review

1. What did early map makers notice about the locations of volcanoes?

2. What causes the region called the Ring of Fire?

3. If you could melt a piece of quartz in some lava, would the lava get more sticky or less sticky? Explain your answer.

4. Where is runny lava found: (a) On a continental plate, or (b) on an oceanic plate?

5. Where is thick and sticky lava found: (a) On a continental plate, or (b) on an oceanic plate?

6. When volcanic island chains are formed, what moves? Pick the correct answer:

   a. the mantle plume   b. the plate above the mantle plume
   c. both the plate and the plume   d. nothing moves

7. Which of the Hawaiian Islands formed first and how long ago did it form?

8. What kind of geologic formation is Loihi? Is it a part of the Hawaiian Chain? Explain your answer.

9. How have scientists figured out that the Pacific Plate is moving at about 9 centimeters per year?

10. The Pacific Plate is moving at 9 centimeters per year.

    a. How long will it take for this plate to travel 4.5 meters?

    b. How far will the plate have travelled in meters after 3 years?

11. What are the names of the items (A–C) on the graphic in Figure 10.10?

12. Name a difference between an island chain and an island arc.

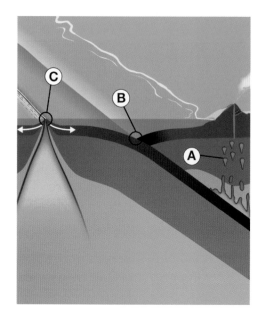

Figure 10.10: *Use this graphic to answer question 11.*

Write an essay about your observations and experiences during a visit to a national park. Write about Yosemite National Park if you have been there. Or, write about another special park you have visited. In particular, write about the geology of the park. Include drawings, diagrams, and/or photographs with your essay.

10.3 Types of Volcanoes

Why do volcanoes come in different shapes? The shape of a volcano and its type of eruption depend on what kind of magma it has. In this section, you will learn about the different types of volcanoes and magma!

Types of magma

Silica in magma Remember, an important property of magma is how much silica it has. One kind of magma has little silica and the other has a lot of silica. Magma with little silica makes runny magma. Magma with a lot of silica makes thick, sticky magma.

Dissolved gas in magma Another important property of magma is how much gas is dissolved in it. Little dissolved gas makes magma that doesn't have bubbles. This magma is "flat"—like soda that has lost its fizz. Magma with a lot of dissolved gas is like soda before you open it. It can be bubbly or, under the right conditions, it can explode out just like when you open a shaken bottle of soda.

Volcanic eruptions The nature of a volcanic eruption depends on what kind of magma is in the volcano. Study the table below and the graphic at the right to see the kinds of eruptions that occur with each kind of magma.

Table 10.1: Comparing magma.

	Low gas content	High gas content
Low silica content	• Runny magma, like syrup • Quiet eruption, lava flows easily	• Runny magma, bubbly • Fire fountain, lava flows easily
High silica content	• Thick, sticky magma • Quiet eruption	• Thick, sticky magma • Explosive eruption

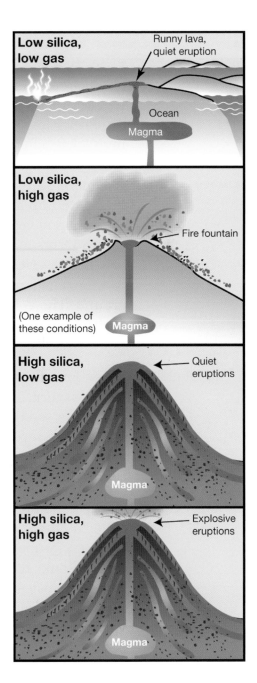

Volcanoes with low silica magma

Shield volcanoes Low silica magma produces a **shield volcano**. This magma can either have low or high levels of dissolved gas. Because low silica magma is runny, it can't build up a tall, cone-shaped volcano. Instead, this magma produces a volcano that is a flattened mound—it resembles a warrior's shield lying on the ground. The volcanoes of the Hawaiian Islands are shield volcanoes. If you have ever visited the Hawaiian volcanoes, you know that they are not explosive.

Shield volcano
Photo by D. Little, USGS.

Fire fountains When low silica magma has high levels of dissolved gas, the gas bubbles out as it reaches the volcano vent. The effect is identical to shaking a soda bottle to produce a shower of soda. The high-gas magma produces a spectacular *fire fountain* (Figure 10.11). The spatters of glowing magma cool in the air and hit the ground as solid lava cinders.

Cinder cones The lava cinders form a cone around the vent called a **cinder cone**. Cinder cones are a common form of volcano. They are often found on the flanks of both shield volcanoes and composite volcanoes (see the next page). Cinder cones may also form in the caldera of dormant volcanoes. Cinder cones are structurally weak because they are simply a pile of rock bits.

Cinder cone
Photo by J. Lowenstern, USGS.

VOCABULARY

shield volcano - a flat and wide volcano that has low-silica magma with low or high levels of dissolved gas.

cinder cone - a volcano that has low-silica magma with high levels of dissolved gas; these volcanoes produce "fire fountain" eruptions.

Photo by R.T. Holcomb, USGS.

Figure 10.11: *A fire fountain in Hawaii Volcanoes National Park. 1972–1974 eruption of the Kilauea Volcano.*

Volcanoes with high silica magma

Composite volcanoes Island arcs and most coastal volcanoes are created at subduction zones. The magma of these volcanoes is thick and sticky because it is silica-rich. Over time, layers of this thick lava and ash build a tall cone called a **composite volcano** (Figure 10.12).

Dissolved gas in sticky magma When silica-rich magma is low in dissolved gas, the magma will come out like toothpaste and form volcanic glass, called obsidian. But if the silica-rich magma contains high levels of dissolved gas, pressure usually builds inside the volcano. The magma of shield volcanoes is so runny that dissolved gas simply bubbles out. But silica-rich magma is too sticky. Before a composite volcano eruption, the magma may be under so much gas pressure that the composite volcano cone bulges (middle image, Figure 10.12).

Pumice and ash When a composite volcano cone bulges like this, either the eruption will subside and the magma will return down the conduit, or the cone will explode. The cone may explode near the vent, throwing a column of gas and lava bits high into the atmosphere. The lava bits puff up and rip apart as the dissolved gas expands inside each bit. This puffing up action produces two forms of rock: pumice and ash. *Pumice* is a dark rock with lots of holes. Pumice has a low density because of its holes (which were made by air bubbles) and will float in water. *Ash* is smaller, like fine sand. Because ash is so fine, it drifts with the wind and may settle over a very wide area.

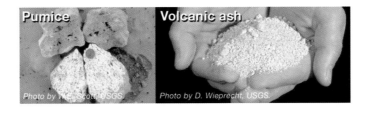

Pumice
Photo by W.E. Scott, USGS.

Volcanic ash
Photo by D. Wieprecht, USGS.

ā VOCABULARY

composite volcano - a tall, explosive, cone-shaped volcano formed by layers of silica-rich lava and ash.

1979
Photo by R.P. Hoblitt, USGS.

Bulge before eruption – 1980
Photo by Harry Glicken, USGS.

After the eruption – 1980
Photo by R.L. Christiansen, USGS.

Figure 10.12: *Mount St. Helens, a composite volcano, before and after an explosive eruption.*

Explosive eruptions

Pyroclastic flows When a column of exploding material collapses, it races down the side of a composite volcano as a **pyroclastic flow**. The speed (more than a 100 km/h), force, and heat (greater than 500 °C) of the pyroclastic flow make it extremely destructive.

Photo courtesy U.S. Geological Survey

pyroclastic flow - a destructive cloud of volcanic material that moves quickly down the side of a volcano after an explosive eruption.

lava bombs - blobs of glowing lava thrown from an explosive eruption.

lahars - a mudflow that results from a volcanic eruption.

Lava bombs Blobs of glowing lava may be thrown far from the base of the composite volcano. These blobs, called **lava bombs**, can be the size of watermelons. Sometimes the composite volcano explodes again, further down its side, adding more material to the expanding lava explosion.

Lahars Mount Saint Helens erupted in Washington State in 1980. This was a classic silica-rich, gas-rich composite volcano eruption. Magma pressure formed a large bulge on the side of the mountain. The eruption was triggered when a portion of the bulge slid off. This created a weakness in the cone that was containing the pressure. An enormous explosion blew off a huge part of the mountain. The combination of landslide, explosion, and pyroclastic flow killed 57 people. If water is present in the ground, mudflows may accompany a composite volcano eruption like this. The mudflows, called **lahars** (Figure 10.13), in this eruption destroyed forests and property and added to the death toll.

Lahar

Photo by Lyn Topinka, USGS.

Figure 10.13: *An example of a lahar, a mudflow that results from pyroclastic flow mixing with water and mud.*

Water and volcanoes

Volcanoes are part of the water cycle
Volcanoes are part of Earth's water cycle. The **water cycle** is a set of processes that keep water moving from place to place. When a volcano erupts, water that is in the magma is released as water vapor into the atmosphere. This water vapor condenses and falls into the ocean as rain. Or, the rain may fall on land and eventually get deposited into the ocean by rivers or streams. Recall that when rivers and streams are swollen by rain, they are able to carry sediments and rocks into the ocean. In this way, the water cycle is connected to Earth's **geological cycle**, a set of processes that keep rocky material moving from place to place in and on Earth.

 VOCABULARY

water cycle - a set of processes energized by the Sun that keep water moving from place to place on Earth.

geologic cycle - a set of processes that keep rocky material moving from place to place on Earth.

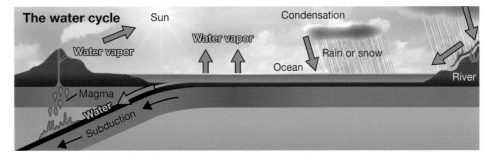

Water in volcanoes
In Section 10.1, you learned that water is important for making magma. Water combines with hot rock when a subducting plate sinks into the mantle. The combination of water and hot mantle rock has a lower melting temperature and the mantle rock melts, forming magma. This magma rises forming a volcano.

Geysers and hot springs
You learned about geysers and hot springs in Chapter 4. These volcanic features are the result of water in the ground coming in contact with magma-heated rock below the surface. The hot rock heats the water. Whether a geyser or a hot spring forms depends on the temperature of the rock, the amount of water present, and the shape of the water passage. Water that evaporates from a geyser or hot spring also becomes part of the water cycle (Figure 10.14).

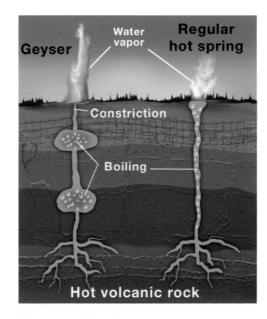

Figure 10.14: *A diagram of a geyser and a hot spring.*

10.3 Section Review

1. What two ingredients in magma affect the type of explosion and shape of a volcano?

2. Under what conditions will magma be very thick and sticky?

3. Describe what a shield volcano's eruption is like. Then, describe a composite volcano's eruption.

4. Compare and contrast pumice, obsidian, and ash.

5. For each of the following statements, indicate which volcano is being described:

    a. a cone composed of layers

    b. forms in calderas

    c. forms from a buildup of lava on the ocean floor

Table 10.2: Summary of types of magma and eruptions associated with various volcano types

	Low gas content	High gas content
Low silica content	• Runny magma, like syrup	• Runny magma, bubbles at vent
	• Quiet eruption, lava flows easily	• Fire fountain at vent, flows away easily
	• Forms shield volcanoes	• Forms shield volcanoes and cinder cones
	• Forms basalt and gabbro rocks	• Forms basalt and gabbro rocks
High silica content	• Thick, sticky magma	• Thick, sticky magma
	• Quiet eruption, lava forms piles	• Explosive eruption, pyroclastic flow, lava bombs
	• Forms composite volcanoes	• Forms composite volcanoes
	• Forms obsidian rock	• Forms granite, andesite, pumice, and scoria rocks

STUDY SKILLS

Keeping up with explosive terms

How can you remember volcanic terms? It helps if you find fun facts about the terms.

For example...

Another name for a composite volcano is stratovolcano. Look up the meaning of the word "stratum."

What characteristic of this kind of volcano do both of these names—composite and stratovolcano—refer to?

Look up the word "lahar." From which language does it come? Is your region likely to have mudflows? Why or why not?

Pick three terms from this chapter. Find fun facts about each term. Write each term and facts about it on an index card.

10.4 Igneous Rocks

Rocks formed from magma or lava are called **igneous rocks**. The kind of igneous rock depends on the type of magma and the conditions under which it cooled.

Types of igneous rocks

Crystals are tightly locked together
Igneous rocks are formed as melted rock cools and crystallizes. A characteristic of igneous rocks is that their crystals are tightly locked together. Melted rock that cools quickly produces small crystals. Slow cooling produces larger crystals.

Crystal size
Crystal size can tell us a lot about how a rock formed. Underground magma cools slowly and produces large crystals. On Earth's surface, magma (lava) cools quickly and produces small crystals.

Basalt versus gabbro
Basalt and *gabbro* are made from the same silica-poor basalt magma. Basalt has fine crystals, but gabbro has large crystals. Can you tell where these rocks formed? You are correct if you thought that basalt is a surface-formed rock and gabbro is formed below Earth's surface.

Granite, rhyolite, and obsidian
Granite, *rhyolite*, and *obsidian* (Figure 10.15) all come from the same silica-rich magma. Granite cools underground and has large crystals. Rhyolite cools on the surface and has fine crystals. Obsidian cools so fast that it has no crystals. Obsidian is often called volcanic glass.

Basalt, granite, and Earth's crust
You learned about the main rock types making up Earth's crust—basalt and granite—in Chapter 7. *Basalt* is the rock that makes up oceanic plates and is more dense than granite. Basalt, as you just learned, has fine crystals and is made from low-silica magma. **Granite** makes up continental plates. It is less dense than basalt, is made of high-silica magma, and has large crystals.

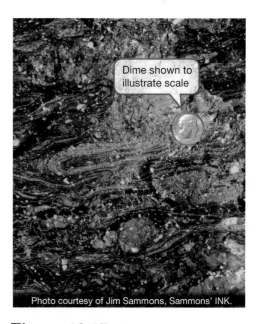

Dime shown to illustrate scale

Photo courtesy of Jim Sammons, Sammons' INK.

Figure 10.15: *Obsidian is often called volcanic glass. Obsidian cools so quickly that it lacks crystals.*

How gas in magma affects igneous rocks You have learned that silica makes magma thick and sticky. Silica also prevents dissolved gas from escaping easily. The same magma that produces granite, rhyolite, and obsidian can also produce pumice. The difference is that the gas in the magma puffs up before the pumice cools to a solid. Pumice is so light due to the trapped bubbles that it floats. At the bottom of the page is an image of a pumice mine (located near a volcano) where pumice is harvested to make abrasive cleaning products.

Scoria is another gas-puffed rock. Scoria may be made of silica-poor basalt magma or silica-rich granite magma. Scoria has a heavier, more crystalline texture than pumice.

Welded tuff The pyroclastic flow from a composite volcano eruption may form a thick layer of hot cinders and ash. This layer is so hot that the pieces become welded together. At first, there may be holes between the pieces. But as the layer gets thicker, the holes become flattened. This type of rock, called *welded tuff,* is often orange-tan in color with small, flat streaks of obsidian in it (Figure 10.16).

Photo courtesy of Jim Sammons, Sammons' INK.

Figure 10.16: *This is a photograph of welded tuff. The spaces made by gas bubbles have been flattened by the weight of material that pressed down while the tuff was still forming.*

Pumice mine, Owen's River Valley, California

The pumice was deposited as pyroclastic flow from a volcano near the mine. Look carefully and you will see the horizontal layers that mark pulses of pyroclastic flow. Pumice is collected for use in commercial cleaning products as an abrasive.

Photo courtesy of Jim Sammons, Sammons' INK.

10.4 Section Review

1. Describe two characteristics of an igneous rock.

2. If lava on Earth's surface cools very quickly, will the crystals in the resulting igneous rock be small or large?

3. Which of the following pieces of information can you learn by looking at an igneous rock. List all correct answers.

   a. how old it is

   b. how fast it cooled

   c. how much it weighs

   d. whether it formed above ground or under ground

   e. how long it will take to metamorphose

   f. what time of day it formed

4. How is gabbro similar to granite?

5. Make a table that compares and contrasts basalt and granite.

6. Granite, rhyolite, and obsidian are shown in Figure 10.17. Determine which photograph represents each rock.

7. You want to take a vacation to a place where you could find igneous rocks. To which of these places would you go? Justify your answer. Note: You could find igneous rocks at any of these places.

   a. Niagara Falls

   b. Las Vegas

   c. The Hawaiian Islands

   d. Your own backyard

8. The Mid-Atlantic Ridge goes through the country of Iceland. Would you expect to find igneous rocks in Iceland? Explain your answer.

Identify these igneous rocks

A

B

C

Figure 10.17: *Use this graphic to answer question 6.*

GEOLOGY CONNECTION
Western Region Volcanoes

Streams of molten lava, rocks glowing fiery red inside, steam spewing from a mountaintop—does this sound like a volcano you could see in Hawaii? It is true that Hawaii has some picturesque and spectacular volcanoes, but there are many volcanoes on the mainland of the United States too.

Why do some regions of the world have volcanoes while others do not? Volcanoes typically happen along the boundaries of the Earth's massive tectonic plates. The plates move and shift, creating both volcanoes and earthquakes. Volcanoes may also occur in the middle of plates or sometimes over places called "hot spots."

In the recorded history of Earth, more than 500 volcanoes have erupted. In the United States, 50 volcanoes have erupted. The three countries with the most active volcanoes are Indonesia, Japan, and the United States. Around the rim of the Pacific Ocean, also called the Ring of Fire, there are more than 1,000 volcanoes.

The western part of United States is in this Pacific Ring of Fire. Alaska, Washington, Oregon, and California all have volcanoes in the ring. Not including Alaska and Hawaii, there are 40 volcanoes in the United States, and you might recognize some of these famous ones out West.

Washington's big five

There are five major volcanoes, called composite volcanoes, in Washington. These steep-sided conical volcanoes are, from north to south, Mount Baker, Glacier Peak, Mount Rainier, Mount St. Helens, and Mount Adams, and with Mount Hood in Oregon, they are part of the Cascade Range, a volcanic arch that stretches from British Columbia to California.

Mount Rainier, at 14,411 feet (4,392 meters), is Washington's highest mountain. Its most recent eruption was in the early 1800s. Located near Seattle, it is closely monitored for activity. Approximately 30 earthquakes occur under Mount Rainier each year, making it a very earthquake active area. In 1899, Mount Rainier became the country's fifth national park.

Ring of Fire

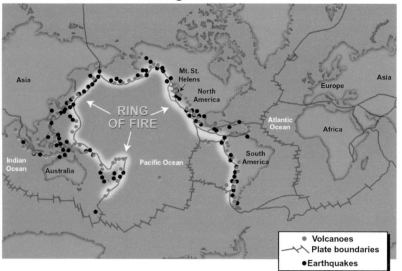

Mount St. Helens erupting in 1980

Nearby stands another famous volcano: Mount St. Helens. It had been quiet for over 100 years until on the morning of May 18, 1980, it erupted violently for nine hours. A magnitude 5.1 earthquake kicked off the huge explosion. In just minutes, the 9,677-foot-high mountain collapsed, reduced 1,200 feet by the explosion and mammoth landslide. So much ash was released that the sky got dark. Recently, Mount St. Helens has erupted again. Scientists view each eruption as a chance to learn more about volcanoes.

Oregon's user-friendly Mount Hood

Moving south along the Cascades, you come to Mount Hood, 11,239 feet high and Oregon's highest peak. The last big eruptions took place 200 and 1,500 years ago. Mount Hood is one of the most climbed peaks in the Pacific Northwest. At 6,000 feet you find the famous Timberline Lodge, built in 1938 and where scenes from *The Shining*, the 1980 movie based on the Stephen King novel, were shot. The slopes of the volcano are used almost year-round for skiing and snowboarding. The nearby ski area is known for having the longest ski season in the United States.

California's hot spots

When you think of California, you typically think of perfect weather, golden beaches, and great surf. But the Golden State is also home to several volcanoes. Active or possibly active volcanoes include Black Butte, Lassen Peak, Long Valley Caldera, Medicine Lake, and Mount Shasta.

Potentially Active Volcanoes of Western United States

Topinka, USGS/CVO, 1999, Modified from: Brantley, 1994, Volcanoes of the United States: USGS General Interest Publication

Still part of the Cascades, and one of the world's largest composite volcanoes (14,161 feet), Mount Shasta is located 265 miles north of San Francisco. The most recent eruption is thought to have occurred in 1786. The mountain is part of the Shasta-Trinity National Forest, the largest national forest in California.

In east-central California, the Long Valley Caldera stands along the east side of the Sierra Nevada. Rocks formed in the past 2 million years from volcanic eruptions cover most of the area.

Our tour comes to an end south of both Shasta and Medicine Lake at Lassen Peak, the baby of the Cascades, one of the youngest of the major volcanoes in those mountains.

Cascades Volcano Observatory

After the eruption of Mount St. Helens, the U.S. Geological Survey created the Cascades Volcano Observatory (CVO). CVO monitors volcanoes and related dangers such as earthquakes and landslides. Thousands of visitors are attracted each year to the spectacular volcanic scenery of the Cascades, but they should not forget the mountains' potential hazards and how they are monitored.

Questions:
1. Why does the Cascade Range have so many volcanoes?
2. Identify and describe two mainland U.S. volcanoes that erupted in the 20th century?
3. What benefits resulted from the eruption of Mount St. Helens?

CHAPTER ACTIVITY The Geological Cycle

The geological cycle is a set of processes that keep rocky material moving from place to place on Earth.

The processes that keep rock material moving through the geologic cycle are:

- weathering of mountains, volcanoes, and rocks into sediments by the water cycle,
- transport, layering, and compaction of sediments to form sedimentary rocks (you will learn about sedimentary rocks in Chapter 11),
- melting of rocks in the mantle when subduction occurs,
- crystallizing of magma and lava to form igneous rocks,
- metamorphism to form metamorphic rocks, and
- the formation of mountains when two continental plates come together.

Plate tectonics plays an important role in the geological cycle. Rocks melt or metamorphose when they are subducted into the mantle. The coming together of tectonic plates creates mountains. Were it not for mountain building, the weathering of rocks over time would leave the continents smooth and flattened.

The combined influence of the Sun's energy and the water cycle weather (wear down) mountains and rocks. *Weathering* is the process of breaking down rocks.

It takes millions of years for one cycle of the geologic cycle to be completed.

What you will do

1. With a partner or group, create a diagram that shows all the parts of the geological cycle.
2. In your diagram, include all the processes listed above in the blue box in your diagram.

3. You may need to make a large sketch to figure out how all the parts work together. Then, make a final version of your diagram in color.

Applying your knowledge

a. What would Earth's surface look like over a long time if mountains stopped being formed?
b. Would the geological cycle work without the Sun? Why or why not?
c. Look around your yard at home or around your school yard. Do you see evidence of the geological cycle at work? Explain your answer.

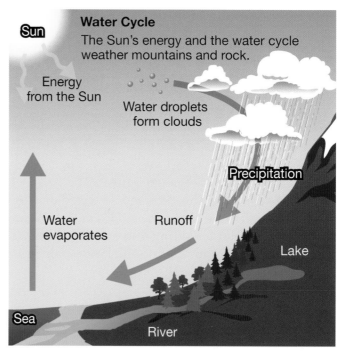

Sun

Water Cycle
The Sun's energy and the water cycle weather mountains and rock.

Energy from the Sun

Water droplets form clouds

Precipitation

Water evaporates

Runoff

Lake

Sea

River

Chapter 10 Assessment

Vocabulary

Select the correct term to complete the sentences. NOTE: Not all terms will be used.

volcano	geological cycle	magma	pyroclastic flow	Ring of Fire
cinder cone	lava	extinct volcano	shield volcanoes	composite volcano
dormant volcano	magma chamber	volcanic neck	active volcano	volcanic island
resurgent dome	igneous rock	basalt	caldera	hot spot
lava lake	dormant volcano	silica	volcanic neck	volcanic island chain
lava bombs	lahars	pyroclastic flow	obsidian	water cycle

Section 10.1

1. The products of an eruption can build a mountainous _____.

2. _____ is magma that has reached and cooled on Earth's surface.

3. A _____ is a place where magma collects underground.

4. A bowl-shaped volcanic feature is a _____.

5. A _____ is a volcanic feature that occurs when water fills a caldera and lava oozes into the water.

6. A _____ occurs when a mound of magma forms on the floor of a caldera.

7. A(n) _____ is a volcano that is erupting or that has erupted recently.

Section 10.2

8. The _____ is a region where about half of the active surface volcanoes on Earth occur.

9. _____ makes magma thick and sticky.

10. A volcanic island forms over a(n) _____.

Section 10.3 and Section 10.4

11. A _____ can form on the sides of either a shield volcano or a composite volcano.

12. After an explosive eruption, a _____ moves quickly down the side of a volcano and can cause a great deal of destruction.

13. Water released from a volcanic eruption can become part of _____, an important cycle energized by the Sun.

14. Low gas, high silica magma forms _____ rocks.

15. High gas, low silica magma forms _____ rocks.

Concepts

Section 10.1

1. What is the difference between a conduit and a vent on a volcano?

2. Describe the three phases of the lifetime of a volcano.

3. Is the material that forms a volcanic neck considered to be solidified magma or lava? Explain your answer.

4. How are pressure and heat involved in melting rock in the mantle?

Section 10.2

5. What is the Ring of Fire? About how much of Earth's volcanic activity is found there?

6. Mount St. Helens formed at what kind of plate boundary?

    a. a subduction zone

    b. a transform plate boundary

    c. a divergent plate boundary

    c. where two continental plates came together

7. How is pressure involved in melting mantle material at a mid-ocean ridge?

8. How does plate tectonics cause volcanic islands to form in chain?

9. What volcanic land feature has helped the east and west coast of North America grow bigger?

10. Describe how the granite domes of Yosemite National Park were formed.

Section 10.3

11. Describe the magma of fire fountain eruptions in terms of silica and gas content.

12. Explain how a shield volcano differs from a composite volcano.

13. Where do composite volcanoes tend to be found?

    a. a subduction zone

    b. a transform plate boundary

    c. a divergent plate boundary

    c. where two continental plates came together

14. The Hawaiian Islands are what type of volcano? What causes these volcanoes to form?

15. Volcanoes found near subduction zones have:

    a.   magma with high silica content

    b.   an explosive eruption

    c.   large amounts of gas released during the eruption

    d.   All of the above

16. What is the difference between a pyroclastic flow and a lahar?

Section 10.4

17. How do igneous rocks form?

18. What about the appearance of an igneous rock gives you a clue about whether it cooled slowly or quickly?

Math and Writing Skills

Section 10.1

1. Mount Kilimanjaro in Tanzania is Africa's highest mountain and a controversial volcano. Research this volcano to find out whether experts think it is extinct, dormant, or active. Write your findings in a short paragraph.

Section 10.2

2. This image shows Hot Creek, a stream that is heated by volcanic activity below the surface. This creek is associated with the Long Valley Caldera in eastern California. The heat in the water is uneven. Some places are cool, but places where hot springs feed into the creek are so hot that you would be scalded. Nevertheless, the creek has fish! Research Hot Creek and describe what causes it to be hot.

Hot Creek, California

Photo courtesy of Jim Sammons, Sammons' INK.

3. Volcanic activity occurs at convergent and divergent plate boundaries. Why do you think this is?

4. A volcanologist finds that the silica content of the volcanic rock near an ancient volcano is high. From this information, describe the probable type of volcano and its eruption. Where might the volcano be located?

Section 10.3

5. The speed of a pyroclastic flow is 100 km/h. How far would this flow travel in 10 minutes?

6. How do volcanoes participate in Earth's water cycle?

7. What role does water play in the geological cycle?

Section 10.4

8. Pumice is mined and used in commercial cleaning products as an abrasive. Research pumice and find out more about its uses.

9. In Yosemite National Park there is a large granite formation called Half Dome. The distance from the bottom of the valley to the top of Half Dome is 1 kilometer. The top of Half Dome is rounded instead of peaked the way most mountains look. How do you think Half Dome formed? To develop a hypothesis, answer the following questions.

    a. What kind of rock is granite?
    b. Did Half Dome form as a result of a volcanic eruption? Did it form as a result of two continents pushing against each other?
    c. Why might Half Dome be rounded?
    d. Develop a hypothesis about Half Dome: In your opinion, how did this rock formation form?

e. Extension: Now research the geology of Half Dome on the Internet or in your local library. How did it form? Compare your research findings with your hypothesis.

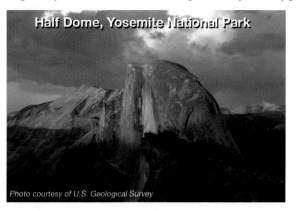
Half Dome, Yosemite National Park
Photo courtesy of U.S. Geological Survey

10. Write a story about the formation of igneous rocks in the rock cycle. Pretend you are the igneous rock being formed, and include as many other fictitious characters as possible.

Chapter Project—Eye-witness Account

Choose a famous volcanic eruption that has happened in the past and research the eruption. Visit the United States Geological Survey web site to find out about present day and past volcanic eruptions (www.usgs.gov).

Write a letter to a local newspaper from the point of view of an eye-witness who survived the eruption. In your letter include details about what happened before, during, and after the eruption. You should include the type of volcano, the type of lava you witnessed during the eruption. Also, include information about the damage and destruction caused by the volcano. Finally, your letter should include the environmental impact that the eruption had. How far around the world was the impact felt? In order to capture the readers attention make your letter as personal and captivating as possible. Include pictures or drawings of the volcano before, during, and after the eruption.

The Shape of Earth's Surface

WHAT CREATED THE GRAND CANYON?

TODAY

GREAT LAKES

12,000 YEARS AGO

TRY THIS AT HOME

Find a plastic bin or a tray that can hold water. In the center of the bin or tray, build a hill out of small rocks, soil, and sand that you find outside. After you have built your hill, blow on it and see what materials move. You may want to use a straw to direct the "wind" that you create. Then, gently pour a glass of water over your hill. What materials are moved by the water? How is the hill changed by the water? How does your hill compare to how land looks after a rain storm? Write a paragraph that describes your observations. Present your observations to your class.

Chapter 11
Water and Weathering

In Unit 2, you learned about energy in the Earth system. In Unit 3, you learned about plate tectonics, earthquakes, and volcanoes. These are examples of Earth systems that are driven by internal energy—energy that comes from the heat of Earth's core. This chapter describes how rock is weathered (broken down) and moved from place to place by water. These processes are driven by external energy—energy from the Sun.

Key Questions

1. *What does a young mountain look like?*

2. *What does a meandering river look like?*

3. *In what kind of rock are most fossils found?*

11.1 **Weathering**

Energy from the Sun warms and cools Earth's surface. It melts and freezes water. It even helps grow the tree roots that eventually can split rocks into pieces. In this section, you will learn how tall mountain ranges eventually break down into the smallest rock particles.

Mountains

Mountains change over time
Mountains—because they are so big and impressive—seem to be unchanging features in a landscape. However, mountains wear down over time. In fact, due to the Sun's energy, wind, and water, mountains begin to crumble as soon as they are formed.

Old versus young mountains
An good example of old mountains are the Smoky Mountains which are part of the Appalachian Mountain range (Figure 11.1). These mountains are very old. The Rocky Mountains in the western United States are younger mountains (Figure 11.2). How do these two mountain ranges differ?

What happens as mountains age?
At one time, the Smokies were as tall as the Rockies and also had sharp peaks. But, since the Smokies are 680 millions of years old (hundreds of millions years older than the Rockies) the peaks have worn down. Eventually, the Smokies will be no more than rolling hills, and the Rockies will look like the Smokies do now.

The Smoky Mountains, Tennessee

Photo courtesy of Jim Sammons, Sammons' INK.

Figure 11.1: *The rounded peaks of the Smoky Mountains near Linville, Tennessee. Vegetation covers the mountains all the way to their peaks.*

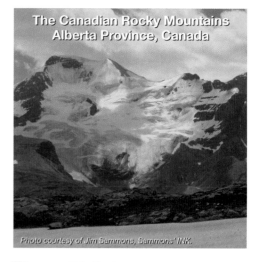

The Canadian Rocky Mountains Alberta Province, Canada

Photo courtesy of Jim Sammons, Sammons' INK.

Figure 11.2: *Sharp peaks of the Canadian Rocky Mountains near Jasper, Alberta Province, Canada.*

Sharp peaks | No vegetation at the peaks

Tall

Millions of years

Sun's energy
Weathering by wind and water ...

"Young" mountains

Round peaks with vegetation

Not very tall

"Old" mountains

Physical weathering

Weathering How is a large mountain broken down into tiny grains of sand? The process of breaking down rock is called **weathering** (Figure 11.3).

Physical weathering Physical forces may break or chip rocks into smaller pieces. This process is called **physical weathering**. Physical weathering may break large blocks loose or chip away tiny grains, one at a time.

Liquid water Liquid water is a physical weathering agent. Rocks break up quickly when running water knocks them against each other. Even running water alone wears away rock. You can see physical weathering by looking at rocks at the base of a waterfall. Running water rounds and smooths the rocks there.

Frost wedging

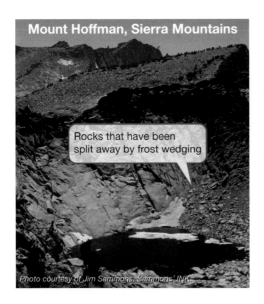

Mount Hoffman, Sierra Mountains

Rocks that have been split away by frost wedging

Photo courtesy of Jim Sammons, Sammons' INK.

Water weathers rock in other ways too. **Frost wedging** is a powerful physical weathering agent. When water cools, it contracts like other matter. But just before it freezes, it expands a little bit! Say a small amount of water enters a tiny crack in the rock. When the water freezes, it expands, making the crack a little wider. More water enters the crack, freezes, and widens the crack even more. Eventually frost wedging splits apart the two sides of the crack. The photo above shows an example of frost wedging near the crest of Mount Hoffman in the Sierra Mountains. Many hand-sized rocks have been split away by frost wedging.

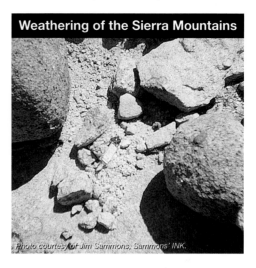

Weathering of the Sierra Mountains

Photo courtesy of Jim Sammons, Sammons' INK.

Figure 11.3: *This course sand and gravel is all that remains of a once-tall peak in the Sierra Mountains.*

Glaciers Frozen water in the form of glaciers is another powerful physical weathering agent. The ice that forms glaciers is a *plastic solid* (a solid that flows). As the ice of a glacier flows down a valley, it grinds the valley floor with pieces of rock caught up in the ice (Figure 11.4). This grinding changes the shape of the valley so that its bottom is rounded.

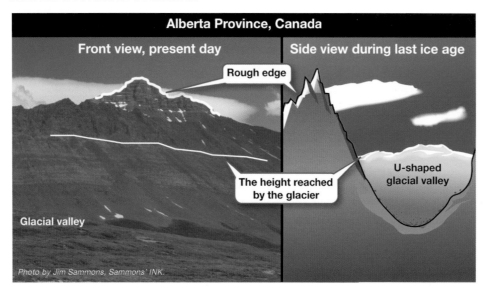

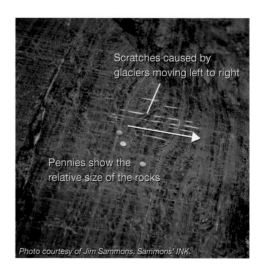

Figure 11.4: *A glacier passed over this rock moving from left to right. The scratches were made by rocks caught in the moving ice.*

A U-shaped glacial valley The image above is of a large valley that held a glacier during the last ice age. The valley floor rises up smoothly in a gentle curve to the ridge above. From the side, this glacial valley is U-shaped. Notice that the highest part of the ridge is rough. This is because the glacier didn't get that high up before it melted. The change from smooth to rough rock is the "bathtub ring" left by the glacier that shows the highest point the glacier reached on the mountain.

Wind Even wind is a physical weathering agent. Wind-blown sand chips away tiny bits of rock from the surface of exposed rock. During this process, the remaining rock can take on unusual shapes and the removed bits eventually become sand (Figure 11.5).

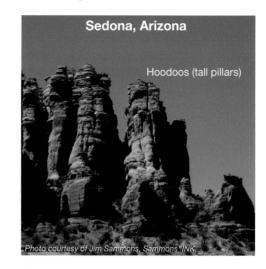

Figure 11.5: *Wind-blown sand has physically weathered this sandstone into tall pillars called Hoodoos.*

Chemical weathering

Chemical weathering
Rock is also reduced to smaller pieces by chemical reactions between water and rock grains. This process is called **chemical weathering**. Some kinds of rock are more easily eroded by chemical weathering than others. For example, marble is chemically weathered much faster than granite. Chemical weathering has worn away the surfaces of many old marble statues (Figure 11.6). This is seen more often in Europe than in the United States because the statues in Europe are older. They have been exposed to chemical weathering for a longer time than most marble statues in the United States.

Physical and chemical weathering
Both physical and chemical weathering can affect rock at the same time. Look at the picture below. Originally there were a few tiny cracks in the rock. Frost wedging probably opened up these cracks. Now chemical weathering is changing the rock mineral so that the sides of the crack are filled with loose grains. You can see the tufts of plants growing in the loose grains of rock.

ⓐ **VOCABULARY**

chemical weathering - weathering of rock that involves chemical reactions.

Figure 11.6: *An old marble statue. Notice that the face of the statue has been worn down by chemical weathering.*

Plant growing in loose rock grains

Opened crack

Photo courtesy of Jim Sammons, Sammons' INK.

Root wedging and rockfalls

Root wedging Plant roots may grow into small crevices. If these plants are sturdy, like trees, they exert force on the rock as they grow. This force is often strong enough to split the rock. This process, called *root wedging*, is a kind of physical weathering (Figure 11.7). However, roots also produce enzymes that attack rock minerals. So root wedging is really a combination of physical and chemical weathering.

Rockfalls Falling rock can break into very small pieces when it hits the ground. The graphic below shows an example of rocks (and trees!) affected by falling rock. Rockfalls can occur when a big chunk of rock is split off of a large landform by frost wedging or root wedging. Rockfalls speed up the weathering process by quickly breaking up large pieces of a rock formation.

Photo courtesy of Jim Sammons, Sammons' INK.

Figure 11.7: *For the moment, the climbers are happy to secure their rope to the small pine tree. Over time, the tree's roots will split away their rocky perch from the cliff by root wedging.*

This pile of rocks is all that remains of a large block of rock that fell from the cliff above.

Large rock pieces shot outward and cut down nearby trees.

Photo courtesy of Jim Sammons, Sammons' INK.

11.1 Section Review

1. You have learned that mountains form when two continents collide. How do mountains turn into small rocks, soil, and sand?

2. Does the Sun play a role in weathering? Explain your answer.

3. Name two differences between old and young mountains.

4. How long does it take for a mountain's sharp peaks to wear down? Chose an answer below and explain your reasoning.

   a. millions of years   b. hundreds of years
      c. about 10 years   d. one year

5. Describe how liquid water and ice affect rocks.

6. What causes a glacial valley to be U-shaped? Write your answer as a short, detailed paragraph.

7. How is frost wedging similar to root wedging?

8. For the following examples, state whether physical or chemical weathering is occurring:
   a. a bicycle left in the rain becomes rusty
   b. your sand castle gets blown away by wind

9. What happens to a rock that experiences physical weathering?

10. What happens to a rock that experiences chemical weathering?

11. Over time, how might the grass growing up through a crack in a sidewalk affect the sidewalk? Use the terms "physical weathering" and "chemical weathering" in your answer.

MY JOURNAL

Find an outdoor place near your house that will not get disturbed. Make a pile of soil and rocks. You may want to put a sign near your pile that says "Do Not Disturb!"

Over the next few days, make regular observations of the pile.

How did the pile change over time? How was the pile affected by physical and chemical weathering?

DO NOT DISTURB!
Scientific observations in progress

11.2 **Moving Sediment**

In Chapter 10, you learned about the water cycle. Water rises in the form of water vapor from oceans, rivers, and even volcanoes! The vapor returns to Earth as rain. The water cycle continues as rain water enters rivers and streams and flows to the oceans, moving sediment along with it. In time, the flowing water moves mountains!

What is sediment?

Where does sediment come from? Weathering breaks rock into bits and pieces called **sediment** (Figure 11.8). When you sit on a sandy beach, you are sitting on sediment that was once a rocky mountain top. How does sediment get from a mountain peak to a beach?

Rivers and streams Wind erodes mountains and moves sediment, but not as well as flowing water. Rivers and streams are bodies of flowing water that carry sediment. A **river** is a large flowing body of water. A **stream** is a small river. The path that a river or stream follows is called a **channel**. As you will learn later, rivers and streams can have one or more channels. Sediment carried by flowing water eventually arrives at the lowest place that it can reach, such as a beach. Then, the sediment is carried into the ocean water by waves.

Athabasca Glacier, Canada
Flowing water is carrying off sediment of all sizes.
The water is cloudy because it is filled with many tiny rock particles.
Photo courtesy of Jim Sammons, Sammons' INK.

sediment - small pieces and grains of weathered rock; also, small pieces of material from living things.

river - a large body of water that flows into an ocean or lake.

stream - a small river.

channel - the path that a river or stream follows.

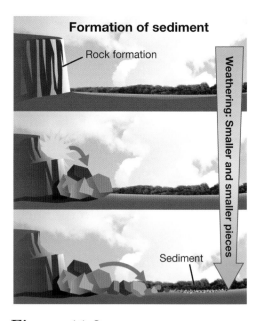

Formation of sediment

Rock formation

Weathering: Smaller and smaller pieces

Sediment

Figure 11.8: *Rocks become sediment because weathering causes them to break down into smaller and smaller pieces.*

Graded bedding

The speed of flowing water
Figure 11.9 shows that you can tell the speed of flowing water by the size of the rock pieces found on a stream bottom. A few years before this picture was taken, knee-deep water was rushing around the stump. Since then, the stream channel has shifted and the old, now dry channel shows clues to how the stream once flowed.

Fast versus slow water
We can tell where the water flowed rapidly in the stream by the pebbles. Fast-moving water carries pebbles. The ground is cut away on both sides of the stump. This means that water moved fast as it flowed around the stump. In front of the stump though, the water was very slow. Small grains of rock settled to the bottom of the slow-moving water forming the *sand shadow* that you see here.

Sediment is sorted by water
When flowing water enters a lake or a pond, the flow stops and the water drops its sediment. First the largest grains settle to the bottom. Next the medium-sized grains settle. Finally the tiniest grains settle. The grains settle in order, making a pattern called **graded bedding**. It's common to find graded bedding in repeating layers, one of top of the other. For example, a stream that feeds into a lake may run fast only during thunderstorms. The stream lays down a graded bed of sediments after each storm.

Figure 11.9: *The stream now (in the background) and the place where it used to flow are shown. The pebbles show where the river flowed quickly. The sand shadow shows where the water flowed slowly.*

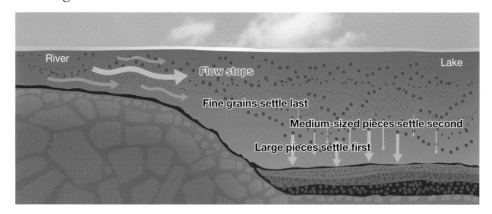

Meandering rivers and braided streams

Meanders Some rivers form S-shaped curves called **meanders** (Figure 11.10). Water flows at different speeds at different parts of the meanders. The fastest flow is on the outside of each curve while the slowest flow is on the inside. Fast-moving water picks up particles. Slow-moving water drops particles so that they settle to the bottom of the river. The fast-moving water wears away the outside river bank and at the same time, slower water adds to the inside bank by dropping sediment. The sediment that settles near the inside bank forms a *point bar*. The point bar adds to the inside of the meander curve and extends it. A *channel bar* is formed by sediment that is eroded from the river bank. The extra sediment is too much for the stream to transport so it settled near the bank.

How rivers move The combination of cutting on the outside bank and extending the inside bank moves the whole meander slowly down a river valley. This process goes on continuously at each meander. If you could watch a meandering river for a hundred years, you would see the meanders making side-to-side looping motions as the meandering river moves slowly down the valley.

a VOCABULARY

meanders - S-shaped curves in a river.

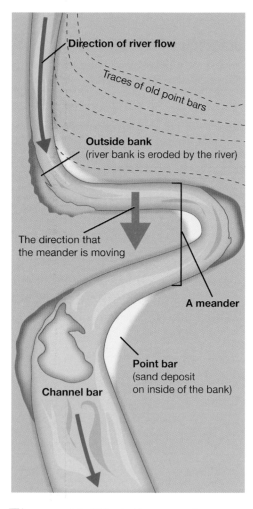

Figure 11.10: *A diagram of a meandering river.*

Meandering scars

This is a picture of the Tuolumne River Valley. Tuolumne is pronounced "two-all-oh-me." Can you see the dark traces of old meanders in the field to the right of the river? These dark traces are called *meandering scars*.

Tuolumne River Valley, Yosemite National Park

Meandering scars

Photo courtesy of Jim Sammons, Sammons' INK.

What is a braided stream?

The channel of a meandering stream moves downhill with time, but it remains a single channel. In contrast, a **braided stream** has many channels that criss-cross each other. Braided streams get their name from the braided appearance of their many channels. The channels of braided streams are constantly changing. New channels are cut and old ones are abandoned in a matter of days or weeks.

Sediment that is being moved by the stream

Braided stream

Photo courtesy U.S. Geological Survey

 VOCABULARY

braided stream - a stream that has many channels that criss-cross each other.

 SOLVE IT!

Here is a map of the Tuolumne River. Use the scale at the bottom of the map to answer these questions. First measure the scale bar using a ruler and then use your ruler to carefully measure the distances on the map.

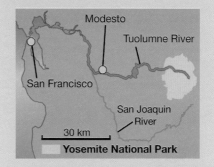

Modesto
Tuolumne River
San Francisco
San Joaquin River
30 km
Yosemite National Park

1. How many kilometers of the river are located in Yosemite National Park?

2. How far would sediment have to travel to go from Modesto to San Francisco?

11.2 Section Review

1. Which of the following would be considered sediment?

   a. mud   b. sand

   c. bits of shells   d. rock pieces

   e. none of the above   f. all of the above

2. How is the water cycle involved in moving rock and sediment from a mountain top to a beach?

3. Is it possible for a piece of a mountain to end up at the bottom of an ocean? Explain your answer.

4. A summary of how water moves rocks is given in Figure 11.11. However, some of the words are missing from this summary. Fill in the blanks using the terms below.

   - small, light grains of rock
   - large, heavy pieces of rock
   - larger rocks
   - fast-moving
   - slow-moving
   - smaller rocks

5. You notice that the bottom of a stream has large pebbles. What does this mean about the speed at which the water is flowing?

6. A lake has one graded bedding pattern. Then, a rain storm causes a stream to flow faster and deposit more sediment into the lake. Draw what this would look like. Hint: Your drawing should have two patterns, one on top of the other.

7. Imagine you could visit a meandering stream 200 years from now. Make a drawing that shows what it would look like today and then what it might look like in 200 years.

8. Now imagine that you could visit a braided stream 200 years from now. Make a drawing that shows what it would look like today and then what it might look like 200 years from now.

Water Can Move Rocks!

a. Slow-moving water has lower energy and can only carry _____.

b. Fast-moving water has higher energy and can carry _____.

c. When slow-moving water speeds up, it can pick up _____ from the stream bottom or stream bank.

d. When _____ water slows down, the larger rocks suspended in the water fall to the bottom of the stream.

Figure 11.11: *Fill in the blanks of this summary box with the correct terms from question 4.*

In this section, you learned that sand on the bottom of a stream indicates slow-moving water. But, when you visit a beach, you often see lots of sand and fast-moving waves. Why might sand be found on a beach even though the waves move fast?

11.3 Sedimentary Rocks

Sedimentary rocks are made of sediments—the rock particles that are produced by weathering. First, wind or water transports the particles to a location like the bottom of a valley or the bottom of a stream. Then pressure and chemical changes cement the particles together to form sedimentary rock.

Types of sedimentary rocks

The size of particles
Sedimentary rocks are identified by the size of the particles that form them. The finest particles are clay and silt. These particles form *mudstone*. Sand particles, larger particles than clay or silt, form *sandstone*. *Conglomerate* is formed by large pebbles and smaller particles. The pebbles make conglomerate look lumpy.

Shell particles form rocks
Sedimentary rock can also be formed from the tiny shells of marine plants and animals. As these organisms die, their shells sink to the ocean floor and form layers of *shell mud*. Over millions of years, these shell mud layers thicken and eventually become sedimentary rock. *Limestone*, a sedimentary rock, is formed this way.

Fossils in sedimentary rocks
Most fossils are found in sedimentary rock layers. This is true for two reasons. First, the processes that bring sediment together also bring together the remains of once-living things. Second, the process of making a sedimentary rock is good for preserving fossils.

Fossil formation
Fossil formation begins when an organism's body is quickly covered in sediments from an event like a mud slide or a sand storm. Body parts that do not rot quickly, like bones and teeth, are buried under sediment layers. After a long time, chemicals in the bones and teeth are replaced with minerals. This process results in a heavy, rock-like copy of the original object—a fossil. Eventually, the sediments and fossil are compressed into sedimentary rock (Figure 11.12).

sedimentary rocks - rocks that are made of sediments.

Organism's body is covered in sediments.

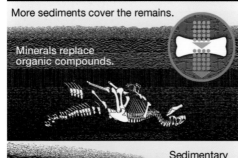
More sediments cover the remains.

Minerals replace organic compounds.

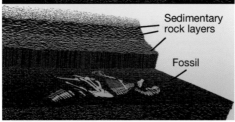
Sedimentary rock layers

Fossil

Figure 11.12: *The process that forms sedimentary rocks also preserves fossils. Most fossils are found in sedimentary rocks.*

Interpreting layers of sediment

Direction of youning Sedimentary rocks hold clues to their past. One of these clues is "the up direction." You learned that large particles settle before small particles, forming *graded bedding*. Figure 11.13 shows three graded bedding patterns. A layer of finest particles is on the top of each pattern. This layer of fine particles helps you know which direction is "up." If you know the up direction, you know the **direction of younging**—this is the direction of younger layers. Graded bedding is preserved when sediments become sedimentary rock.

Cross bedding Sometimes bedded sediment is cut away by fast-running water. Then, more sediment is laid over the cut layer. This leaves a layer that ends abruptly as another layer passes over it. This pattern of **cross bedding** is common in sedimentary rocks that formed in stream and riverbeds.

direction of younging - the order in which sedimentary rock layers are formed—from larger to finer particles.

cross bedding - when a graded bedding pattern in a sedimentary rock is cut off and covered with another graded bedding pattern running in another direction.

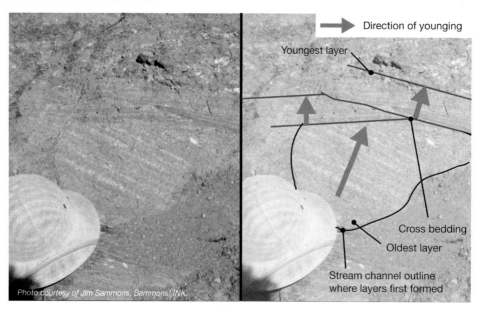

Direction of younging

Youngest layer

Cross bedding

Oldest layer

Stream channel outline where layers first formed

Photo courtesy of Jim Sammons, Sammons' INK.

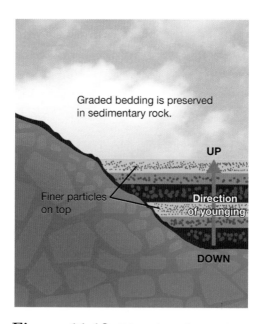

Graded bedding is preserved in sedimentary rock.

UP

Finer particles on top

Direction of younging

DOWN

Figure 11.13: *Direction of younging. This graphic shows three graded bedding patterns.*

11.3 Section Review

1. Which location would most likely produce sedimentary rocks, a dried-up lake bed or the side of a volcano? Explain your answer.

2. Make a sketch of what you think the following sedimentary rocks would look like: mudstone, sandstone, and conglomerate. Be careful about drawing correctly-sized particles for each type of rock, but don't worry about the colors.

3. What kinds of sediments form limestone? How does this sedimentary rock form?

4. Why are many fossils found in sedimentary rocks?

5. State whether these statements are true or false. If a statement is false, rewrite the sentence so that it is true.

   a. When sediment settles on the bottom of a lake, the largest pieces of rock settle last.

   b. In a graded bedding pattern, the finest particles are the top layer.

   c. The direction of younging is the direction in which the top layer is the largest particles and the bottom layer is the finest particles.

6. The graphic on the previous page illustrates a rock that has a cross bedding pattern. Where were the layers of this cross bedding pattern formed long ago?

   a. at the bottom of a stream   b. in Earth's mantle
   c. inside a volcano   d. on a glacier

STUDY SKILLS

One way to learn new words is to write sentences using the words.

To help you learn the new words in this chapter, write a story about the life of a rock.

Your story should begin with the rock as part of a mountain top.

Use at least three new words that you learned in this chapter.

CHALLENGE

You have learned about sedimentary rocks in this chapter. In previous chapters, you learned about igneous and metamorphic rocks.

How are these types of rocks different from one another?

Write a paragraph that answers this question.

GEOLOGY CONNECTION

A World Heritage Site: Carlsbad Cavern

What do Cave Man, Christmas Tree, Texas Toothpick, and Witch's Finger have in common? They are sights you can see in New Mexico at Carlsbad Caverns National Park, which includes Carlsbad Cavern and more than 100 known caves. A cavern is a large cave or a large chamber in a cave. The Carlsbad park was designated a national park in 1930.

Ben Sublette was the first recorded explorer of Carlsbad Cavern. In 1883 he lowered his 12-year-old son, Rolth, into the cave on a rope. Later, a curious cowboy named Jim White spent years exploring the cave. He took photographer Ray V. Davis with him on one trip and posted the photos in the town of Carlsbad in 1915. People were amazed by the images, and White offered tours. He became the park's first chief ranger. Today, more than 500,000 people visit Carlsbad Caverns National Park each year.

How was Carlsbad Cavern formed?

Carlsbad Cavern is in the Guadalupe Mountains, a Permian-aged fossil reef. The Permian age is a geological period of time 230 million to 286 million years ago, when all the continents were joined together into one landmass called Pangaea. In the region of Carlsbad Cavern, there was an inland sea surrounded by a 400-mile-long reef called Capitan Reef. It was formed from sponge, algae, and seashell remains. The reef also contained the mineral calcite. Over time, the sea dried up and the reef was covered by thousands of feet of sediment. Sediment can be sand, gravel, dirt, or anything that sinks to the bottom of a sea.

Several million years ago, Earth's crust moved and the land rose up to form the Guadalupe range, which is made of Capitan Reef limestone. Weather caused erosion and exposed the buried limestone reef.

Most limestone caves are created when surface water seeps into cracks and dissolves the limestone. Surface water includes rives, lakes, and oceans, and it contains carbonic acid, which erodes limestone.

Limestone caves are usually wet and contain streams, lakes, or waterfalls. But the caves in the Guadalupe Mountains are dry. So how did the chambers of Carlsbad Cavern form?

NPS Photo by Peter Jones

Rain, mixed with acid from the air and soil, dissolved the limestone to create chambers. Acid rain alone did not do all the work. Oil and gas deposits located under the reef contained hydrogen sulfide, which mixed with groundwater to create sulfuric acid. Strong sulfuric acid dissolved the limestone, creating large pathways. As the mountains lifted, the land rose above the groundwater. The water drained away—leaving behind all the caves and chambers.

The Big Room

Carlsbad Cavern contains the Big Room, one of the world's largest underground chambers. The Big Room is the largest room in the cavern and the largest cave chamber in the United States. It is located 754 feet below the surface, is 25 stories high, and is one-third of a mile wide. Just how big is the Big Room? According to the National Park Service, it could hold about six football fields. Visitors reach the chamber by elevator. Once there, they can walk a one-mile path that circles the Big Room.

Cave formations

The entrance to Carlsbad Cavern was created over the last few million years. Erosion and collapsing land created a natural opening. Then air was able to enter the cave. Water from rain and snow combined with the air to dissolve the cavern's calcite. Water also deposited calcite to create the formations that decorate the cave. This process of creating cave formations, or *speleothems*, began 500,000 years ago.

There are many types of speleothems including stalactites and stalagmites. Stalactites are also called dripstones and form on the ceilings and walls of the cave. Stalagmites form from cave floors.

NPS Photos by Peter Jones

Other U.S. caves

There are more than 40,000 known caves in the United States. Mammoth Cave in Kentucky is the world's longest cave with more than 350 miles of passageways. Black Chasm Cavern in Volcano, California, has a variety of formations, many of them with unusual twisted shapes. Moaning Caverns in Vallecito, Calif., has a vertical chamber so large it could hold the Statue of Liberty. It may also contain the oldest human remains in North America.

> **Questions:**
> 1. Describe how Carlsbad Cavern was formed.
> 2. What is a speleothem? List and describe two kinds of speleothems.
> 3. What impact has weather had on the formation of Carlsbad Cavern?

CHAPTER ACTIVITY: Features of Rivers and Streams

Running water is a powerful force that shapes the landscape. The power of running water is related to the slope and shape of the river, and the volume of water flowing in the river. Flowing water erodes sediment from the bottom and sides of the river and moves the sediment farther downstream. Study the images below to learn the names of river and stream features and then go on a scavenger hunt to find where on the globe you will find these features. Use the Internet and other resources to look for images and information.

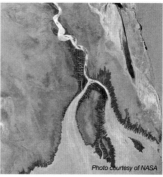

Photo courtesy of NASA

River delta: The mouth of a river that flows into an ocean or lake.

V-shape valley: When a river cuts a mountain it forms a V-shaped valley (a U-shaped valley is formed when a glacier moves through mountains).

Photo courtesy of U.S. Geological Survey

Meander: S-shaped curves in a river.

Waterfall: Falling water that results when a river flows from a high to a low place in its path (such as over a cliff).

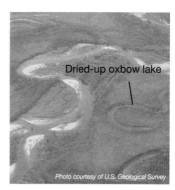

Dried-up oxbow lake

Photo courtesy of U.S. Geological Survey

Oxbow lake: A meander that breaks off from the main river channel.

Photo courtesy of U.S. Geological Survey

Alluvial fan: A fan-shaped area of sediment caused by a fast-flowing stream slowing down as it flows onto flatter land.

Photo courtesy of U.S. Geological Survey

Flood plain: Flat land nearest a river that usually occurs at a distance from the source of the river. A flood plain is very good land for growing plants because the flooding of the river deposits nutrients in the land. However, flood plains are not good places for building because of the flooding.

Chapter 11 Assessment

Vocabulary

Select the correct term to complete the sentences.

weathering	physical weathering	sedimentary rocks
frost wedging	chemical weathering	meanders
river	graded bedding	cross bedding
stream	direction of younging	channel
braided stream		

Section 11.1

1. _____ is when rock is broken down into smaller pieces.

2. Frost wedging is an example of _____.

3. The process of breaking rock down chemically is called _____.

4. _____ occurs when water enters a crack in a rock, freezes, and expands so that the rock splits in two pieces.

Section 11.2

5. A _____ is a small river.

6. The path that a river or stream follows is called a _____.

7. The channel of a meandering _____ is S-shaped.

8. _____ is a pattern of large to small sediment pieces that results when sediment settles to the bottom of a lake or pond.

9. S-shaped curves in a river are called _____.

10. A _____ has many channels that criss-cross.

Section 11.3

11. _____ are made of layers of sediments.

12. The _____ for a sedimentary rock indicates which way is "up" for the rock—in other words, which layer formed first (the bottom layer) and which sediment layer formed last (the top layer).

13. _____ occurs when graded bedding patterns cut off and cover each other.

Concepts

Section 11.1

1. What is one clue that tells you that a mountain is young versus being very old?

2. Explain the difference between physical and chemical weathering.

3. Do physical and chemical weathering cause the same results? Explain your answer.

4. How is water involved in physical weathering? How is water involved in chemical weathering?

5. How do glaciers weather valleys?

6. How do trees weather rocks?

Section 11.2

7. What kinds of things could you do to turn a large piece of rock into sediment?

8. Under what kind of river conditions is a sand shadow created?

9. Why do storms cause a new graded bed pattern to form on the bottom of a lake or river?

10. What is the difference between a point bar and a channel bar?

11. Is this an image of a meandering river or a braided stream? Explain your answer.

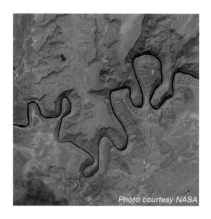

Photo courtesy NASA

Section 11.3

12. Name one feature of sedimentary rocks that is used to tell one from another.

13. Which of these sedimentary rocks has the smallest particles: conglomerate or mudstone?

14. Why are fossils often found in sedimentary rocks?

15. Which direction is the direction of younging for this sedimentary rock?

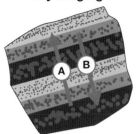

Which is the direction of younging?

A sedimentary rock

Math and Writing Skills

Section 11.1

1. Pretend you are a journalist for your local newspaper's *Health and Science* section. There has been recent buzz about the increase in acid rain in the local area. From studying earth science in school, you know that acid rain causes chemical weathering. However, many citizens do not understand the impact of acid rain.

   a. Research acid rain and its effects on the environment on the Internet or in your school library.

   b. Write a newspaper article explaining how acid rain could impact local geologic features and important stone statues in your town.

   c. Make sketches to illustrate your article or include images that you find in your research.

2. You have learned that the Sun's energy in combination with wind and water cause weathering of mountains to sediment. There is one other important factor that contributes to weathering—gravity! Why might gravity play a role in weathering? You can read about gravity in Chapter 5.

3. Over a few days time, a student collected data on how a pile of soil eroded. One measurement made was the height of the pile of soil. Here is her data:

Day	Height of pile (centimeters)
1	25
2	23
3	20
4	10
5	8
6	7
7	6
8	5

a. Make a graph of the student's data. Be sure to label the x- and y- axes and give your graph a title.

b. From the graph, what can you say about how the pile of soil eroded?

c. From this graph, write a story about what happened to the pile over the 8-day period?

Section 11.2

4. Answer true or false to the following statements. If the statement is false, rewrite it so that it is true.

a. Slow-moving water tends to carry larger rocks.

b. Fast-moving water has higher energy than slower-moving water.

c. When slow-moving water speeds up, it can pick up larger rocks from the stream bottom or stream bank.

d. Larger rocks carried by fast-moving water stay suspended in the water when this water slows down.

5. The table below shows how a river's volume of water flow (in cubic meters per second) and amount of transported sediment (in metric tons per day) change over eight months.

Month	Volume of water flow (m^3/second)	Sediment Load (metric tons/day)
December	1.0	125
January	1.2	175
February	1.6	300
March	3.0	675
April	4.6	1500
May	3.2	1000
June	2.8	800
July	2.2	525

a. Construct a line graph comparing the month and the volume of flow.

b. Construct a line graph comparing the month and the load.

c. When was the river's volume of flow the greatest? When was the river's volume of flow the least? When was the river's sediment load the least?

d. Is there any relationship between the volume of flow and the load? If so, explain.

e. Propose a hypothesis to explain the changes over the months in the volume of flow and the load.

6. Two processes that are important for sediments to become sedimentary rock are *compaction* and *cementation*. Research these terms to find out what they mean and write a definition for them in your own words.

7. There are different types of sedimentary rocks. Rocks made of layers of rock particles are called *clastic* sedimentary rocks. Rocks made of bits of living material like shells are called *biological* sedimentary rocks. And some sedimentary rocks are made when minerals crystallize—these are called *chemical* sedimentary rocks. In the chapter you learned about the following sedimentary rocks. Identify each as being clastic, biological, or chemical.

   a. Mudstone

   b. Sandstone

   c. Conglomerate

   d. Limestone

8. A thin layer of sedimentary rocks covers much of Earth's land surface. Underneath this thin layer are igneous rocks (andesite and granite, for example) and metamorphic rocks. Why does this pattern of rocks on Earth's surface make sense?

Chapter Project—Sedimentary Rock Hunt

Sediment is everywhere! For this chapter project you will go on a geological "dig" to find five sedimentary rocks. First, research sedimentary rocks to find out where they might be found in nature and what they look like. Then, go on your "dig" to find the rocks. It may take a while to find this many rocks in your area so be patient. Keep in mind that rocks are not only outdoors. Your house, the mall, local stores, benches, playgrounds and other areas may also have many sedimentary rocks for you to find.

As you find a sample, bring it or a photograph of it to class.

Chapter 12
Beaches

You have learned that weathering eventually causes mountains to become tiny pieces of rock called sediment. And you have learned that streams and rivers carry this sediment to bodies of water like ponds, lakes and oceans. This chapter is a continuation of that story. Sediment that reaches the ocean is first deposited on the beach. But beaches are just a brief resting stop for sediment. After sediment leaves a beach, it continues its journey to the deep ocean floor.

Key Questions

1. *Why are beaches sandy?*

2. *What is sand made of?*

3. *What is the difference between a winter beach and a summer beach?*

12.1 The Shallow Marine Environment

Read the section title. You have probably heard each word before. *Shallow* means water that is not deep. **Marine** is a term that describes anything that has to do with the ocean. *Environment* refers to the characteristics of a place. So, a shallow marine environment is the area near the ocean where the water is shallow. In this section, you will read about what happens to sediment in a shallow marine environment.

The parts of a beach

Beach zones   The *foreshore* in the shallow marine environment lies between the high and low tide lines (Figure 12.1). A **beach** is a sandy zone above the foreshore. Marine biologists have a different name for the foreshore. They call it the **intertidal zone**.

Onshore and offshore regions   Below the foreshore is the *shoreface*. The shoreface is always underwater. Passing waves affect the sediments of the shoreface, especially the upper part nearest the beach. Waves smooth land surfaces. Because waves have little effect on the lower part of the shoreface, the surface of this region is bumpy. Anything that is on the beach, foreshore, or shoreface is onshore. Anything beyond the shoreface is offshore.

VOCABULARY

marine - a term that describes things that are part of or from the ocean.

beach - a sandy zone above the foreshore in a shallow marine environment.

intertidal zone - the zone of a marine environment between the high and low tide lines; also called the foreshore.

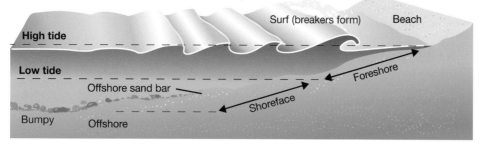

A shallow marine environment at high tide

Figure 12.1: *The range of land between the high and low tide lines is called the foreshore. Sea level is the average ocean height between the high and low tide levels.*

Sandy beaches and tidal flats

Beaches have sand
Sand is the most obvious feature of a beach. The light-colored, rounded grains slip easily through your hands. (Figure 12.2). Sand is not sticky. Blankets and towels only need a quick shake to remove sand before they are put away for the next beach trip.

Tidal flats have mud
Tidal flats, often part of *salt marshes,* are located in the intertidal zone (Figure 12.3). However, tidal flats are different from beaches. Tidal flats often have sandy areas, but most of a tidal flat is dark, sticky mud. And the sticky mud can smell very bad! Why are tidal flats different from beaches?

Why are tidal flats and beaches different?
Tidal flats and beaches are both made of sediment. Streams and rivers carry the sediment down from the mountains and other high places. The sediment includes small, medium, and large particles when it arrives at both areas. What happens to the sediment after it arrives is what makes tidal flats and beaches different.

ā VOCABULARY

tidal flat - a flat, muddy area in the intertidal zone.

Figure 12.2: *People enjoy the clean, light-colored, rounded sand grains that slip easily through their hands.*

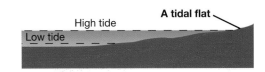

Figure 12.3: *A tidal flat is in the same area as a beach.*

This is a tidal flat in a salt marsh. You can see dark mud clinging to the students' shoes.

This is a summer beach. Sand covers every surface and no rocks are exposed.

Photos courtesy of Jim Sammons, Sammons' INK.

Waves and sand

Tidal flats do not have waves Waves are the key difference between tidal flats and beaches. Tidal flats are not like beaches because they are not affected by waves. Waves change the size of sediment particles. A sample of tidal flat mud contains different kinds and different sizes of sediment particles.

Waves at the beach If you have ever stood on a beach, you know that waves seem to come in and go out from the edge of the beach. If you have swam at the beach, you know it is a thrilling experience. As each wave passes over you, you feel the strong rush of water. The rush and crash of the waves churns the sandy ocean floor. Sand grains are broken into smaller pieces.

What is sand? The largest particles are heavy enough to settle to the ocean floor. The smallest particles and broken grains are carried out to sea with the waves and ocean currents. The remaining particles, called *coarse sand,* build the beach (Figure 12.4). The coarse sand grains tumble and roll over each other with every passing wave. The tumbling action wears away any sharp edges or corners. It also polishes the grains. The only grains that are hard enough to stand this harsh treatment are the minerals—light-colored quartz and feldspar. Both quartz and feldspar contain silica. Beach sand is made of visible, rounded grains of quartz and feldspar.

Quartz

Photo courtesy U.S House Subcommittee on Energy and Natural Resources

Feldspar

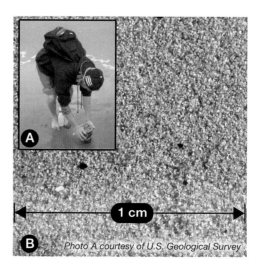

Figure 12.4: *(A) Scientists use special digital cameras to photograph and then measure the size of sand grains on a beach. (B) This image of sand grains is one centimeter across. By studying sand grains on a beach over time, scientists can determine how much wave energy affects the beach.*

SOLVE IT!

Image B in Figure 12.4 is 1 centimeter across. Count how many grains you see going across the bottom of the image.

Multiply the number you get by 100 to estimate out how many grains would fit along a length of one meter.

Waves

Wind causes waves   Ocean waves at a beach occur as a repeating pattern of wave crests and troughs. A **crest** is the high point of a wave, and a **trough** is the low point. The height of a wave is the distance between the wave crest and trough.

Wave height   The wind is the most common cause of ocean waves. The height of a wave is influenced by:

- The strength of the wind.
- How long the wind blows.
- How much open water the wind blows over.

Wavelength   The distance between two wave crests is called the **wavelength** of a wave. The ability of a wave to disturb the ocean bottom as it approaches a beach depends on its wavelength. A passing wave can "reach" down about half its wavelength. That means that a wave with a wavelength of 10 meters can only disturb the ocean bottom if it is five meters deep or less.

Waves stir up sediment on the ocean bottom   Most waves will reach deep enough to affect the part of the shoreface nearest the beach. The lower part of the shoreface is only affected by the strongest waves with the longest wavelengths.

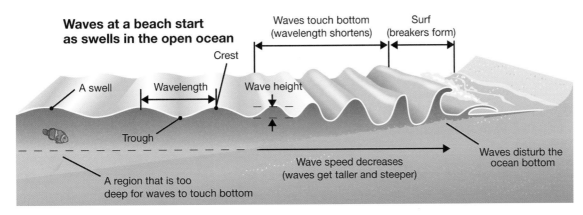

Waves at a beach start as swells in the open ocean

Crest

A swell

Wavelength

Wave height

Trough

A region that is too deep for waves to touch bottom

Wave speed decreases (waves get taller and steeper)

Waves touch bottom (wavelength shortens)

Surf (breakers form)

Waves disturb the ocean bottom

VOCABULARY

crest - the high point of a wave.

trough - the low point of a wave.

wavelength - the distance between two wave crests, or the distance between two wave troughs.

Swells

In the open ocean, most waves look like moving humps of water called swells. Swells can travel great distances over open water without losing much energy because although the swell moves, the water stays close to the same place.

If you could watch a blob of water as a swell passed by, you would see it move in a circle. First the blob would drop and move toward the approaching swell. Then the swell would lift the blob and push it forward. Finally, the blob would drop back to its starting place. Because the blob would end up right where it started, little energy is lost. That's why swells can travel great distances without losing much energy.

By the time a swell reaches a beach, if it has a lot of energy, it can become a huge breaker! A breaker is a wave that becomes foamy as it hits the beach.

12.1 Section Review

1. What are the two names given to the area that lies between the high and low tide lines?

2. Why is the lower shoreface bumpy?

3. What is different about the sediment you find at a beach versus a tidal flat?

4. What natural phenomenon happens at beaches but not at tidal flats? How does this phenomenon affect the sediment found at these locations?

5. What can scientists learn from studying and measuring the size of sand grains at a beach?

6. How do waves affect the smoothness of sand grains?

7. Beach sand is made mostly of what two minerals?

8. What causes waves?

9. What three factors affect the height of a wave?

10. Why are swells able to travel great distances without losing much energy?

11. The wavelength of a wave in the open ocean is 12 meters. At what depth will it begin to stir up sediments as it comes toward the beach?

    a. 5 meters   b. 6 meters
    c. 12 meters   d. 24 meters

12. Challenge questions:

    a. What is the difference between high tide level, sea level, and low tide level at a beach or tidal flat?

    b. Most coastlines on Earth experience high and low tide levels at least once a day. What causes the water level to change at coastlines?

CHALLENGE

Tidal flats and beaches are special environments. Use the Internet or reference books to find out what kinds of plants and animals live in tidal flats. Then, find out what kinds of plants and animals live on beaches. Make a poster to display what you learn.

STUDY SKILLS

Surf while you study

You can improve how fast you learn by applying your knowledge to new situations.

For example, the answer to review question 9 is related to why some of the biggest breakers are found at the shore lines of the Hawaiian Islands. These big breakers are why the sport of surfing is very popular there.

Do some Internet surfing to find out why Hawaii is such a good spot for big breaking waves.

12.2 Waves Shape Beaches

The shape and appearance of a beach is determined by its waves. In this section, you will learn more about waves, sand, and beaches.

Beaches in winter and summer

Winter versus summer beaches You have learned that fast-moving water will pick up large, heavy particles, and that slow-moving water will drop these particles. Winter waves are stronger than summer waves on the east and west coasts of the United States. Gentle summer waves tend to carry sand from deeper water onto beaches. The stronger winter waves carry the sand back to deeper water (Figure 12.5). This back-and-forth action creates two distinctly different environments on the same beach, a summer beach and a winter beach (Figure 12.6).

What is a bony beach? Waves that create summer and winter beaches are not the same year after year. Just like one summer may have a little more or less rain than another, waves may be more or less energetic from year to year. During the winter, the sand that is removed from the beach winds up in sandbars, not too far out from shore. During a harsh winter, the beach may be eroded by a series of very strong storms. High-energy waves carry away more sand than usual, carrying the sand further out from the shore. After a harsh winter, it may take years for the beach to recover from the erosion. During this recovery time, beach regulars will call it a "bony beach" because the beach is full of rocks.

How does a beach get too much sand? On the other hand, the gentle waves of a mild winter may not remove all of the summer sand. In this case, when the next summer arrives, the beach may start out with an extra amount of sand, and the summer waves will build up even more sand. After several mild winters, the sand may reach unusually high levels.

A winter beach

Photo courtesy of Jim Sammons, Sammons' INK.

Figure 12.5: *This is a winter beach. Compare this image to the summer beach image in Section 12.1.*

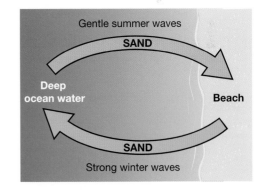

Gentle summer waves
SAND
Deep ocean water
Beach
SAND
Strong winter waves

Figure 12.6: *Gentle summer waves carry sand from deep ocean water to beaches. Strong winter waves carry the sand from the beaches to deep ocean water.*

Losing and gaining sand

Beaches lose sand

The amount of sand that is moved from the beach to the deep ocean by the summer-winter wave cycle is not even. Over time, more sand is lost than is returned in summer. This sand is lost because eventually it is carried too far from shore for gentle waves to return it. In some places the shore is more durable than others. Waves will cut away the softer rock on both sides of these more durable places. Eventually, the durable places, called sea stacks, will stand in the water separated from the shore.

Rivers and streams supply new sand

Beaches never completely wear away because rivers and streams bring new sand from the mountains to the beaches. But this sand doesn't stay in one location. Instead, it flows along the coast.

What is longshore drift?

A **coast** is the boundary between land and a body of water like the ocean. This flow of sand along a coast is called **longshore drift**. The beach sand that is lost to deep water is replaced by new sediments flowing from a river or stream. Therefore, sandy beaches do not stay the same—they are constantly changing due to waves, longshore drift, and replenishment by rivers and streams.

VOCABULARY

coast - the boundary between land and a body of water like the ocean.

longshore drift - the flow of sand along a coast.

Sea stacks

Figure 12.7: *Some sediment is taken from beaches by the action of waves against the shore. In some places the shore resists wearing away. Waves cut away the softer rock on both sides of these more durable places. Eventually, the durable places, called sea stacks, will stand in the water separated from the shore.*

Small stream

Stream mouth

Here is a small stream flowing from a reservoir into the ocean. Longshore drift has carried sand from left to right along the coast. Longshore drift has shifted the stream mouth so far to the right that the stream flows along behind the beach.

Photo courtesy of Jim Sammons, Sammons' INK.

How does longshore drift work?

Waves carry sand in the direction they move

Longshore drift shapes beaches. First of all, waves carry sand grains in the directions that they move. For example, as a wave moves toward and away from the beach, it drags sand grains forward and backward. If a wave came in a straight line to the beach, sand would go up and back the same path. The sand grains would end up just about where they began before the wave broke. Longshore drift occurs because waves approach the beach at an angle. This means the waves come in at one direction (the *upwash*) and then leave the beach at a different angle (the *backwash*). This process causes sand grains to move along the coastline of a beach.

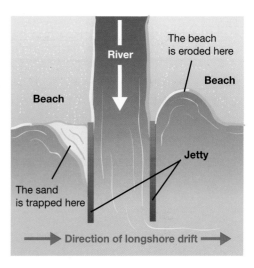

Figure 12.8: *A jetty is a barrier to longshore drift. Sand gets trapped on one side of the jetty, but the beach erodes on the other side.*

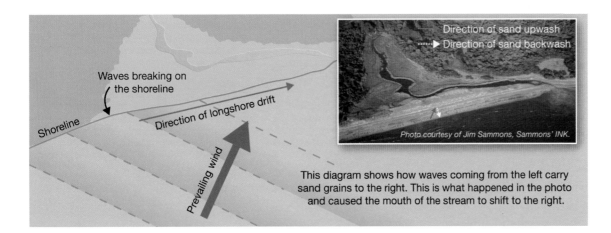

This diagram shows how waves coming from the left carry sand grains to the right. This is what happened in the photo and caused the mouth of the stream to shift to the right.

Barriers to longshore drift

Because the sand of a beach is constantly coming and going, a beach is like a river of sand. Evidence of the flow of sand at a beach can be seen wherever there are barriers to longshore drift. A *jetty* is a barrier that is built to control or slow down ocean currents near a coast (Figure 12.8). Another barrier is a *breakwater*, which protects a harbor from waves.

| **What happens to sand at a barrier** | When a jetty or breakwater is located off the coast of the ocean, longshore drift will be disrupted. Sand will quickly build up on the side of the barrier where the waves first hit. At the same time, the beach will erode away on the other side of the barrier. |

| **Protecting a harbor leads to a new problem** | Many breakwaters have been built in front of marinas or harbor entrances to protect them from high waves. But soon after solving the problem of high waves, a new problem appears. The water behind the breakwater is calmer than it used to be. The calm water drops its sediment and the marina or harbor entrance fills with sand (Figure 12.9). The only solution is to remove the breakwater or use pumps, called *dredges*, to remove the sand. |

| **Continental shelves and canyons** | Eventually, beach sand finds its way to the edge of the **continental shelf** and drops off into very deep water. Sand drifting down the steep face of a continental shelf cuts into the shelf just like streams cut into valleys. These cuts are called *submarine canyons*. As a canyon is cut, the cut grows in the direction of the shore. Some canyons are so close to the shore that sand moving along the coast by longshore drift lands in the canyon and gets deposited directly into the deep ocean basins. Beaches can lose a lot of sand quickly at submarine canyon locations. |

Figure 12.9: *A breakwater is a barrier to longshore drift that protects harbors. Excess sand can build up near a breakwater.*

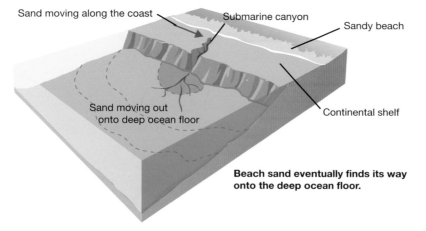

Beach sand eventually finds its way onto the deep ocean floor.

12.2 Section Review

1. Which season is known for having stronger waves on the east and west coast of the United States? Which season has weaker waves?

2. How do these seasonal waves affect the shape of a beach?

3. Why is a winter beach sometimes called a bony beach?

4. Which beach profile (A or B) in Figure 12.10 is a summer beach? Which profile is a winter beach?

5. Is the amount of sand moved between the beach and deep ocean water equal over time? Explain.

6. What is the main source of beach sand?

7. If a dam was built to block a river from flowing toward a beach, what might happen to this beach over time?

8. Answer true or false. If a statement is false, rewrite it so that it is true.

   a. Longshore drift occurs when waves move toward and away from a beach along the same path.

   b. A jetty is a barrier that disrupts longshore drift.

   c. A breakwater is a large wave.

   d. Submarine canyons prevent beaches from losing sand.

9. What are sea stacks?

10. How does longshore drift move sand along the beach?

11. What happens when a barrier is built in front of marinas or harbors to protect boats from high waves?

12. Sand drifting down the steep face of a continental shelf creates cuts or valleys, which over time, can migrate toward the coast, becoming quick pathways for sand to move to deeper waters. What are these valleys called?

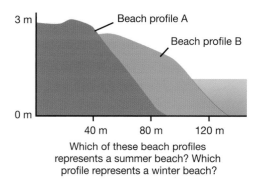

Figure 12.10: *Use this graphic to answer question 4.*

From Sea to Shining Sea

The first verse of Katharine Lee Bates's poem *America the Beautiful* (1913) ends with 0this memorable line: "From sea to shining sea." She was envisioning the Atlantic and Pacific oceans that border the United States, but what comes to mind in your "America the beautiful"? The Rocky Mountains, perhaps? The Mississippi River, or the Grand Canyon? One of the Great Lakes? How about a beach beside those shining seas? Beaches are geological formations, and they are both plentiful and varied in this country.

If you have been to the seaside, you know that beaches have big things in common: sand, water, and waves. But they differ in ways people might not notice if they never see other beaches. What are the sand, wind, and waves like? These elements differ depending on location.

Waves are the big thing

Waves are what shape beaches: smaller ones build up beaches, larger waves take sand out to sea. Wave size is affected by wind, land formation, and the distance a wave travels. In the United States, prevailing winds blow from west to east. So if you live on the Pacific Coast, winds blow in the same direction that waves move. These winds increase wave energy and create larger waves.

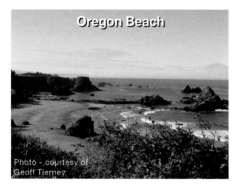
Oregon Beach
Photo - courtesy of Geoff Tierney

On the East Coast, winds blow against the waves. So there the winds decrease the energy of waves, creating smaller waves.

Along both coasts, the continental shelf extends into the ocean. The continental shelf is the underwater part of a continent that ends in a steep slope to the ocean floor. The West Coast shelf is narrow and slopes sharply. On the East Coast, the shelf is wider and slopes gradually. Friction from the gradual slope causes East Coast waves to slow down and decrease in size. West Coast waves are not slowed by such friction and so they are larger when they reach shore.

North Carolina Beach
Photo - courtesy of NOAA
Cap. Albert E. Theberge

Beach by beach

Keep in mind that winds, waves, tides, and currents all change—and all change what a beach looks like. Its location also changes a beach's size and shape, its sediment and color.

Look at the Pacific Coast in Oregon: Over eons, rock from mountains was moved by rivers and slowly turned into smaller sediment. The beaches may have fine sand or coarse sand with cobblestones. Beaches in the rugged Northwest are not as big as those on the Atlantic Coast; instead, many small beaches and coves dot the coastline. Oregon has the largest area of coastal dunes in all of North America.

Looking south, California has numerous beaches of varying shape, size, and texture. In Northern California, the coast is rugged with strong surf, and there are many cove beaches made of granite from the sea cliffs. On the central coast along the Big Sur, steep cliffs drop into the ocean.

Big Sur
Photo - courtesy of Geoff Tierney

In Southern California, beaches are larger and made of white sand. Sand colors vary depending on the mineral content: At Carmel Beach, ground quartz and feldspar have created white beaches; at Sand City, iron has created amber-colored sand.

On the Atlantic Coast, the Carolinas have miles of white sand beaches. Most South Carolina beaches are wide and flat, and in the south of the state, the coast includes salt marshes, rivers, and creeks. To protect South Carolina beaches from erosion, sea oats are planted on sand dunes to keep them in place.

Sea oats on a beach
Photo - courtesy of NOAA - Cap. Albert E. Theberge

Looking north to New England, sandy beaches are a nice complement to the area's rocky coastline. Metamorphic rock with quartz meets the sea along the coastline in Maine.

Cape Cod in Massachusetts was shaped by large ice sheets in the last ice age. As ice melted, the sea level rose. The action of water and waves and tides loosened and moved glacial deposits to create sandy beaches and bays.

Next time you visit the sea, enjoy how it shines— and see how the wind, the waves, the sand all have made it unique.

Quoddy Head, Maine
Photo - courtesy of NOAA
Cap. Albert E. Theberge

Questions:

1. What factors influence wave size?
2. Why are West Coast waves bigger than East Coast waves?
3. Describe several big differences between East and West coast beaches.
4. Explain why sand color may vary from beach to beach.

CHAPTER ACTIVITY Beach Trip

In this activity, you will go on a beach trip to make observations. Among the things to take with you—take what you have learned from this chapter and its investigations!

Materials

- Supplies for a beach trip (Be sure to bring sunscreen!)
- Field guides to help you identify beach animals and plants
- A notebook or sketch book
- Pencil or pen
- Colored pencils
- A ruler
- Sampling bottles
- Binoculars
- A camera

What you will do

1. Schedule a beach trip with your family or perhaps you will take a beach trip with your whole class.
2. Before the beach trip, write down your predictions for what the beach will be like once you are there. If you have visited this beach before, use your prior experience to help you write your paragraph. If you have never been to this beach, make predictions about what you will see based on reading this chapter.
3. Make a checklist of the items you will need for your beach trip. What kind of beach supplies will you need—a towel? snacks? sunglasses? Be sure to take the items listed in the materials list above.
4. At the beach, use the table to guide your observations. You may want to make a copy of this table in your notebook or sketch book.
   Notes for making observations: If permitted at the beach, collect a small sample of sand to take home. See if you can determine how big your sand grains are using a ruler, but they may be too small to measure easily! Use your binoculars to quietly observe any birds you see from a distance so you don't disturb them. Take photographs too.
5. Observations table:

Things to observe	Observations
Cloud cover Is it cloudy or clear?	
Weather What is the weather like?	
Temperature Is it cold, warm, or hot?	
Waves Are the waves big, medium, or small?	
Sand What color is the sand? Describe the size and shape of the sand.	
Animals What animals do you see? How many of each animal do you see?	
Plants and seaweed What kinds of plants and seaweed do you see?	

6. Make a large bird's eye view diagram of your beach (a diagram that shows what the beach looks like from the air). Make other sketches of the beach and its wildlife.

Applying your knowledge

a. After your beach trip, compile your sketches, photographs, and written observations into a scrapbook.
b. Based on your observations and sketches, how is the sand deposited on the beach and how it is affected by waves?
c. Is your beach being eroded by waves? If so, how?
d. Does your beach have a jetty? Do you see evidence of how the jetty might be affecting the beach? If so, describe what you see.
e. Share your scrapbook with your class.

Chapter 12 Assessment

Vocabulary

Select the correct term to complete the sentences.

longshore drift	continental shelf	intertidal zone
marine	coast	beach
tidal flat	crest	trough
wavelength		

Section 12.1

1. Sea water, a fish that lives in the ocean, and seaweed are all part of the _____ environment.

2. The sandy zone above the foreshore in a shallow marine environment is called a _____.

3. The _____ lies between the high and low tide lines.

4. A _____ is a muddy, flat area in the intertidal zone.

5. _____ is the distance between two wave crests.

6. The _____ is the high point of a wave while the _____ is the low point.

Section 12.2

7. In the end, beach sand finds its way to the boundary between the ocean and land called the _____.

8. The flow of sand along the coast is called _____.

9. Eventually, beach sand moves out to the _____ and then drops off into deep water.

Concepts

Section 12.1

1. How does the surface of the lower shoreface bottom compare to the upper shoreface bottom? Why?

2. What is meant by the term sea level?

3. Where does the sand on a beach come from? What is sand made of?

4. What is the difference between the sediment in a tidal flat and the sediment at a beach?

5. Which condition below *does not* affect the height of a wave?

   a. how long the wind blows

   b. the strength of the wind

   c. how much open water the wind blows over

   d. whether the wind is from the north or the south

Section 12.2

6. Is it possible for a beach to get too much sand? If so, how does this happen?

7. What are sea stacks?

8. When sediment reaches a beach from a river, does it stay in one place? Describe at least one thing that can happen to this sand.

9. What is the difference between a jetty and a breakwater?

10. Look at Figure 12.8 in the text. Make a sketch of this diagram and indicate the place that would be best to have a public beach. Explain your answer.

Math and Writing Skills

Section 12.1

1. For some people, the coast is their favorite place to be. Write a paragraph or story about visiting a beach, intertidal area, or tidal flat. Your story can be real or made up. However, you must describe the appearance of the coastal area in your story or paragraph.

2. The intertidal zone can be a place with many different kinds of organisms. Some of these include barnacles, sea stars, crabs, and many different varieties of seaweed. Find out for yourself about the organisms of the intertidal. Pick one organism and write about it.

3. One type of seaweed called the sea palm (*Postelsia palmaeformis*) lives on the northern west coast of the United States. You have read that waves can break down rocks to sand. Research this fascinating seaweed and find out how it is adapted to survive waves. If you have trouble finding information, find a picture and predict from its appearance how it survives.

4. Which situation would potentially make a bigger wave?
   a. If wind blew over the ocean surface for a distance of 10 kilometers.
   b. If wind blew over the ocean surface for a distance of 5 kilometers.

5. Which situation would potentially make a bigger wave?
   a. If wind blew at a speed of 10 kilometers per hour over the ocean.
   b. If wind blew at a speed of 30 kilometers per hour over the ocean.

6. A wave coming in towards a beach has a wavelength of 12 meters. At what depth will it disturb the ocean bottom?

Section 12.2

7. Imagine you are a particle of sand on a beach. What effect would longshore drift have on you? Write a short paragraph in answer to this question.

Chapter Project—Looking at Sand

Gather sand samples in jars or bags from your own travels or ask friends to send you samples of sand (if they live on or near a beach). Note: Only collect samples if it is permitted at the beach! Make sure each sample of sand you collect is labeled with its location and date. When you have gathered at least three samples, look at each one. Place some of each sample in separate dishes. Copy the table below on a separate piece of paper and fill it in as you make your observations.

In order to determine the types of materials present, you may have to get help from your teacher. Quartz and feldspar are common minerals in sand. Magnetite is common in California sand and can be identified by passing a magnet through the sand—the magnet attracts the particles. You may need a magnifying glass to see and identify particles that are parts of shells.

Location	Size and shape of the grains	Color or colors of the grains	Which types of weathered material are present?					What do your observations tell you about the how much weathering by waves occurs at this beach?
			Quartz (mineral)	Feldspar (mineral)	Shell fragments	Magnetite (mineral)	Other types of materials	

Chapter 13
Natural Hazards

Two great energy sources drive Earth's processes. Energy from the Sun drives the *external energy system,* while energy from Earth's hot core drives the *internal energy system.* Most natural hazards are related to one of these two energy systems. *Natural hazards* are events that can change and damage human and animal habitats. Earth's weather is part of the external energy system. What natural hazards are weather-related? The movement of the lithospheric plates is part of the internal energy system. What kinds of natural hazards are powered by Earth's internal energy?

Key Questions

1. *Does the Sun cause some natural hazards?*

2. *How do natural hazards affect habitats?*

3. *How does learning about earth science help you to stay safe?*

13.1 What Is a Natural Hazard?

A **natural hazard** is an event in nature that can cause extensive damage to land and property, and that threatens human lives. In this section, you'll be introduced to natural hazards. In Section 13.2, you'll learn about different kinds of hazards.

Energy for natural hazards

Two energy sources
Most natural hazards are related to one of two energy sources—the Sun, or Earth's hot core. Earth's weather, driven by the Sun, is part of the *external energy system*. Weather-related natural hazards include hurricanes, flooding, and slumping. Plate tectonics, driven by the hot core, is part of the *internal energy system*. Natural hazards related to plate tectonics include earthquakes, tsunamis, and volcanic eruptions.

Earth science helps people
Earth scientists can provide life-saving information in the event of a natural hazard. For example, because it is unlikely that humans will ever be able to stop a volcano from erupting, it is important to understand how volcanoes work. A volcanologist is an earth scientist who studies volcanoes (Figure 13.1).

Technology helps people
Satellite and computer technology, and good communication also help protect people from natural hazards. Communication systems allow officials to alert people quickly if a natural hazard is about to happen. Before 1960, hurricanes, for example, could hit a coast without warning. Since 1960, weather satellites have helped predict and track hurricanes. Figure 13.2 shows a satellite image of Hurricane Hugo about to make landfall on the coast of South Carolina in 1989. Government organizations like the National Hurricane Center (NHC) monitor storms that might become hurricanes. The NHC issues hurricane watches and warnings so that people can evacuate a threatened area.

natural hazard - an event in nature that can cause extensive damage to land and property, and that threatens human lives.

Figure 13.1: *A volcanologist speaking to the media.*

Figure 13.2: *A weather satellite image of Hurricane Hugo making landfall on the coast of South Carolina.*

Reducing the risks of natural hazards

Where do you live? Earth is an amazing place and this is especially true because there are so many interesting and scenic places to live. Where on Earth do you live? What's the best thing about where you live? What's the worst? It's possible that a potential natural hazard may be the worst thing, but it doesn't have to be. It's a good idea to study earth science so you understand natural hazards and how to stay safe!

Predicting natural hazards Some natural hazards, like hurricanes, can be predicted. Others, like earthquakes and volcanic eruptions, are very difficult to predict. Nonetheless, scientists who study natural hazards understand a great deal about why they occur and can judge when people should be warned.

Staying safe The time line for a hazard affects how the government manages resources to help the most people during a natural hazard. A *time line* is a description of what will happen during a particular event. Understanding the time line of a hazard is important in order to be able to take steps to reduce risks so that people do not get hurt and property is not damaged. For example, in an area with earthquakes, it is important to follow a plan like the one in Figure 13.3. But, the government has to be careful in how it issues warnings about hazardous events. If a warning is issued too early and the event doesn't happen, people may stop taking warnings seriously! This could lead to people getting hurt if an event eventually happens. As you read, ask yourself these questions:

- What natural hazards might occur where I live?
- How can I reduce the risks associated with a natural hazard?
- Do I know enough about this hazard to keep myself safe?
- Do I know what to do if the government issues a warning about the hazard?

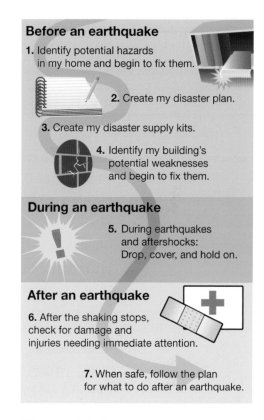

Before an earthquake

1. Identify potential hazards in my home and begin to fix them.

2. Create my disaster plan.

3. Create my disaster supply kits.

4. Identify my building's potential weaknesses and begin to fix them.

During an earthquake

5. During earthquakes and aftershocks: Drop, cover, and hold on.

After an earthquake

6. After the shaking stops, check for damage and injuries needing immediate attention.

7. When safe, follow the plan for what to do after an earthquake.

Figure 13.3: *Steps to earthquake safety.*

13.1 Section Review

1. An earthquake can occur on the ocean floor where there is no human property and there are no people. Would this earthquake be considered a natural hazard? Explain your answer.

2. What energy source powers plate tectonics?

3. What energy source powers Earth's weather systems?

4. Name two natural hazards that occur as a result of plate tectonics.

5. Name a natural hazard that is related to weather.

6. How do earth scientists help keep people safe from natural hazards?

7. Hurricane hunters (Figure 13.4) include airplane pilots that fly into hurricanes. They can measure the wind speed of the hurricane and help track the hurricane. Why do you think taking these measurements helps keep people safe from hurricanes?

8. Before 1960, people living on the coast of the U.S. could not depend on hurricane warnings for protecting themselves. Why?

9. Can all natural hazards be easily predicted? Why or why not?

10. What is one thing you can do to protect yourself from risks associated with a natural disaster?

11. What is one danger associated with giving people a warning for a natural hazard that does not occur?

12. Write down three things you learned from studying the earthquake plan from Figure 13.3 (previous page).

13. A *habitat* is an environment in which an organism lives. How might a natural hazard affect the habitats of plants, animals, and people? Write your thoughts in a paragraph.

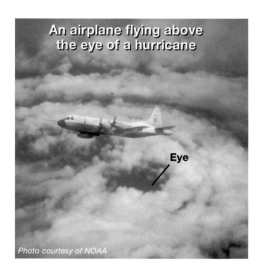

An airplane flying above the eye of a hurricane

Eye

Photo courtesy of NOAA

Figure 13.4: *A hurricane hunter flying above the eye of a hurricane. The eye is a still place that is circled by the hurricane winds.*

MY JOURNAL

There are four questions at the bottom of the previous page. Write responses to these questions on your own. Then, ask a parent or guardian to answer the questions. Talk about your responses together.

13.2 Natural Hazards Driven by External Energy

The Sun is Earth's external energy source. As you learned in Section 13.1, hurricanes, flooding, and slumping are some natural hazards that are driven by external energy from the Sun. In simple terms, a **hurricane** is wind that blows at speeds greater than 119 kilometers per hour (74 miles per hour). **Flooding** is an event that occurs when water overwhelms normally dry land. **Slumping** is an event that occurs when soil particles become surrounded by water so that the ground sinks or "slumps."

Hurricanes

Wind, waves, and rain	Hurricanes start as tropical storms and form over oceans. With the right ocean temperature, air moisture, and winds, a tropical storm can become a hurricane. For a coastline, the arrival of a hurricane means severe and dangerous winds, high waves, and a lot of rain.
Hurricane season	During an average hurricane season (June 1 to November 30), six storms may form in the Atlantic Ocean, and over a three-year period an average of three hurricanes may hit the U.S. coast. The year 2005 was unusual in terms of hurricanes, with many "firsts." For example, it was the first year with four major hurricanes hitting the U.S. (Figure 13.5). One of these hurricanes was Hurricane Katrina that made landfall in New Orleans.
How places are affected by hurricanes	As long as hurricanes are at sea and away from ships, they are not threatening. Hurricanes become particularly hazardous to people and property when they arrive on land. Wind and waves damage property, and heavy rains cause flooding. The strong waves are called a *storm surge*. A storm surge is as dangerous as the wind so it is always important to leave a coastal area when a hurricane warning has been issued. After Hurricane Katrina, a storm surge breached the levees between Lake Pontchartrain and New Orleans, causing about 80% of the city to flood.

VOCABULARY

hurricane - wind that blows at speeds greater than 119 kilometers (74 miles) per hour.

flooding - an event that occurs when water overwhelms normally dry land.

slumping - an event that occurs when soil particles become surrounded by water so that the ground slides or "slumps." Slumping is a form of mass wasting which is the falling of rock and soil due to the influence of gravity.

Figure 13.5: *2005 was a record season for hurricanes.*

What you can do to stay safe

As stated in Section 13.1, hurricanes are a predictable natural hazard. However, it is only possible to predict the general path of a hurricane. It is hard to pinpoint where a hurricane will make landfall until a few hours before. This means that preparations have to be made along a wide band of possible landfalls to keep people safe. Therefore, it is important to pay attention to hurricane watches and warnings.

- A *hurricane watch* issued for your area means that there is the possibility of hurricane conditions within 36 hours. If you hear that a watch has been issued, you should make a plan with your family to evacuate the area as safely as possible.
- A *hurricane warning* issued for your area means that there is the possibility of hurricane conditions (sustained winds of at least 119 kilometers per hour) within 24 hours or less. If you hear that a warning has been issued, you and your family should begin to evacuate the area as quickly and as safely as possible.

Hurricane categories

The Saffir-Simpson Hurricane Scale (above right) rates the intensity of hurricanes (from 1 to 5) based on wind speed. The scale helps determine how much flooding and property damage might occur if a hurricane makes landfall. A tropical storm becomes a hurricane when the wind speed reaches 119 kilometers per hour or more.

Saffir-Simpson Hurricane Scale

Name	Wind speed	Damage	Storm surge
Tropical depression	> 63 kph	Little	None
Tropical storm	63 - 119 kph	Minor flooding	Very minor
Category 1 hurricane	120 - 153 kph	Minimal damage	1.2 - 1.5 m
Category 2 hurricane	154 - 177 kph	Moderate	1.6 - 2.4 m
Category 3 hurricane	178 - 209 kph	Extensive	2.5 - 3.7 m
Category 4 hurricane	210 - 249 kph	Extreme	3.8 - 5.5 m
Category 5 hurricane	< 250 kph	Catastrophic	> 5.6 m

kph = kilometers per hour

SOLVE IT!

When Hurricane Andrew hit Florida in 1992, its winds were 265 km/h and it produced a storm surge of 5.2 meters. What category was Hurricane Andrew on the Saffir-Simpson Hurricane Scale?

Do research to find out more about Hurricane Andrew. How does Hurricane Katrina, which hit New Orleans in 2005, compare to Hurricane Andrew?

Flooding

Rain causes flooding

Flooding commonly occurs when heavy rain or snowmelt add more water to a river than it can carry. The extra water overwhelms normally dry land areas. Fortunately, this type of flooding is usually predictable several days in advance. However, heavy rainfall can occur so quickly that the land cannot absorb the water. The result is a *flash flood*. Central Texas has been called "Flash Flood Alley" because it has more flash floods than any other place in the U.S. Figure 13.6 lists a few flood safety tips.

River valleys and snowmelt

A river valley is created when rivers carve into mountains. Valleys are low-lying land features that are surrounded by higher land features such as mountains. River valleys are changing environments because the amount of water that flows into them changes. The amount of water increases or decreases based rain or snowmelt. Colonial mountain people of the Appalachian Mountains learned early on that the only safe place to build their homes was on the high hills. The rivers of this region often become full of water and dangerously fast in the spring after the snow melts. As a fast flowing, full river roars through a valley, plants and other important parts of a habitat (animal or human) will be swept away.

Storm surges

Storm surges from hurricanes and other storms can cause coastal flooding. If these wind-driven waves occur at high tide, the combination can raise the sea level high enough to flood towns and cities that lie close to or below sea level.

Floodplains

The area that floods near a river is called a **floodplain**. This area is usually located some distance from the source (headwaters) of the river. A flood plain is very good land for growing plants because seasonal flooding of the river deposits nutrients in the soil. However, because flooding occurs regularly, these areas are not ideal for buildings and homes.

Stay safe in the event of a flood

- Pay attention to all National Weather Service Flood watches and warnings.
- Practice and maintain a flood safety plan with your family.
- Cars and trucks should never attempt to drive through moving water because flood waters can be very strong. The U.S. National Weather Service says "Turn Around Don't Drown!"

Figure 13.6: *Flood safety.*

Slumping

The difference between dry and wet soil

When soil is dry, friction between the grains of soil keeps it firm enough that you can build a house on it. However, if the soil is wet, the spaces between the grains are full of water. The water makes the grains slippery and friction is a lot lower. Wet soil is squishy. If you have walked on wet soil, you know that your feet sink into it!

What is slumping?

Slumping is a natural hazard that describes what happens when loose soil becomes wet and slides or "slumps" like a tired person (Figure 13.7). As with flooding, slumping can happen after a period of very heavy rainfall. Houses are at risk of being destroyed by slumping when they are built on steep, loose soil or below hills that are made of loose soil. A house could be destroyed if it slides down with the soil or if the soil on a hill above falls on the house!

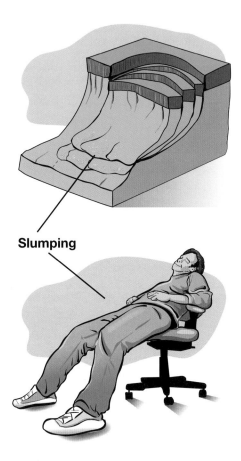

Slumping

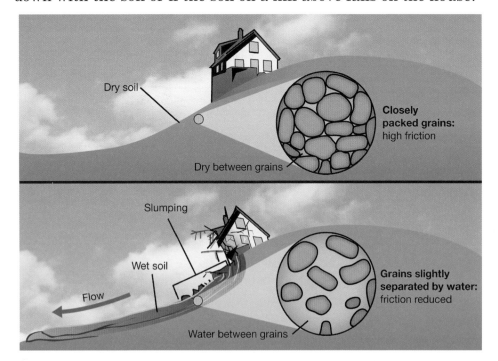

Figure 13.7: *Loose soil experiences slumping (top). A tired person can slump just like the ground! (bottom).*

Wildfires

Wildfire   **Wildfire** is an unwanted fire that burns in a forest or other natural area. Three ingredients make a fire—fuel, oxygen, and heat. Our atmosphere is about 20% oxygen and a forest or grassland provides a lot of fuel for a fire. Lightning and even volcanic eruptions can provide heat to start fires. However, careless people start nine out of ten wildfires! The number of wildfires started by people can be reduced by educating everybody about fire safety.

Preventing forest fires   You have probably encountered fire prevention rules if you have visited a wilderness area. Often camp stoves are allowed at a campsite, but campfires are forbidden. This is because many campers do not realize how easy it is for wildfires to start. A smoldering twig from a campfire or a burning cigarette, even if it is buried, can start a forest fire by burning underground until it ignites something dry, like leaves. Forest fires are much more likely to occur after a dry period than after a rainy period since a smoldering object is likely to burn out on wet or moist ground.

Fighting forest fires   Rain is a factor in causing damage during hurricanes, flooding, and slumping. However, rain can also help stop a forest fire. A heavy rain can cause a forest fire to eventually die out. Hot, windy weather makes fighting fires difficult. Fire crews try to stop fires by removing fuel from their path. They do this by cutting or burning away a line, called a *firebreak* in front of the fire (Figure 13.8). Firebreaks are effective and are the first line of defense for firefighters. But, firebreaks are easily jumped by a forest fire when strong winds carry burning embers over them.

Beneficial fires   Sometimes forest rangers and officials let fires burn a forest because a fire can benefit a natural area. A controlled fire can burn away dry, dead twigs that could fuel a large wildfire in the future. Fires also cause some plant seeds to germinate and grow. After a fire, the soil is filled with nutrients and supports new plant life.

Photo courtesy National Park Service.

Figure 13.8: *A firebreak is a line that is cut or burned away in front of a wildfire. Firebreaks are very effective and are the first line of defense for firefighters.*

13.2 Section Review

1. What is the main difference between a tropical storm and a hurricane?
2. What is the difference between a hurricane watch and a hurricane warning?
3. On the Saffir-Simpson Hurricane Scale, which is more intense: a Category 4 hurricane or a Category 5?
4. When does flooding happen inland (away from coastlines)?
5. When does coastal flooding occur?
6. During what time of year is a river valley likely to be flooded? Explain your answer.
7. Where and when might you see a sign that says "Turn Around Don't Drown"?
8. How can flooding be beneficial to the land?
9. What happens, on a small scale, when water gets in between grains of soil?
10. What happens, on a large scale, when water gets in between grains of soil?
11. What three ingredients make a fire?
12. Name a natural phenomenon that starts wildfires.
13. Why do land managers and the USDA Forest Service work so hard to educate people about preventing wildfires?
14. Weather plays a role in both causing and stopping forest fires. Do you agree with this statement? Justify your answer.
15. How do firefighters try to remove fuel from a fire's path?
16. Is there such a thing as a fire that benefits a forest? Explain your answer giving three reasons that justify it.

CHALLENGE

It is important to stay safe when a destructive natural event, like an earthquake or a hurricane, occurs.

You have learned one slogan for helping people stay safe during a flood.

Choose a natural hazard and research how people can stay safe during this event if it occurs.

Then, make up a slogan to help people remember at least one of the important safety tips.

Make a colorful sign that advertises your slogan. You may want to come up with a logo for your slogan as well.

13.3 Natural Hazards Driven by Internal Energy

Earthquakes, tsunamis, and volcanoes are driven by Earth's internal energy source—its core. You have learned about these natural hazards in previous chapters.

Earthquakes

A sudden movement in Earth's crust   In Chapter 9 you learned that earthquakes are the result of sudden movement in Earth's brittle crust. The energy released by this movement is carried by seismic waves. These waves cause sudden, violent movement when they arrive at Earth's surface.

Scales to measure earthquakes   Of course, strong movements at Earth's surface cause more damage than weak movements. However, other factors also contribute to the amount of damage done by earthquakes. This is why there is more than one scale for measuring earthquakes. The *Richter scale* is based on the measurements of seismic waves and gives a sense of the energy released by an earthquake. The *Mercalli Intensity scale* is based on the amount of earthquake damage (review Table 9.1).

Liquefaction   Soil types can affect the amount of damage caused by earthquakes. When seismic waves pass through the ground, the soil can act as a liquid. This is called **liquefaction** (Figure 13.9).

Liquefaction caused the cracking of this paved road.

Photo courtesy of U.S. Geological Survey

The 1989 Loma Prieta earthquake caused a lot of damage in San Francisco. The area most damaged had been built on top of San Francisco Bay mud.

liquefaction - when sediment shakes so much during an earthquake that it acts like a liquid.

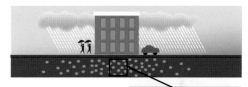

- Water-saturated soil
- Particles slightly separated
- Water pressure is low

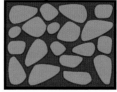

Liquefaction
- Particles are further separated
- Water pressure is high

Figure 13.9: *Liquefaction occurs when soil is saturated with water. An earthquake increases pressure on the soil so that the particles separate with water between them. The result is that the soil acts like a thick liquid!*

Buildings and earthquakes

Brittle versus flexible materials

Earthquake vibrations easily damage heavy, brittle building materials like brick, mortar, and adobe. More-flexible building materials include wood and steel (Figure 13.10). Steel is a strong but flexible building material. Buildings with well-designed steel supports are less likely to be damaged during quakes.

Building height

Taller buildings are often more susceptible to earthquake damage than single-story buildings. However, this is not always true. Mexico City had short, medium, and tall buildings before an earthquake struck in 1985. After the quake, many of the medium-height buildings were destroyed. Why would short and tall buildings survive, while medium-height buildings were destroyed?

When earthquake vibrations match the sway of a building

Buildings naturally sway back and forth. Short buildings sway faster than tall buildings. In the Mexico City earthquake, the swaying of the medium-height buildings happened to match the earthquake vibrations. This made the medium-height buildings sway so much that they collapsed. The medium-height buildings—with the right timing of the push from the quake—were shaken apart. This is similar to how you can make someone go higher on a swing if you push them at the right time (Figure 13.11).

Easily damaged by earthquakes	Earthquake resistant
Brittle building materials	Flexible building materials
brick	steel
mortar	wood
adobe	

Figure 13.10: *Brittle versus flexible building materials. More-flexible materials are better able to absorb energy from earthquakes so possible damage is diminished.*

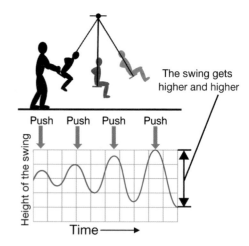

The swing gets higher and higher

Figure 13.11: *Each push of a swing at the right time increases the height of the swing.*

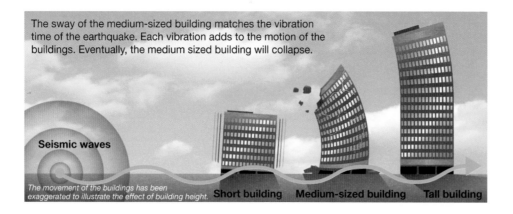

The sway of the medium-sized building matches the vibration time of the earthquake. Each vibration adds to the motion of the buildings. Eventually, the medium sized building will collapse.

Seismic waves

The movement of the buildings has been exaggerated to illustrate the effect of building height. **Short building   Medium-sized building   Tall building**

Tsunamis

A "harbor wave" Tsunami is a Japanese word that means "harbor wave." Sudden movements of the sea floor cause tsunamis. These movements may be earthquakes, volcanic eruptions, or sediments slumping on a steep underwater face. You have learned that earthquake energy is spread by seismic waves. In a similar way, energy from these underwater movements is spread as a wave on the ocean surface.

Tsunamis in the open ocean In the open ocean, wind-driven waves and tsunamis are about the same height. But the wavelength of a tsunami is much longer than the wavelength of a wind-driven wave. The wavelength of a wind-driven wave may measure 20 to 40 meters from crest to crest. It may take ten seconds or so for a wind-driven wave to pass by. Wind-driven waves are small splashes compared to tsunamis. The wavelength of a tsunami is hundreds of kilometers long! Because the surface of Earth is curved, you can't see enough of it to detect the crest of a tsunami as it approaches! If a tsunami approached your ship, you would see only a flat sea. As it passed under the ship, the tsunami would cause the ship to rise gently, about ten meters, and then gently settle back after several minutes.

Tsunamis in shallow water When a tsunami approaches land, the lower front edge of the wave begins to drag on the shallow bottom. As the front slows, the back of the wave catches up. This shortens the wavelength. Shortening the wavelength makes the wave crest higher. It's this enormous crest of water, often 20 meters high or more, that comes crashing over beaches and harbors.

VOCABULARY

tsunami - a huge ocean wave caused by underwater earthquakes, volcanic eruptions, or slumping.

Read more about tsunamis

Find out more about tsunamis by reading the Chapter 9 Connection titled *2004 Indian Ocean Earthquake and Tsunami*. In this reading you will learn how a 10-year-old girl saved the day by remembering what she learned in her science class. You will learn a clue that indicates that a tsunami is coming, and you will learn about the very important tsunami warning networks.

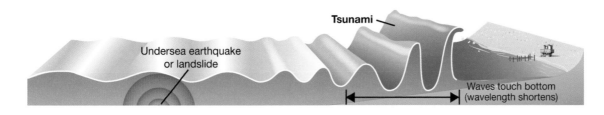

Tsunami — Undersea earthquake or landslide — Waves touch bottom (wavelength shortens)

Volcanic eruptions

Shield and composite volcanoes Volcanic eruptions from shield volcanoes are mild because they release runny lava. Of the 50 states in the U.S., only Hawaii has shield volcanoes. Active volcanoes found in the continental states are all composite volcanoes located near plate boundaries.

Predicting an eruption Composite volcanoes are formed from thick, sticky magma. The thick magma blocks the escape of gas and lava when the volcano is active. This makes a composite volcano like a shaken soda bottle with a loose cap. Scientists can tell that a composite volcano is becoming more active, but it's hard to tell exactly when or how it will erupt. Sometimes composite volcanoes seem ready to erupt, only to become quiet again for awhile.

Predicting a lava flow Glowing lava from shield volcanoes moves slowly enough that people can usually get out of the way. The path that lava will take can be predicted from earlier flows and from maps that show low areas that would make good pathways. The main threat posed by lava flow is destruction of property. Anything that will burn bursts into flame at the first touch of lava. Some structures are set on fire just by radiant heat, before the lava even touches it. The immediate danger passes after lava cools and becomes solid rock.

A town versus a volcano Cooled lava may block or fill harbors, streams, and lakes. In 1973, lava from a volcano on Iceland named Eldfell ("fire mountain" in Icelandic), was flowing toward an important fishing port near the town of Vestmannaeyjar (Figure 13.12). Firefighters saved the harbor by spraying the lava with water to cool and harden the flow. Although the harbor was saved and few people were injured, most of the town was destroyed. About 300 buildings burned or were buried by the lava flow. The residents of the town rebuilt it and used the cooling lava to create a heating system!

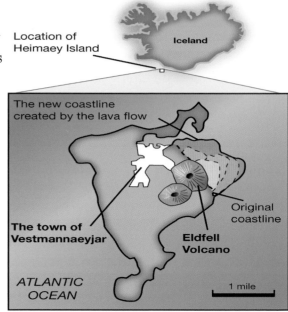

Figure 13.12: *This map shows how far into the fishing port the lava reached. The cooled lava flow made the island bigger and improved the harbor.*

SOLVE IT!

Use the scale on the map to measure the distance from the vent of Eldfell to the new coastline created by the lava flow in 1973.

Is Iceland a big country or a small one? Justify your answer using the scale.

Pyroclastic flow   Pyroclastic flow is many times more dangerous than lava flow. A composite volcano sends an eruption column into the air. Shortly afterward, a wave of hot, toxic gases, ash, and larger fragments races down the side of the cone. The energy of this wave is enormous. A tourist, driving his car as fast as he could, was unable to outrun pyroclastic flow from the Mount St. Helens eruption. At times he was going more than 90 miles per hour! He only lived to tell about it because the flow stopped shortly after it caught up to him. Pyroclastic flow is forceful as well as fast. In the same Mount St. Helens eruption, hundreds of trees were knocked flat by the force of the pyroclastic flow.

Pompeii   The Roman town of Pompeii was overrun by pyroclastic flow when Mount Vesuvius erupted in 79 C.E. Hot gases and ash quickly suffocated the inhabitants. Several additional flows buried the town under a thick blanket of ash. Pompeii remained buried until art collectors and scientists began removing the ash 1,700 years later. Hollow casts, formed by the bodies of the dead, were discovered as the ash was removed. The casts were filled with plaster so that today we can see these people in their last moments (Figure 13.13). The force of the pyroclastic flow struck down people who were outdoors. Many of the plaster casts show people shielding their faces from the hot gases and ash.

Lahars   Lahars are mudflows that result from water mixing with loose material on the steep sides of a volcano. Lahars are common on most composite volcanoes because these volcanoes have steep sides with plenty of loose material on them. Because of their height, these volcanoes also often get plenty of water in the form of snow or rain. The mudflows of lahars can carry large boulders. Lahars can be dangerous because they often follow riverways that lead to town. The river path brings the lahar right into town, boulders and all!

A victim of the Mt. Vesuvius eruption (hollow area under ground)

Plaster is poured into the cast

Plaster hardens and the form is carefully dug up

Figure 13.13: *The two photographs show plaster casts of people who were caught by the Mount Vesuvius eruption near Pompeii. The lower part of the graphic shows how these plaster casts were made.*

Ashfall Volcanic ash is made of tiny, cooled bits of magma. The ash is very fine because the magma explodes apart as trapped gases bubble out. Ash drifts with the wind because it is so fine. Eventually, it settles to the ground. This settling is called *ashfall*. The wind determines the direction and distance of ashfall.

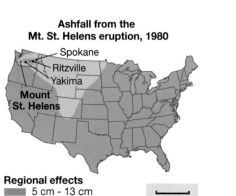

Ashfall from the Mt. St. Helens eruption, 1980

Spokane
Ritzville
Yakima
Mount St. Helens

Regional effects
- 5 cm - 13 cm
- 1 cm - 5 cm
- Trace amounts to 1 cm

600 km

VOCABULARY

volcanic ash - fine particles of cooled magma.

landslide - a large mass of soil or rock that slides down a volcano or mountain. Landslides can be caused by volcanic events, earthquakes, or other factors. Landslides are a form of mass wasting which is the falling of rock and soil due to influence of gravity.

Volcanic ash is abrasive and can damage delicate machinery. It jams moving parts and fills any low area. Streams may be dammed and farm crops buried. Like snow, ash adds weight to roofs of buildings. Unless the ash is removed, the roof may collapse. The weight and the danger become greater if rain soaks the ash. Unlike snow, the ash will not melt and go away, it must be removed.

Landslides A **landslide** (a form of "mass wasting") occurs when a large mass of soil or rock on a steep slope slides down and away (Figure 13.14). Landslides are common on composite volcanoes. The slope is steep and the material is loose. Landslides may be triggered as magma rises and falls inside the volcano. This rising and falling often causes the side of the volcano to move. The Mount St. Helens eruption began when an earthquake occurred and one side of the volcano collapsed resulting in the largest landslide ever recorded. The landslide left a weak place in the side of the volcano that could no longer hold in the magma that had been building up inside the volcano for two months. The landslide and the subsequent eruption killed 57 people and destroyed 230 square miles of forest.

Landslide

Photo by Robert L. Schuster, USGS.

Figure 13.14: *A landslide that occurred in La Conchita, California in 1995.*

13.3 Section Review

1. One earthquake measurement scale is based on damage caused.
   a. What is the name of this scale?
   b. What is the highest value on the scale?

2. Name one thing that determines whether or not an earthquake causes a lot of damage, or just a little damage.

3. Flexible building materials like wood and steel help a building survive an earthquake because:

   a. they reflect earthquake energy.   b. they block earthquake waves.
   c. they absorb earthquake energy.   d. None of these.

4. Name three underwater movements that can cause tsunamis.

5. How do the wavelengths of tsunami waves compare to the wavelengths of wind-driven waves?

6. What happens when a tsunami reaches shallow water?

7. Answer the following questions about volcanoes.
   a. Which is the only state in the U.S. to have shield volcanoes?
   b. In the continental U.S., which type of volcanoes are especially hazardous?
   c. What natural hazard caused the Mt. St. Helens eruption?

8. Why is a pyroclastic flow so dangerous?

9. A mudflow occurs that results from water mixing with loose materials on the side of a volcano. Name this type of event.

10. List three effects of ashfall on the local environment.

11. Describe how landslides occur.

CHALLENGE

Follow these steps then present your work on a poster or make a book!

1. Pick a natural hazard. Here is a list to choose from:

- hurricane
- flooding
- slumping
- earthquake
- tsunami
- volcanic eruption

2. Research on the Internet or in a library to find the name and date of the most recent event of this type of natural hazard. The U.S. Geological Survey website (www.usgs.gov) has good information about natural hazards.

3. Find out how the habitats of plants, animals, and people were affected by this event.

4. Find out how the habitats are recovering now that the event is over.

5. Make a list of tips for how to stay safe during this type of natural hazard.

GEOLOGY CONNECTION The Shake, Rattle 'n' Roll of Earth

If you live in a region where there are snowstorms or hurricanes, you receive warning days in advance. Scientists use weather equipment and computers to predict such dangerous storms. But what about other natural hazards? In many parts of the world, earthquakes are a huge concern. Scientists are trying to learn as much as they can about earthquakes, in the United States and worldwide, so as to be able to predict when and where they will occur.

Where Earth quakes …

Did you know that earthquakes could occur almost anywhere? Between 1974 and 2003 in this country, only eight U.S. states recorded no earthquakes: North Dakota, Wisconsin, Iowa, Florida, Delaware, Maryland, Connecticut, and Vermont. Guess which state has the most?

Alaska is so far the most earthquake-prone state, with a magnitude 7 quake occurring almost yearly. It was on March 28, 1964 at Prince William Sound in southern Alaska that the largest recorded earthquake in the United States (for that matter, in the Northern Hemisphere) occurred, a magnitude 9.2. Luckily, it was a holiday (school was out, some businesses were closed) in a state not densely populated, or many more than 115 people would have died.

Southern California quakes, too

The Southern California Earthquake Center (SCEC) was founded in 1991, with headquarters at the University of Southern California. This is a perfect location to research earthquakes; the area is a natural laboratory with many active faults. The center's focus is learning why earthquakes happen and finding ways to predict them. The scientists' goal is to provide the public with life-saving information.

Earthquakes occur when mammoth plates beneath Earth's surface grind and scrape against each other, one sometimes pushing from underneath the other's edge. California has two huge plates, the Pacific Plate and the North American Plate. The boundary between them is the famous San Andreas Fault. The slab of granite in the photo on the previous page has been forced up along the fault by movement of the Pacific and North American Plates.

The San Andreas Fault is more than 800 miles long and as much as 10 miles deep. The fault moves an average of about two inches per year. Researchers at SCEC monitor the movement of this fault, these plates, and many other changes in Earth's crust.

Top Ten Earthquake States

Ranking	State	No. of Earthquakes 1974-2003	Percent of total
1	Alaska	12,053	57.2%
2	California	4,895	23.2%
3	Hawaii	1,533	7.3%
4	Nevada	778	3.7%
5	Washington	424	2.0%
6	Idaho	404	1.9%
7	Wyoming	217	1.0%
8	Montana	186	0.9%
9	Utah	139	0.7%
10	Oregon	73	0.3%

Earthquake myths

If the SCEC is to prepare people for a possible earthquake by communicating safety information, it must also educate people to discard the myths about earthquakes. One myth is that big earthquakes happen only in early morning. Many do, but in fact, earthquakes can occur at any time of day. Another myth is that earthquakes are more common in hot, dry weather. In fact, there is no link between weather and earthquakes, which is logical when you think that quakes begin many miles below Earth's surface, where weather is not a factor. Many people believe that standing in a doorway is the safest place to be in an earthquake. But, in fact, doorways in modern houses are no stronger than other parts of the house. Experts say the safest place to be during an earthquake is under a table.

Did you feel it?

People usually turn to their televisions and radios for immediate news. Now the Internet has made its way into the news business and become another main source of fast information. Within minutes, data can be uploaded and available to millions of people. The U.S. Geological Survey (USGS) has a website called "Did You Feel It?" where people who experience an earthquake can share information. They can go online, enter their ZIP code, and answer a list of questions. Some of those are: "Did the earthquake wake you up?" and "Did objects fall off shelves?" With all of this information, the USGS efficiently produces maps of shake intensities and damage. These Community Internet Intensity Maps, or CIIMs, provide valuable data to researchers.

There is still so much to learn about earthquakes. Scientists continue to gather data and perfect their monitoring tools. They hope to be able someday to reliably predict when these natural hazards will occur. People might have time to protect themselves, and many thousands of lives worldwide could be saved.

Questions:

1. Where do earthquakes most commonly occur in the United States?
2. What are the focus and main goals of the Southern California Earthquake Center (SCEC)?
3. What information does the Southern California Integrated GPS Network (SCIGN) provide researchers about earthquakes?
4. How has the Internet become a valuable tool in earthquake research?

Composite and Shield Volcanoes

With a partner, use these diagrams to make clay models of two types of volcanoes —shield and composite volcanoes. Your models will show a cross-section of each volcano. You learned that shield volcanoes can be found in Hawaii and tend to have gentle eruptions. Composite volcanoes, which are found in the continental U.S., have explosive eruptions.

Materials

- Several colors of clay, including red for new lava/magma
- Wire or slicing tool to cut clay models in half
- Construction paper on which to place the models
- Toothpicks with labels

What you will do

1. Both volcanoes should have a magma chamber, vent, and crater. Your volcanoes will be built as though they are currently erupting, so make sure that your new lava/magma (red) is a different color than the old lava.

2. When you finish building your volcano, cut it in half to see a cross-section.

3. Then use your toothpicks to label the following parts:
   Composite volcano—ash, old lava, magma, new lava, magma chamber, vent, crater
   Shield: magma—new lava, old lava, magma chamber, vent, crater

Applying your knowledge

a. How are the volcanoes different in shape?
b. How are the volcanoes different in explosivity?
c. Why is "composite" a good term for the composite volcano?
d. Why is the term "shield" a good term to describe the shield volcano?

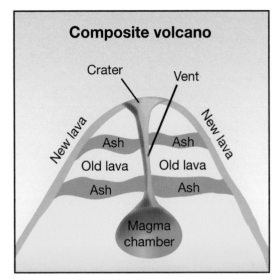

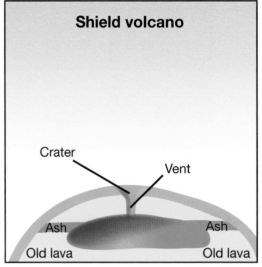

Chapter 13 Assessment

Vocabulary

Select the correct term to complete the sentences.

landslide	wildfire	flooding
tsunami	liquefaction	slumping
natural hazards	tsunami	floodplain
hurricane	volcanic ash	landslide

Sections 13.1 and 13.2

1. Scientists like volcanologists inform people about events called _____ which can cause damage and threaten human lives.

2. _____ is a natural hazard that occurs when the ground becomes so wet that it sinks.

3. _____ start as tropical storms and form over oceans.

4. _____ is a natural hazard that can occur after heavy rainfall.

5. _____ is a natural hazard common in dry, forested areas.

6. The land near a body of water like a river that experiences flooding is called a _____.

Section 13.3

7. The combination of an earthquake and wet sediment can cause _____.

8. A(n) _____ can be caused by an undersea earthquake or by sediments slumping underwater.

9. _____ can cover large areas after a volcanic eruption.

10. Earthquakes or volcanic eruptions can a trigger a(n) _____.

Concepts

Section 13.1

1. Why is earth science an important scientific field regarding natural hazards?

2. Why are hurricanes easier to predict than earthquakes?

3. What are some important parts of a natural hazards safety plan. List at least three parts.

Section 13.2

4. A hurricane is a huge wind storm, but it does more than just produce strong wind. What are some effects of a hurricane on a location once it reaches land?

5. What is the difference between a category 1 hurricane and a tropical storm?

6. While listening to the radio, you hear that a weather service is reporting that a hurricane is expected to make landfall on a coastal region within the next 12 hours. Would this radio message be a hurricane warning or a hurricane watch?

7. How is snow involved in causing flooding of an area?

8. Why should a car or truck never attempt to drive through a river that has washed over a road?

9. What role does friction play in preventing slumping of land?

10. What is a firebreak?

11. Fire can be beneficial to a forest. How?

Section 13.3

12. Why is it helpful to have multiple scales by which to measure earthquakes?

13. If you experienced an earthquake and wanted to use your experience to figure out its rating, would you check the Richter scale or the Mercalli Intensity Scale? Justify your answer.

14. Describe how the height of a building can determine whether or not it is seriously damaged by an earthquake.

15. How do tsunamis become such huge waves?

16. Is it possible to predict a volcanic eruption? Explain your answer.

17. Discuss the dangers of a gentle eruption of runny lava from a shield volcano versus an explosive eruption from a composite volcano.

18. Why is pyroclastic flow from a volcanic eruption so devastating?

19. What determines the direction and distance of an ashfall?

20. The rising and falling of the side of a volcano due to the rising and falling of magma inside a volcano can trigger a _____.

21. _____ can be very dangerous because they often run into riverbeds on which towns are built.

Math and Writing Skills

Section 13.1

1. Where do you live?

   a. Write a paragraph describe the climate and environment in which you live. Describe the kinds of natural hazards that people need to be aware of in your area.

   b. For one natural hazard that you may be affected by, write a plan for staying safe if a natural hazard event ever occurs. Talk to your family before, during, and after you have written your plan.

2. In the image below, a seismologist is standing next to a seismograph recording of the Loma Prieta earthquake. How are seismologists important in a natural disaster situation? See Chapter 9 to read about what seismologists do.

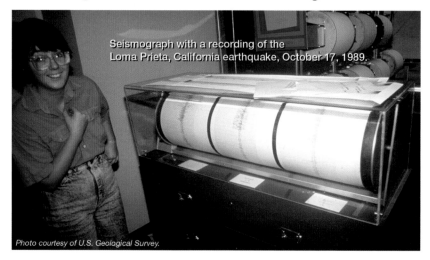

Seismograph with a recording of the Loma Prieta, California earthquake, October 17, 1989.

Photo courtesy of U.S. Geological Survey.

Section 13.2

3. The following table lists hurricanes and tropical storms that occurred during 2004. Identify the Saffir-Simpson Hurricane Scale rating for these storms.

Hurricane	Wind speed (kph)	Category
A	169	
B	210	
C	63	
D	125	
E	260	

Section 13.3

4. In order to push someone on a swing, you have to push them at the right time. If you do this, the swing goes higher and higher. How is pushing someone on a swing related to how seismic waves damage buildings?

5. Ashfall from the eruption of Mount St. Helens covered a large area.

 a. Using the scale on the map below, what was the greatest distance covered by the ashfall from the volcano?

 b. Which city—Spokane or Ritzville—had ashfall that was 5 cm-13 cm deep?

Ashfall from the Mt. St. Helens eruption, 1980

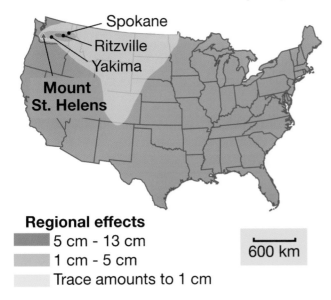

Regional effects
- 5 cm - 13 cm
- 1 cm - 5 cm
- Trace amounts to 1 cm

600 km

Chapter Project—Natural Hazard Time Lines

Pick one of the listed natural hazards or another that has happened in the past and create a time line for this event based on your research. Be creative in how you present your time line.

- The 1906 earthquake that destroyed old San Francisco was over in minutes, but the fires raged on for three days. This is because when earthquakes strike cities, fire often adds to the destruction. Gas pipes are broken and electrical lines fall down. To make matters worse, water mains often break so there is no water to fight the fires. Research the San Francisco earthquake and create a time line for what happened before, during, and after the earthquake.

- The Roman town of Pompeii was overrun by pyroclastic flow when Mount Vesuvius erupted in 79 C.E. Hot gases and ash quickly suffocated the inhabitants. Several additional flows buried the town under a thick blanket of ash.

- Others include:
 The eruption of Mount St. Helens in Washington in 1980.
 The landslide that occurred near San Bernardino, California in December 25, 2003.
 The 2004 Indonesian tsunami.
 Hurricane Katrina in 2005.
 Flooding and landslides in Haiti in 2004 (aftermath of Hurricane Jeanne).
 Pakistan-India border earthquake that struck in October 2005.

WHAT IS IN THIS JAR?

WHAT IS THE ROLE OF SUNLIGHT IN A FOOD CHAIN?

WHERE DO FISH GET ENERGY TO GROW AND SWIM?

TRY THIS AT HOME

Water—an important resource in all ecosystems—comes to your house through pipes. Every month the water company measures how much water you use and charges you for it. Find out how much water your family used last month by looking at the water bill.

After studying the water bill, come up with one strategy that your family can use to conserve water. Give this strategy a try and see if it works for conserving water and saving money next month!

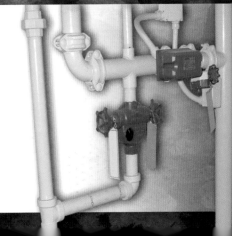

Chapter 14
Resources

Hoover Dam, near Las Vegas, Nevada, towers more than 200 meters above the raging Colorado River. This gigantic concrete structure is known as one of the greatest engineering projects in the world. Hoover Dam is called a *hydroelectric plant* because it turns the energy of falling water into electricity. The dam is important to the American southwest, because it brings water and electricity to millions of people. Using a natural resource like water to make electricity is one way to meet our growing demand for energy. What other natural resources do we use in our daily lives? Read this chapter to find out!

Key Questions

1. *What are some of Earth's resources?*

2. *Where do we get the energy for making electricity and for running automobiles?*

3. *What does it mean to conserve Earth's resources?*

14.1 Natural Resources and Energy

For tens of thousands of years, people have depended on Earth's resources for food, clothing, shelter, energy, medicine, and even entertainment, arts, and riches. What are the basic resources that Earth has to offer?

Natural resources

Material resources
A **natural resource** is a feature of Earth that benefits people. Earth's natural *material* resources are things like air, fresh water, and soil. What would happen if any of these resources were missing? Study the scenes below and find the material resources. How does each of these benefit people?

Energy resources
Some natural resources are used to supply energy to our busy world. Important *energy* resources are:

Energy Resources	
the Sun	tides
wind	coal, oil, natural gas
moving water	nuclear (radioactivity from uranium)
Earth's internal heat	biomass fuel (such as wood)

ă VOCABULARY

natural resource - a feature of Earth that benefits people.

MY JOURNAL

A forest can be considered a natural resource. Why do you think this is so?

Write an essay that answers this question.

Energy and daily life

Energy use   Your alarm clock rings and you wake up for school. You shower, brush your teeth, dress, and grab a quick breakfast before catching a bus. This is how the day starts for hundreds of thousands of students all across the country. What part of that simple morning routine requires electricity and transportation energy? Almost all of it!

Electricity   The first electric light company in the U.S. was started in 1878. Since then, our use of electricity has grown each year. What do you need to make electricity? You need an energy source. Earth's natural energy sources are used to make electricity. Think of all the ways you use electricity each day. The average American household uses about 10,000 kilowatt-hours of electricity each year. How much energy is that? If your body were able to utilize electricity as an energy source (rather than food) that much energy could keep you running for almost five months!

Transportation   Electricity is not the only modern use of natural energy sources. Transportation uses a lot of energy too. In the United States alone, about *130 billion gallons* of gasoline are consumed each year. Where does gasoline come from? Gasoline is made from crude oil, which is pumped out of the ground, either on land or from the ocean floor.

Heating and consumer products   In addition to being used for gasoline, oil can be used to heat homes. **Petroleum** is another name for oil, which is often used to heat homes. *Petrochemicals* are compounds made from oil. Petrochemicals are used to make plastics, medicines, cosmetics, and paints. Look around you now and see how many items are made of plastic. It takes petroleum to make all of those things.

petroleum - another name for the natural resource called *oil*.

CHALLENGE

Why do we need petroleum?

Petroleum is not just used to make gasoline—it is used to make many products we use daily. Here are some examples:

- plastic
- asphalt for paving roads
- synthetic rubber
- paraffin wax
- fertilizer
- detergents
- photographic film
- packaging materials
- paint
- carpet backing
- synthetic clothing fibers such as kevlar, nylon, polyester, acrylic, and spandex
- cosmetics

Make a sketch of one room in your home, and label all of the things made from petroleum.

14.1 Section Review

1. Define the term *natural resource*, and list all of the natural resources that exist in the area directly around your school.

2. List at least four major natural resources that you see in *each* scene above.

3. What two things in our modern lives require a lot of Earth's natural energy sources?

4. What is gasoline made from?

5. What is a petrochemical? What types of products can be made from petrochemicals?

6. What natural resource is plastic made from?

7. Study the bar graph in Figure 14.1 and answer the following questions.

   a. What type of information does this graph give you?

   b. How would the graph look if many more people in the United States used public transportation?

   c. "Americans love their cars." Does this graph support that statement? Why or why not?

Transportation energy use in the United States

Data from the U.S. Department of Energy, Transportation Energy Data Book, Edition 24

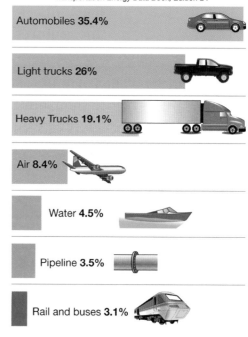

Automobiles **35.4%**

Light trucks **26%**

Heavy Trucks **19.1%**

Air **8.4%**

Water **4.5%**

Pipeline **3.5%**

Rail and buses **3.1%**

Figure 14.1: *Use this bar graph to answer question 7.*

14.2 Supplying Our Energy Needs

Think of how much you need electricity and how much you rely on motor vehicles every day. Making electricity and driving motor vehicles cause us to use Earth's energy resources.

Making and transporting electricity

Starting at the power plant
To find out how electricity is made and transported, let's trace the energy pathway. Look at the diagram below. Electricity is made in a power plant. Most power plants burn fossil fuels (natural resources like coal, oil, or natural gas) to produce heat. Next, this heat is used to boil water. The steam from the boiling water turns a turbine. The turbine turns a generator which produces electricity.

Electricity is carried by wires
Electricity leaves the power plant and is carried to your house by wires. The fuel energy from the coal, oil, or natural gas changes its form several times on the way to your home. With each change, some energy is converted to heat. In fact, most of the energy that is transferred from fuels like coal, oil, and natural gas will eventually become heat energy. Some will be used, but most will be unusable.

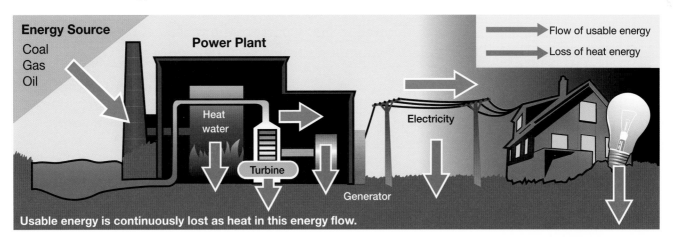

Energy Source
Coal
Gas
Oil

Power Plant

Flow of usable energy
Loss of heat energy

Heat water

Turbine

Electricity

Generator

Usable energy is continuously lost as heat in this energy flow.

Electricity from fossil fuels

What is a nonrenewable resource?

A **nonrenewable resource** is not replaced as it is used. **Fossil fuels** are good examples of nonrenewable resources. Fossil fuels are found within the rocks of Earth's surface. They are called fossil fuels because they were formed hundreds of millions of years ago by processes acting on dead plants and animals. The three major fossil fuels are coal, oil, and natural gas.

Fossil fuels

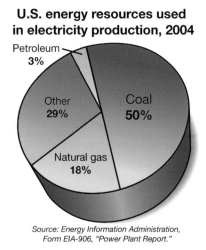

U.S. energy resources used in electricity production, 2004

Petroleum 3%
Other 29%
Coal 50%
Natural gas 18%

Source: Energy Information Administration, Form EIA-906, "Power Plant Report."

Earth's coal, oil, and natural gas deposits took hundreds of millions of years to form. Because it took so long for these resources to form, they are considered nonrenewable resources. Natural gas is pumped out of gas pockets both onshore and offshore. Coal is a solid fossil fuel that is mined from the ground in many places across the United States. Crude oil is drilled out of natural deposits both onshore and offshore. Crude oil deposits are located in many parts of the world, including the United States. Oil, coal, and natural gas can all be used to make electricity.

The future of nonrenewable resources

Nonrenewable resources like coal, oil, and natural gas are not replaced as they are used. This means that someday we will not have enough coal, oil, and natural gas to produce the electricity we need. How are we preparing for the future when these resources are no longer available? Perhaps we can use the energy of atoms, wind, or sunlight. Did you notice the "other" category in the pie chart above? Read on to find out about this category.

VOCABULARY

nonrenewable resource - a natural resource that is not replaced as it is used.

fossil fuels - substances found in Earth's crust that were formed over millions of years from the remains of dead organisms.

SOLVE IT!

Study the pie chart (also known as a circle graph) and answer these questions.

1. Which fossil fuel is used the most to make electricity?

2. Which fossil fuel do you think is found in the largest amount in the United States?

3. What resources do you think make up the "other" category? (Hint: read ahead to learn about renewable resources that can be used to make electricity.)

Electricity from nuclear energy

What is nuclear energy? The United States gets about 20% of its electricity production from nuclear power plants. The fuel is a nonrenewable resource called *uranium*. Uranium is an extremely high-energy source of heat. Uranium atoms split apart in the nuclear reactor and the energy released is used to heat water and make steam. The steam drives a turbine, which spins a generator to produce electricity.

U
92
uranium

Uranium is an element, and you can find it listed on the periodic table of elements. Elements are the most basic substances. Uranium has characteristics that make it very useful as a fuel for nuclear reactors. Uranium is naturally radioactive, and it releases particles from its atoms that have a lot of energy.

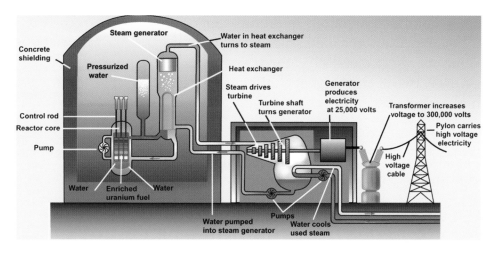

Do some research on uranium.

1. How is uranium used to produce electricity? (Hint: if you can describe the process shown in the picture to the left, you will have your answer!)

Advantages and disadvantages of nuclear energy The main advantage of using nuclear energy to produce electricity is that it doesn't pollute the air like fossil fuel power plants do. We will discuss the problems of pollution in the next section. There are no new nuclear power plants being built in the United States. In fact, all plants that have been scheduled to be built since 1973 have been canceled. Why is this happening? One reason is that used uranium fuel from a reactor stays dangerously radioactive for a long time. Storage of nuclear waste has always been a major disadvantage of nuclear power plants. When scientists find a way to dispose of spent nuclear fuel safely, nuclear energy will be more widely used to produce electricity.

2. Nuclear power plants do not pollute the air like fossil fuel plants do. However, there is a big drawback to nuclear power plants. What is it?

Electricity from renewable resources

Renewable resources A **renewable resource** can be replaced naturally in a relatively short period of time. The Sun and wind are renewable resources that can be used as energy sources. Figure 14.2 shows that nine percent of all resources used to make electricity in 2004 were from renewable resources.

Solar energy The Sun is our biggest source of light and heat. In fact, 99 percent of the energy used to heat Earth and all of our buildings comes from the Sun. The Sun's energy is often called **solar energy**. A solar cell can convert solar energy to electricity. Solar energy is plentiful and clean. However, two of the biggest challenges with using solar energy to make electricity are:

1. a backup energy source must be used on cloudy days

2. solar energy is very spread out, so it must be collected from a huge area to be a significant source of energy

Wind energy A wind energy system captures the energy of motion from moving air (wind) and turns the energy into electrical energy. California was the first U.S. state to build large *wind farms* (areas where wind turbines are located). Today, California produces more electricity from wind energy than any other state in the U.S. In fact, wind is the world's fastest-growing energy source used to make electricity. Wind is a clean, plentiful fuel source. What disadvantages are there to using wind as an energy source? Well, the wind does not always blow when electricity is needed, and right now the cost of building a wind farm is greater than the cost of building a power plant that uses fossil fuel to make electricity.

Other renewable energy sources It is also possible to use moving water (hydroelectric), hot spots near Earth's surface (geothermal), fuels made from once-living things like wood or corn (biomass), and tides to produce electricity.

VOCABULARY

renewable resource - a natural resource that can be replaced.

solar energy - energy from the Sun.

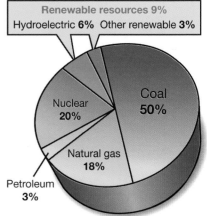

U.S. energy resources used in electricity production, 2004

Renewable resources 9%
Hydroelectric **6%** Other renewable **3%**

Nuclear **20%**

Coal **50%**

Natural gas **18%**

Petroleum **3%**

Source: Energy Information Administration, Form EIA-906, "Power Plant Report."

Figure 14.2: *Renewable resources were used to make 9% of the electricity produced in 2004.*

Evaluating resources used to produce electricity in the U.S.

For discussion This evaluation chart compares different resources that can be used to make electricity in the U.S. An evaluation chart is a powerful tool used to organize large amounts of information. According to the chart, which resources will the U.S. be using less and less of in the future? Which resources will be used more as time goes by? Can you explain why?

Using the evaluation chart

This evaluation chart was adapted from several similar charts, and some of the high, medium, and low ratings are open to debate; the information is not meant to represent specific scientific research data —it is meant to stimulate discussion.

Resource	What is the chance that this source can be used *50 years from now?*	What level of *cost* is involved with using this system?	What level of *impact* does using this resource have on the environment?
Nonrenewable resources			
Petroleum	Low	High	Medium
Natural gas	Medium	High	Low
Coal	High	Medium	Very high
Nuclear	Medium	Very high	Very high
Renewable resources			
Hydroelectric (dams)	Low	Medium	Low
Solar	High	High	Low
Wind	High	Medium	Low
Geothermal (using Earth's energy)	Medium	Medium	Medium
Biomass (burning wood and agricultural waste)	Medium	Medium	Medium

Transportation and energy sources

Gasoline use If you were asked to estimate how many automobiles there are in the United States, what number would you guess? According to the U.S. Department of Transportation, there were *over 132 million automobiles* in the United States in 1997. What is the main energy source used for operating automobiles? If you guessed petroleum, you are correct. Gasoline is made from petroleum. Americans use about 375 million gallons of gasoline *every day*. It is important to know that the U.S. does not produce enough crude oil to make all of the gasoline used by American motorists. The United States produces only about 40 percent of the crude oil it uses. Where does the rest come from? It is imported from other countries.

Efficiency What does it mean to say that a machine or a process is efficient? If a machine is *efficient,* the machine is able to use most of its energy source to do a job. For efficient machines, very little of the energy source is converted to unusable energy like heat. Efficiency is a very important idea to understand when you are learning about how we use different energy sources. A bicycle is a very efficient machine (Figure 14.3). When you ride a bicycle, almost 80 percent of the energy you put into pedaling the bike is converted to motion. Automobiles, however, have a low efficiency. Only about 20 percent of the gasoline energy is converted to motion. Most of the energy is lost as unusable heat.

Usefulness and trade-offs If bicycles are so efficient, why don't we use them more, instead of automobiles, when we travel? You know the answer to that question! Cars can take us where we want to go much faster and more conveniently than bicycles can. Bicycles aren't as useful to us as cars are. Useful energy sources are sources that meet our needs *and* have the right balance of cost and efficiency.

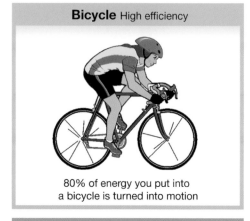

Bicycle High efficiency

80% of energy you put into a bicycle is turned into motion

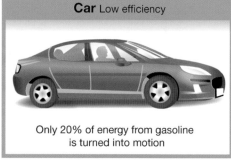

Car Low efficiency

Only 20% of energy from gasoline is turned into motion

Figure 14.3: *Bicycles are efficient but they are not useful for most transportation needs!*

Comparing notes

For discussion   Compare gasoline-powered cars to cars of the future. What will cars of the future use for energy sources? What type of car will you drive some day?

14.2 Section Review

1. Some of the energy that comes from burning a fossil fuel can be turned into electricity, but most of the energy is lost. Explain why this is a true statement and identify the unusable or lost energy.

2. Define *nonrenewable resources* and list three used for making electricity.

3. Define *renewable resources* and list three that can be used for making electricity.

4. List one major advantage and one disadvantage of making electricity in a nuclear power plant.

5. List two advantages and disadvantages of using solar energy to make electricity.

6. List two advantages and disadvantages of using wind energy to make electricity.

7. Study the pie chart below. Redraw your own version of this pie chart as it will most likely look *fifty years from now*. Use the evaluation table in this section that compares energy resources to help you decide how to draw your graph.

U.S. energy resources used in electricity production, 2004

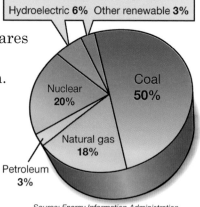

Renewable resources 9%
Hydroelectric **6%** Other renewable **3%**

Coal **50%**

Nuclear **20%**

Natural gas **18%**

Petroleum **3%**

Source: Energy Information Administration, Form EIA-906, "Power Plant Report."

Hybrid car

Hybrid Cars

The entire world, not just the United States, depends on oil—mostly for transportation energy. What are scientists doing to prepare for the time when there is not enough oil to meet the world's needs? One new type of car that will help reduce our need for oil is a hybrid car. Do some research and find out how hybrid cars might help reduce our need for oil. Write an essay on what you learn.

14.3 Resources and Conservation

In this chapter you have been learning about Earth's material and energy resources. Natural resources benefit people, and it is important to think about how we can take care of Earth's resources. **Resource conservation** happens when people protect, preserve, and manage Earth's natural resources.

Air—an important resource

Air is everywhere　Air is a very important natural resource, even though you may forget that it is all around you. Air is a mixture of nitrogen, oxygen, carbon dioxide, water vapor, and other gases. We do not need to worry that the air will get "used up," because there are natural cycles that keep the supply steady. However, these natural cycles can't always keep the air clean.

Air pollution　**Pollution** is a change to the environment (air, water, or soil) that is harmful to humans or other living things. Some changes to the air can have harmful effects on humans and other living organisms. Air pollution (Figure 14.4) is caused by tiny particles and gases called **emissions** that are released into the air. What produces emissions that pollute the air?

- power plants that use fossil fuels to make electricity
- motor vehicles (trucks, cars, airplanes, etc.)
- factories
- erupting volcanoes

Reducing pollution　The United States government has passed laws to control the levels of emissions from power plants, factories, and motor vehicles. If you use less electricity, you can help keep the air clean too.

VOCABULARY

resource conservation - protecting, preserving, and managing Earth's natural resources.

pollution - a change to the environment that is harmful to humans or other living things.

emissions - tiny particles and gases released into the air.

Figure 14.4: *Air pollution is caused by emissions from some factories, power plants, and motor vehicles.*

The water supply

Earth is a watery planet

The amount of water on Earth today is about the same as it was during the age of dinosaurs, 65 to 220 million years ago. About 70 percent of Earth's surface is covered by water. That's a lot of water! However, only a small amount of this water is useful to humans. Why can't humans use more than a small part of Earth's water supply? About 97 percent of Earth's water is salt water. That leaves only 3% as fresh water. About 70 percent of this fresh water is frozen, and the rest is found in rivers, streams, lakes, ponds, and even below the ground in layers of soil and rock. If this is true, and Earth has been around for such a long time, why haven't we run out of water? Earth's water is recycled by natural processes.

Water pollution

Earth's water supply will stay steady, but the water that humans can actually use is a precious resource which we must use with care. Water can be polluted by changes that are harmful to people or other living things. How does water get polluted?

- towns and cities can pollute the fresh water supply with wastes that are washed down sinks, toilets, and showers
- industries like factories and power plants produce wastes that can pollute water
- pesticides and fertilizers from farms can end up in the water supply
- oil spills from large ships that transport oil across the oceans can cause serious pollution problems

What can you do?

Using less water at home and at school can certainly help by putting less demand on the water supply. Also, never pour things like paint, paint thinner, motor oil, or garden chemicals on the ground or down the drain. Your town or city has probably has a special collection area for these hazardous substances.

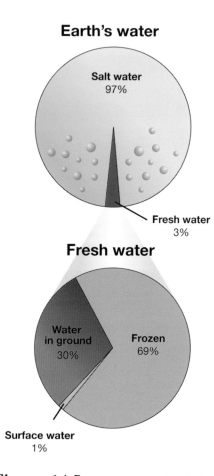

Figure 14.5: *The top pie chart shows how much of Earth's total water is salt water, and how much is fresh. The bottom pie chart shows how much of the fresh water is frozen, and how much is in the ground and on the surface.*

Land, forests, and wildlife resources

Land and soil Earth's land and soil are used to benefit people in many ways, and everyone must share these nonrenewable resources. How is land used to benefit people?

- Mining minerals: a *mineral* is a nonliving substance found in Earth's crust. Gold, iron, and tin are minerals that are called metals. Coal, oil, sand, and salt are also examples of minerals.
- Development: people use land to build houses, schools, and industries.
- Agriculture: growing crops and raising animals for food are important land uses.

What minerals are mined from Earth in the United States? Do some research and make a list of these minerals. Which ones are mined in your state?

Forests and fisheries Think of all the products we use that come from forests. Maple syrup, rubber, fruits, and nuts come from living trees. Lumber for constructing buildings and furniture comes from trees that have been cut down. Paper is another important forest product. Don't forget that trees and other plants produce oxygen that humans and other organisms need to survive. Fish are also valuable resources. Both trees and fish are renewable resources, but we cannot use them up faster than they are replenished, or the supply will decrease quickly.

What can you do? Do you recycle paper, metal, and plastic in your home and school? Recycling programs all over the country have been put in place to help reduce the solid waste that takes up so much of our land space.

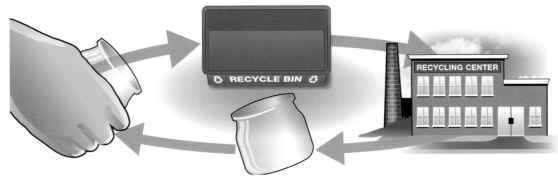

Trash takes up space in landfills: recycle and re-use!

RECYCLE BIN

RECYCLING CENTER

A resource conservation issue: global warming

Global warming Have you ever heard the phrase "global warming"? This is an important concern that has received a lot of attention in recent years. *Global warming* refers to our ability to increase the temperature of Earth's climate by increasing the amount of certain gases in the atmosphere—mostly carbon dioxide.

Carbon dioxide and global warming There is very little carbon dioxide in the atmosphere, compared to the amounts of nitrogen and oxygen (Figure 14.6). Does this surprise you? The amount of carbon dioxide in Earth's atmosphere is just enough to trap heat from the Sun to make Earth warm and comfortable. Earth would be too warm with too much carbon dioxide, and too cold if the carbon dioxide level was too low. When we use fossil fuels, we add more carbon dioxide to the atmosphere. Increased levels of carbon dioxide can contribute to global warming. Using public transportation, using less electricity (turn out the lights!), and driving hybrid vehicles can all help reduce carbon dioxide levels.

Consequences The amount of carbon dioxide in the atmosphere has increased by about 30 percent since the 1800s. Also, Earth's average surface temperature has increased 0.6 to 1.2 degrees Fahrenheit over that same time period. These increases are not huge, but they are enough to have warmed the North Pole and caused the sea level to rise 4 to 10 inches. Have you heard about any other consequences of global warming?

Trees and air quality One acre of trees can provide oxygen for about 20 people each day. This same acre of trees can also absorb emissions, including carbon dioxide. Trees are not the solution to the problem of increased carbon dioxide levels, but they can certainly help!

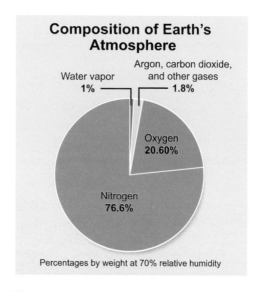

Figure 14.6: *There is very little carbon dioxide in Earth's atmosphere, compared to the amount of nitrogen and oxygen.*

Figure 14.7: *Trees can improve Earth's air quality.*

14.3 Section Review

1. What does it mean to conserve Earth's natural resources?

2. Why is air an important natural resource?

3. List four possible causes of air pollution.

4. Why can humans only use a small part of Earth's water supply for drinking, cleaning, and other daily needs?

5. Why is water an important natural resource?

6. List four possible causes of water pollution.

7. Describe two things you can do to help conserve Earth's water resources.

8. Study the fresh water pie chart in Figure 14.5. What percentage of fresh water can readily be used for drinking water and other needs? Why?

9. Make your own illustration of natural resources provided by trees. Draw a living tree and show on your diagram all of the different products that can come from different kinds of living trees. Draw a tree that has been cut down and show on your diagram all the different products that can come from trees that have been harvested. Be creative!

10. Why are fish considered a natural resource? Is this a nonrenewable or a renewable resource? Explain your answer.

11. Land is a natural resource. List at least three ways that land and soil are used to benefit humans.

12. How can global warming cause the ocean levels to rise? What problems could increased ocean levels cause?

13. Do some research to find at least two consequences of global warming, in addition to rising ocean levels.

What percent of *your* state do you think is covered by water? What state do you think has the greatest area covered by water? Write down your predictions, then do some research to find the answers to these questions. (Hint: http://ga.water.usgs.gov/edu/wetstates.html is a website maintained by the United States Geological Survey that will give you information on this topic.)

The Roads to the Mighty Redwoods

Have you ever gone over the river and through the woods to Grandmother's house? If she lived near one of the redwood groves in Northern California, you just might have crossed a river or creek on the way—and seen the tallest and biggest trees in the world among these mighty redwoods.

Over 65 million years ago a dozen species of redwoods existed on Earth. Today, only three species remain. What could have happened to cause the loss of so many tree species? Scientists believe that changes in the Earth's climate caused the trees' extinction. Millions of years ago Earth was warmer and wetter. Over time the climate became colder and drier. The three species that survived had to adapt to this new environment.

Different roads lead to different woods

The dawn redwood was thought to be extinct up until its "discovery" in 1944. You must travel to remote valleys in China to see this redwood, the smallest of the three species. Dawn redwoods grow to about 70 feet and are only a few feet in diameter. These redwoods grow well in a colder climate.

A different road leads to the Sierra redwood, also known as the giant sequoia. This species is found on the western side of the Sierra Nevada, the "snowy range" that lies mostly in eastern California. Sierra redwoods have adapted to the snow and freezing temperatures of the area. They are not the tallest variety of redwoods, but they have the largest trunk size. They are the most massive living organism known. The largest is located in Sequoia National Park, in the southern

Photo courtesy National Park Service

Sierra Nevada. Can you imagine a tree 275 feet tall and 26.5 feet in diameter? Can you believe that it may reach 2,500 years of age? This mighty tree goes by the name of General Sherman. In the park are several sequoias that are named after United States presidents.

The road to the third species of redwood stretches along a 450-mile coastal strip from southern Oregon to south of Monterey, California. Here you find the tallest trees in the world, the coast redwoods. They have adapted to a climate of heavy fog, which helps to protect them in the dry summers and cold winters.

The tallest living coast redwood is 367 feet 5 inches. That's taller than a 30-story building—and, in fact, taller than the Statue of Liberty, which is 305 feet from the ground to the tip of the torch. This mighty redwood goes by the name Mendocino. It is growing in one of the remotest parts of California's Montgomery Woods State Reserve, in the heart of the Coast Range. Its age is estimated at between 600-800 years. Its diameter has been measured at 10 feet 4 inches, which is wider than the average car.

Forests and redwoods as resources

Less than 200 years ago, the redwood forest spread over nearly 2 million acres. While all but 100,000 of those acres are still covered in redwood forest today, only about 68,000 remain that have never been logged.

What are the pressures on this great natural resource? First, lumber was in demand as more settlers made their way to

Northern California in the 1840s and '50s. The Gold Rush increased that demand. The logging industry, settlers, and individuals began cutting down forests. This lumber was used for buildings, railroad ties, barns, and fences. Large sections of forest were removed in a process called clear-cutting, in which a large portion of the trees were removed at one time. Early clear-cutting methods sometimes damaged the ecosystems. Efforts continue today to balance the social, economic, and environmental concerns to conserve this natural resource. Organizations such as Save-the-Redwoods League buy land and donate it to government park services.

Saving the redwoods

In 1902, in the Santa Cruz Mountains south of San Francisco, Big Basin Redwoods State Park was established. California's oldest state park is home to the largest stand of coast redwoods south of San Francisco. The original park started with 3,800 acres of protected redwoods. Today, the park covers 18,000 acres.

State park employees perform many important duties. For example, visitors to Big Basin may cross paths with Park Ranger Gary Brennan. His responsibilities include law enforcement, visitor information, and protection of the park. He patrols roads blanketed in the same fog that reaches across the forest and protects and preserves the magnificent and mighty redwoods.

Park Ranger Gary Brennan

Questions:

1. Why do scientists think there are so few redwood species alive today?
2. What are the names of the three species of redwoods that are alive today?
3. Write a couple of sentences about why you think redwood forests are a "great natural resource."

Conserving Resources

There are two types of natural resources, nonrenewable and renewable. A nonrenewable natural resource cannot be replaced, and a renewable natural resource is in constant supply. You have studied these different types of natural resources in this chapter. Nonrenewable natural resources are often used more than renewable natural resources, despite the fact that they will eventually run out.

In this activity you will form an action plan for one type of natural resource used in your school. First, identify the different ways natural resources are used in your school. Then, choose to study the use of one of these resources. Finally, you and your peers will devise an action plan to decrease the waste, and conserve more of this natural resource!

What you will do

1. In your group list all of the ways natural resources are used in your school.
2. Now, choose to analyze the use of one of these natural resources in your school. Check your choice with your teacher, so all of the groups are not doing the same thing.
3. In your analysis you need to collect data. This may be in the form of a survey, interview, reading a meter, or some other way. It is important to not only record the amount of the resource that is used, but also how it is used. This way, when it comes time to design an action plan you will be able to analyze ways that resources have been wasted. For instance, if windows are left open often, energy is wasted and if students don't print paper double-sided, paper is wasted!
4. Design a way that your group will collect data, and record data. Again, check over your data collection and recording method with your teacher before continuing.
5. Once your data collection method has been approved, and you have designed an appropriate method of collection, collect your data. Divide the responsibilities for data collection.
6. After collecting data, write a report about your findings.
7. As a group, design an action plan and make a poster that explains the problem (overuse of natural resources) and the solution (action plan to conserve natural resources).

Applying your knowledge

a. What natural resource did your group decide to study?
b. Summarize your group's findings from collecting data.
c. After your action plan has been in effect for a month, write a paragraph explaining whether or not your message to conserve natural resources is working. If something does not seem to be working, decide on new strategies to communicate with people.

Chapter 14 Assessment

Vocabulary

Select the correct term to complete the sentences.

solar energy	nonrenewable resource	resource conservation
emissions	renewable resource	fossil fuels
natural resources	pollution	petroleum

Section 14.1

1. Another name for the natural resource called oil is _____.

2. Earth's _____ are features that benefit people — like air, fresh water, soil, minerals, trees, and petroleum.

Section 14.2

3. _____ are substances made from things that were once alive.

4. A _____ is a natural resource like uranium or coal that is not replaced as it is used.

5. The Sun's energy is often called _____.

6. A _____ is a natural resource like the Sun, wind, or trees that can be replaced in a relatively short period of time.

Section 14.3

7. Tiny particles and gases released into the air are called _____.

8. If you practice _____, you are protecting, preserving, and managing Earth's natural resources.

9. _____ is a change to the environment that is harmful to humans or other living things.

Concepts

Section 14.1

1. Generate a list of anything that can be considered a natural resource.

2. Look around you right now and name five objects that would not exist if there was no petroleum.

Section 14.2

3. Describe the three fossil fuels and where they can be found.

4. Sort the list of energy resources into *renewable* and *nonrenewable* resources.

   nuclear, natural gas, hydroelectric, solar, biomass, wind, oil, coal, geothermal

5. Refer to the chart "Evaluating resources used to produce electricity in the U.S." to answer the following questions:

   a. Name a resource that has a high chance of being used 50 years from now, has a medium level of cost, and a low impact on the environment.

   b. Is this source of energy being used to produce electricity in your state? Write down where you got your information from to answer this question.

   c. Study the chart and choose the resource that you think will be used to make the most electricity 50 years from now. Justify your answer with information from the chart.

6. Look at the "Comparing notes" illustration that shows a notebook comparison between current cars and future cars. Choose one of the following future cars. Research and find information on your chosen future car to write a notebook list like the one in the illustration.

   Future cars to choose from: electric car, solar car, fuel cell car, biofuel car, hybrid car

Section 14.3

7. Why is air an important natural resource?

8. Describe two things *you* can do to help reduce air pollution.

9. How does water become polluted?

Math and Writing Skills

Section 14.1

1. Study the bar graph "Transportation energy use in the United States", found on the 14.1 section review page. Write a paragraph that tells in words what information this bar graph gives about daily life in the United States.

Section 14.2

2. Use the graph to answer the questions:

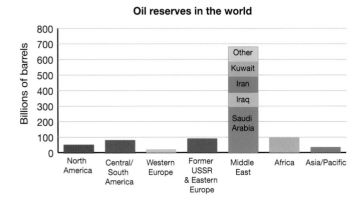

Oil reserves in the world

a. Which area of the world has the most oil in reserves? How many billions of barrels does this area have?
b. Which specific country has the most oil in reserves? How many billions of barrels does this country have?
c. Which area of the world has the least oil in reserves? How many billions of barrels does this area have?
d. What percentage of total world oil does North America have in reserves?
e. EXTENSION: Research the following question—what percentage of total world oil does North America use?

3. Use the graph to answer the questions:

a. What percent of total energy used in California is from oil and gas?
b. What type of energy is used least in California?
c. What is the total percent of nonrenewable energy use in California?
d. What is the total percent of renewable energy use in California?
e. Based on your analysis of the graph above, how successfully do you think California is conserving natural resources for energy use?

Percent of total energy used in California

Biomass, wind, solar 3%
Hydro 2%
Geothermal 4%
Nuclear 6%
Coal 7%
Oil and gas 78%

Section 14.3

4. Find out about recycling plastics in your community. Prepare a brochure that provides information on how to recycle plastics.

Chapter Project—Can You Conserve?

Keep a journal for 1 week of the different ways you use natural resources. Don't forget to include electricity use! Keep track of heat used, lights turned on, oven use, shower use, paper used, plastic bottles, etc. Give as much detail as you can about the amount of resources used and the time of day they are used.

After you have kept detailed notes for one week of how you use natural resources, identify two areas that you can practice better resource conservation. Create a poster of an action plan that shows how you will conserve these resources. Be creative and practical!

Chapter 15

Ecosystems

A California sea otter wakes up from a nap and unwraps itself from the large frond of kelp that was keeping it from floating away while sleeping. The playful sea otter dives to the ocean floor, looking for tasty sea urchins that are feeding on the kelp. After bringing a sea urchin to the surface, the sea otter floats on its back in the sunshine, opens the urchin by banging on it with a rock, and eats it. The ocean water, kelp, sea urchins, sea otter, sunshine— indeed, all of the living and nonliving things that interact in this coastal marine area— make up an *ecosystem*. What types of ecosystems are found where you live?

Key Questions

1. *What is an ecosystem?*

2. *What is a common way to show "who eats whom" in an ecosystem?*

3. *Why are ecosystems in a "delicate balance"?*

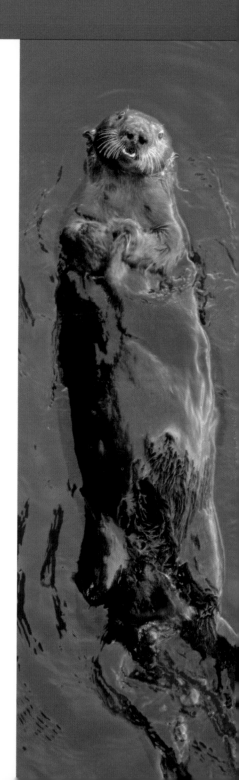

15.1 Ecosystems and Energy

Did anyone ever ask you the question: "Where do you get your energy?" Energy enters our world from the Sun—but how does the Sun's energy become your energy? Read this section to find out.

What is an ecosystem?

Organizing living things   Individual living things can be grouped into higher levels of organization. Living things of the same type are grouped into *populations*. Populations of different types of living things are grouped into *communities*. Different communities form *ecosystems*, which make up the *biosphere*.

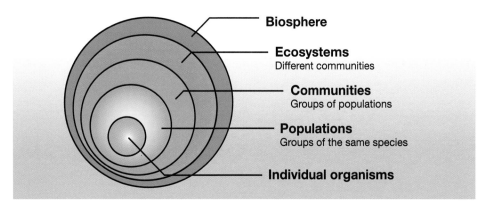

- **Biosphere**
- **Ecosystems**
  Different communities
- **Communities**
  Groups of populations
- **Populations**
  Groups of the same species
- **Individual organisms**

Ecosystems   A tropical rainforest is an example of an ecosystem. An **ecosystem** is made up of a group of living things and their physical surroundings. A tropical rainforest ecosystem is made up of the plants and animals that live there, plus nonliving things like soil, air, water, sunlight, and nutrients. The living and nonliving parts of an ecosystem work together like a team.

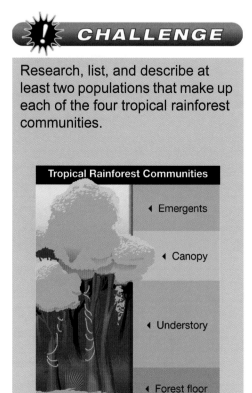

ⓐ **VOCABULARY**

ecosystem - a group of living things and their physical surroundings.

Photosynthesis and energy

Sunlight Sunlight is almost always the first type of energy to enter an ecosystem. How is energy from the Sun useful to an ecosystem? You may already know that some living things, like plants, are able to capture the energy from sunlight (Figure 15.1). When another living thing in an ecosystem eats a plant, it is gaining energy that came first from the Sun.

Photosynthesis **Photosynthesis** happens when a plant uses the Sun's energy to turn water and carbon dioxide into useful molecules such as sugars and starches. A company that bottles orange juice once advertised that there is a little sunshine in every bottle. There is some scientific truth to that advertisement!

VOCABULARY

photosynthesis - the process plants use to make food from sunlight, water, and carbon dioxide.

Figure 15.1: *Ferns can survive with very little sunlight. A cactus needs a lot of sunlight to grow.*

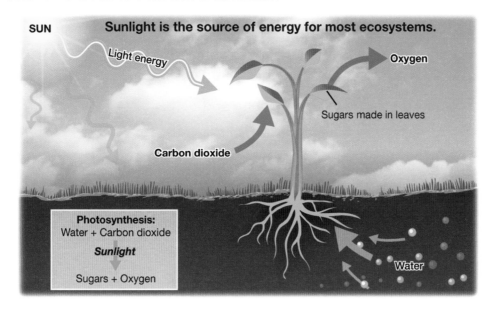

SUN

Sunlight is the source of energy for most ecosystems.

Light energy

Oxygen

Sugars made in leaves

Carbon dioxide

Photosynthesis:
Water + Carbon dioxide
Sunlight
Sugars + Oxygen

Water

Living parts of an ecosystem

Producers
Most ecosystems get their energy first from sunlight. A **producer** is a living thing, like a plant, that can take the Sun's energy and store it as food. Another word for "produce" is *make*. Producers make their own food. Kapok and banana trees are common producers in a tropical rainforest ecosystem.

Consumers
Other members of ecosystems cannot make their own food. A **consumer** must feed on other living things to get food and energy. Another word for "consume" is *eat*. Consumers eat other living things. A **herbivore** is a consumer that eats only plants. A **carnivore** is a consumer that eats only animals. A consumer that eats both plants and animals is called an **omnivore**. There are many consumers in a tropical rainforest ecosystem. Insects, caterpillars, and monkeys feed on the plants and trees. These herbivores are eaten by carnivores such as ocelots and pumas. What about you? Are you a herbivore, carnivore, or an omnivore?

Decomposers
Producers and consumers in an ecosystem create waste and both eventually die. If waste and dead organisms are not somehow broken down, the nutrients they contain would not become available for other living organisms in that ecosystem. The waste would pile up and potentially harm living things. Imagine what it would be like in your neighborhood if the trash was not taken away—you would not be able to stay there for very long without getting sick. A **decomposer** is a living thing that consumes waste and dead organisms to get energy. "Decompose" means to *break down*. Decomposers break down material from waste and dead organisms, and the molecules are returned to the ecosystem. Fungi and bacteria are decomposers in many ecosystems (Figure 15.2). Decomposers are important and can be called *nature's recyclers*.

VOCABULARY

producer - a living thing that can make its own food.

consumer - a living thing that eats other living things for food and energy.

herbivore - a consumer that eats only plants.

carnivore - a consumer that eats only animals.

omnivore - a consumer that eats both plants and animals.

decomposer - a living thing that breaks down waste and dead things.

Figure 15.2: *Mushrooms are fungi that help decompose fallen branches and leaves on the forest floor.*

Nonliving parts of an ecosystem

Water and sunlight

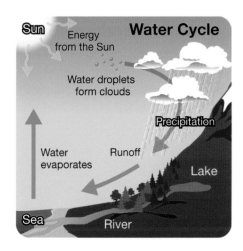

Living things need water and sunlight. The Sun is always there, but what about water? Water supply depends on the *water cycle*. Nature allows water to recycle so it can be used in many ecosystems. Look at the picture to the left. Where does the energy come from to make the water cycle work? That's right, the Sun is the source of energy.

Carbon and oxygen

Even though we can't see them, carbon and oxygen are important members of ecosystems. The Carbon-Oxygen cycle describes how the ecosystem uses these important elements. Carbon is present in both air and water as carbon dioxide gas. Oxygen is also a gas that is found in air and water. Producers take in carbon dioxide during the process of photosynthesis, and release oxygen. Consumers take in oxygen for their life processes and release carbon dioxide. When you breathe in, your body gets the oxygen it needs. When you breathe out, your body gets rid of carbon dioxide. This carbon dioxide is needed by producers in your ecosystem.

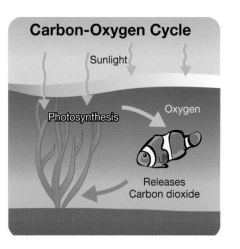

STUDY SKILLS

Understanding a cycle diagram

Refer to the water cycle diagram on this page to practice this study skill.

1. Place your finger on a part of the cycle. A cycle repeats over and over, so it does not matter where you begin.

2. Follow the arrows in the diagram while tracing your finger along the pathway.

3. Read each label and make sure you understand what happens during each step.

4. Refer to the diagram and write down a few sentences about what happens in the cycle from start to finish.

Living and nonliving parts of an ecosystem

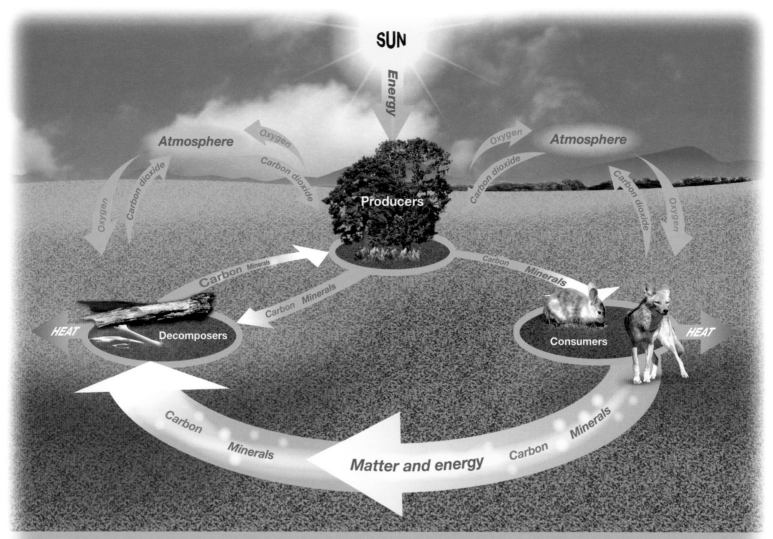

Living and nonliving parts of an ecosystem are linked together by recycling matter and energy.

15.1 Section Review

1. What is an ecosystem?

2. Use the terms *producer, consumer,* and *decomposer* to label each member of the meadow ecosystem: grass, grasshopper, frog, snake, hawk, and fungus.

3. What process changes light energy into chemical energy (energy that can be used by organisms other than producers) in an ecosystem?

4. How are matter and nutrients cycled back into the ecosystem from which they came?

5. A _____ is the type of organism that undergoes photosynthesis, converting energy into a usable form of food for other organisms in an ecosystem.

6. What form of energy is lost by moving from producer to consumer to decomposer in an ecosystem?

   a. light

   b. heat

   c. food energy

7. Research the term *chemosynthesis* on the Internet. After researching the term, explain what chemosynthesis is. Then provide an explanation for why the statement, "all living things require energy from the Sun" is ***not true***.

8. BONUS QUESTION: What is the name of the cactus pictured to the right?

The Sonoran Desert covers about 120,000 square miles in southwestern Arizona, southeastern California, and parts of Mexico. Divide your journal page into two columns labeled *Producers* and *Consumers*. Do some research and list five different common producers and consumers in the Sonoran Desert.

15.2 Food Chains and Food Webs

All living things need energy. Off the California coast, an ocean plant called kelp is eaten by sea urchins. Sea otters eat the sea urchins. In turn, a sea otter might be eaten by a shark. The sequence of "who eats whom" is called a food chain.

What is a food chain?

A simple food chain
A **food chain** shows how each member of an ecosystem gets its food. A simple food chain links a producer, an herbivore, and one or more carnivores (Figure 15.3). Arrows in the food chain show how energy is passed from one link to another.

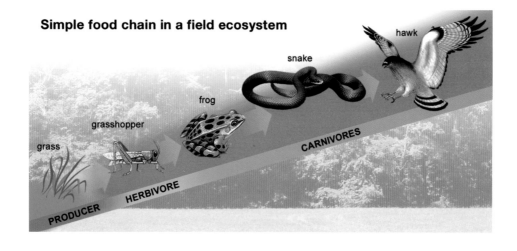

Producers are plentiful
What is the most plentiful member of a field ecosystem? You might answer "carnivores," since there are three examples of carnivores in the illustration above. However, grasses and other producers are much more plentiful than carnivores. This food chain shows how each member of the ecosystem gets its food. It is not meant to show how many of each type of organism there is in the ecosystem.

food chain - shows how each member of an ecosystem community gets its food.

Figure 15.3: *How would these members of a meadow ecosystem be linked in a food chain?*

Energy and food chains

Energy decreases as you move up in a food chain

There are more producers than herbivores or carnivores in an ecosystem community. When an herbivore eats a plant, only some of the plant's energy becomes part of the herbivore's body. The rest is lost as waste or heat. Also, when a carnivore eats another animal, only some of that energy becomes part of the carnivore's body. The amount of energy that gets passed along from the original producer becomes less and less as you move up a food chain.

Energy pyramid

A diagram in the shape of a pyramid is a good way to show how energy moves from one feeding level to the next in a food chain. Why is the pyramid a good shape for the diagram? Because a pyramid is wide at the base and narrow at the top. As you move up the pyramid from producer to consumer, the diagram gets smaller and smaller to show how less and less energy is available.

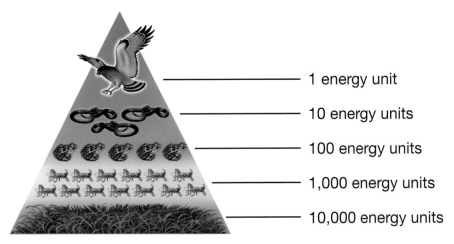

1 energy unit

10 energy units

100 energy units

1,000 energy units

10,000 energy units

An energy pyramid shows how many units of energy there are at each level of a food chain.

VOCABULARY

energy pyramid - diagram that shows how energy moves from one feeding level to the next in a food chain.

SOLVE IT!

There cannot be too many links in any food chain because the animals at the top of the energy pyramid would not get enough energy to stay alive.

1. Describe a pattern that you see in the pyramid's energy unit numbers.

2. How many times more energy units does the grass have than the grasshopper?

3. How many times more energy units does the frog have than the snake?

Food webs

What is a food web?

Most animals are part of more than one food chain. They eat more than one kind of food to get enough energy and nutrients. You can connect many food chains to form a food web. How many simple food chains are shown in the food web below?

VOCABULARY

food web - a group of overlapping food chains in an ecosystem.

MY JOURNAL

The food web members pictured on this page are: seaweed, worm, zooplankton (tiny floating animals that eat producers), snail, crab, sardine (small fish), striped bass (large fish), seal, and gull. Make a sketch of each simple food chain that makes up the web, and label each member with its common name.

15.2 Section Review

1. How is a food web different from a food chain?

2. Circle all of the terms that apply to the organisms in Figure 15.4:

   a. Field mouse: consumer, omnivore, herbivore, carnivore, producer, photosynthesizer, plant, animal

   b. Red fox: consumer, omnivore, herbivore, carnivore, producer, photosynthesizer, plant, animal

   c. Green plant: consumer, omnivore, herbivore, carnivore, producer, photosynthesizer, plant, animal

   d. Snake: consumer, omnivore, herbivore, carnivore, producer, photosynthesizer, plant, animal

3. Sketch the correct food chain for the organisms pictured in Figure 15.4. (Hint: foxes are known to eat reptiles!)

4. Name a marine animal that could be at the top of the marine food web pictured on the previous page, with arrows linking it to both the sea otter and striped bass.

5. Why is a pyramid a good shape for a diagram that shows how energy moves from one feeding level to the next in a food chain? Be sure your answer includes the word *energy*.

Figure 15.4: *Use this figure to answer questions 2 and 3.*

15.3 Ecosystems—A Delicate Balance

The ways that living things in a ecosystem relate to one another creates a natural balance. Most of the relationships in an ecosystem involve food. Other interactions are affected by human activity in positive and negative ways.

Interactions

Competition   Members of an ecosystem often compete for food. **Competition** happens when two or more species depend on the same food source or any limited resource. For example, on Sable Island off the coast of Nova Scotia, gray seals and harbor seals compete for the same food (Figure 15.5). Both types of seals feed on tiny fish called *sand lances*. Scientists have discovered that gray seals dig into the ocean floor to find the fish hiding there. Harbor seals follow schools of sand lances and eat fish that wander away from the school. The gray seals are thriving, but the harbor seal population has been decreasing. The gray seals seem to have a more successful feeding behavior, and they are winning the competition.

Predator-prey relationships   Sharks in Sable Island's offshore waters are known to eat seals. Animals that feed on other animals are called **predators**. In this example, the sharks are predators and the seals are **prey**. The sharks like to eat both kinds of seals, but harbor seals are smaller and easier to catch. Predator-prey relationships help keep a natural balance in an ecosystem.

Symbiosis   There are many cases where two different types of living things live closely together for long periods of time. This type of interaction is called **symbiosis**. In symbiosis, at least one member always benefits from the interaction. A remora is a small fish that follows sharks around and eats their scraps. The remora benefits from the shark, but the shark does not benefit from the remora.

competition - happens when members of an ecosystem depend on the same limited supply of food.

predators - animals that feed on other animals.

prey - animals that are killed for food by a predator.

symbiosis - an interaction where two species live together for a long time and at least one of the species benefits.

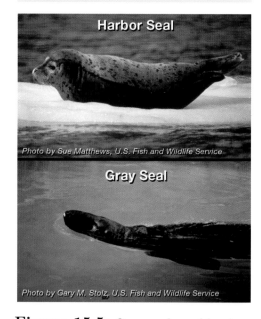

Figure 15.5: *Gray seals and harbor seals compete for the same food off the coast of Sable Island in Nova Scotia.*

Pollutants

What is a pollutant? Human activities affect ecosystems in both positive and negative ways. One negative effect is pollution. A **pollutant** is something that causes harm to a living thing. Three things often determine how harmful a pollutant is:

1. the pollutant's ability to cause harm
2. the amount of pollutant in the air, water, or soil
3. how long the pollutant stays in the air, water, or soil

Sulfur dioxide is a pollutant Sulfur dioxide is a chemical that is a good example of a pollutant (Figure 15.6). When sulfur dioxide is present in large amounts in the air, it can make breathing difficult even for healthy people. It also reacts with water in the atmosphere to make acid rain. Acid rain can kill trees and harm life in lakes, ponds, and streams. Sulfur dioxide enters the air from fossil fuel power plants, automobiles, and even volcanoes.

Mercury is a pollutant Mercury is an element that can be found naturally in an ecosystem. Human activities like industry also cause the release of mercury into the environment. It is taken in by members of an ecosystem and it builds up in their bodies. When the amount of mercury in a living organism gets high enough, the animal or plant can be harmed and may even die. Mercury is commonly found in fish. Because mercury is stored up in the fatty tissues of the fish over its entire lifetime, the level of the mercury in the fish may be thousands of times higher than the level of the mercury in the water (this is also known as biomagnification).

VOCABULARY

pollutant - a variable that causes harm to an organism.

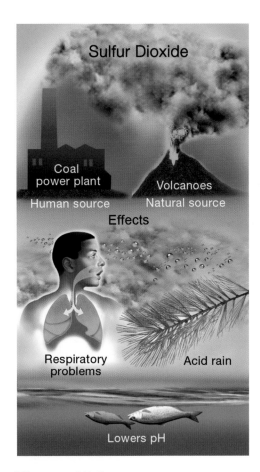

Figure 15.6: *Sulfur dioxide is a pollutant.*

Sea otters and the marine ecosystem

California sea otters

California sea otters are playful members of the California coastal marine ecosystem. They are listed under the federal Endangered Species Act, and they are called a "fully protected mammal" under California state law. What happened to cause the sea otters in California to become endangered? They were hunted by humans until the population became very small. Since 1977, the number of sea otters has been growing, but they are still considered a "threatened" species.

Keystone species

Sea otters are called a *keystone species*. This means that they are very important members of the marine ecosystem. The feeding habits of sea otters directly affect animals and plants that are lower in the food chain. Sea otters play an important role in maintaining the healthy balance of the kelp community. Kelp is a large sea plant that can form underwater forests (Figure 15.7).

The ecosystem balancing act

Sea otters are important to the health of a kelp forest because they eat sea urchins, abalone, and other shellfish that feed on the kelp. Without sea otters, the shellfish population would eat too much of the kelp and destroy the kelp forest. Why is the kelp forest important? It is home to many fish, shellfish, and other marine life. Can you see how an ecosystem and all of its members interact in a delicate, natural balancing act?

Figure 15.7: *An underwater kelp forest is home to many fish, shellfish, and other marine life.*

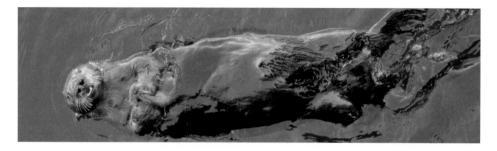

Water quality

Marine and freshwater ecosystems

Perhaps you live in a coastal region, where marine ecosystems are part of your everyday life. But even if you live far inland, you are part of another kind of aquatic environment—a freshwater ecosystem. We depend on fresh water for drinking, for staying clean, and for farming and industries. Humans can't live apart from a freshwater ecosystem!

Water quality testing

Because clean water is so important to our daily lives, we must protect the health of freshwater ecosystems. Governments and civic groups test the quality of surface water regularly (Figure 15.8).

Observing a body of water

To learn about the water quality of a pond, river, or lake, you would first make careful observations. You might ask, "What does the pond water look like or smell like? What animals and plants are living in the pond? Where is the pond located? Are there houses or farms nearby? Is the pond near a factory?" Common tests used to see if surface water is healthy are described below.

Temperature

The water temperature of a pond is measured three or more inches below the surface of the water. The higher the water temperature, the less dissolved oxygen there may be in the water. Dissolved oxygen is needed by most organisms living in the pond.

Turbidity test

The turbidity test measures the cloudiness of water. If the water is cloudy due to suspended sediment, sunlight is blocked, and pond plants do not grow well. This can be harmful, because pond plants are needed as food for other living things in the pond. A *secchi disk* provides an easy way to measure turbidity (Figure 15.9). The disk is lowered into the water until the black and white panels are no longer visible to a person looking into the water. The rope holding the disk is marked at meter and half-meter intervals to measure the depth of the disk when it disappears from view underwater.

Photo courtesy of U.S. Department of Agriculture - NRCS

Figure 15.8: *Testing water quality in a pond ecosystem.*

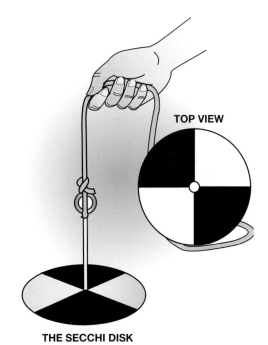

TOP VIEW

THE SECCHI DISK

Figure 15.9: *A Secchi disk.*

More water quality tests

Dissolved oxygen test

Oxygen enters fresh water from the air and the photosynthesis of aquatic plants and microscopic organisms called phytoplankton. Water quality is higher when dissolved oxygen levels are high. Water samples for a dissolved oxygen test should be taken away from the water's edge and about three inches below the surface.

Biological oxygen demand test

The biological oxygen demand test is a two-part test. Two water samples are taken at the same time. Dissolved oxygen is measured in the first sample right away. The second sample is shielded from light and measured at a later time. The amount of oxygen in the first and second samples is compared to find out how much oxygen was used by bacteria as they decompose organic material.

Nitrate and phosphate tests

Nitrates and phosphates are chemicals that can enter ponds that are near farms, fertilized lawns, or septic tanks. Excess nitrates or phosphates can cause large growths of algae, a type of rootless, stemless plant commonly found in ponds. Decomposers feed on the decaying algae and use up valuable oxygen. This endangers the health of the pond ecosystem.

pH test

The pH scale ranges from 0 to 14 (Figure 15.10). Pure water is pH 7 (neutral). Surface water ranges from about 6.5 to 8.5. Most organisms in an aquatic ecosystem function best when the water pH is about 7. Many life processes do not function well when pH is too high or low. For example, fish have trouble reproducing when the pH of their water environment is too low (acidic).

Summary

These water quality tests help make sure that the water we need stays clean and safe. When test results show that a body of water is unhealthy, government and civic groups can work together to find the causes and decide on a way to make the aquatic ecosystem healthy once again.

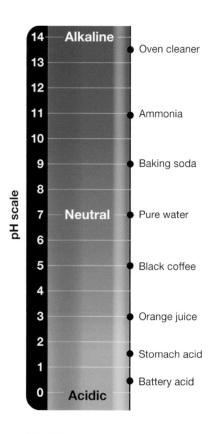

Figure 15.10: *The pH values of some common solutions. The pH of a solution is a measure of how acidic (pH 0 to 7) or basic (pH 7 to 14) it is.*

15.3 Section Review

1. Read each description of an ecosystem interaction and decide whether it is an example of *competition, predator-prey relationship,* or *symbiosis*.

   a. Sweet potato plants release chemicals that keep other nearby plants from growing.

   b. Tickbirds sit on a black rhinoceros and feed on the ticks that infest the thick skin of the rhino. The rhino benefits because it gets ticks removed from its body; the tickbirds benefit because they have a source of food.

   c. A hawk captures and eats a rabbit.

2. Name one type of air pollutant and one type of water pollutant. Why are these substances harmful to air and water?

3. Water quality is very important to the health of a pond. Complete the water quality test chart that has been started for you. Be sure to fill in all the blanks!

Water Quality Test	What it tests for	Results for a healthy pond
Temperature	How warm or cold the water is	Cold water has more oxygen available for living things than warm water
Turbidity	The cloudiness of the water	Clear water allows sunlight to get to the pond plants, which helps them grow
Dissolved oxygen		
Nitrates		
pH		

Black-Tailed Prairie Dog

The black-tailed prairie dog is a keystone species in a prairie ecosystem. Do some research to find at least three reasons why this animal is considered a keystone species.

BIOLOGY CONNECTION: A Forest in the Ocean

Have you ever taken a hike through a forest? You probably saw many, many trees, tall and short, and animals like birds, chipmunks, snakes, maybe even a deer or a fox. Now, have you ever swum through a forest? Fish do. Sea urchins do. Sea otters do, too. Indeed, the ocean has its own forests—kelp forests—much like forests on land.

Kelp forests are found all along the cool waters of the Pacific coast, as far north as Alaska and as far south as southernmost California. Kelp forests are also found along the shores of South America, southern Australia, and South Africa. In general, kelp grows in waters of about 50-60°F.

Kelp and its characteristics

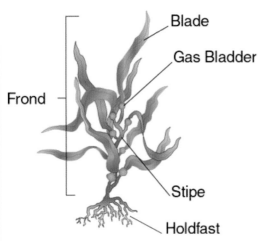

Kelp is a type of algae or seaweed that grows in cool, clear ocean water. The three main parts of a kelp plant are the holdfast, the stipe, and the blade. The holdfast looks like a root, but it does not gather nutrients like land-plant roots. Instead, it keeps the kelp plant in place by growing over rocks and wedging into cracks. The stipe is like a stem; nutrients are transported up and down it. This food transportation system allows kelp to grow larger than other types of algae. The blade is the flattened, leaf-like part of kelp. It is inside the blade that food is made. Here, cells absorb water and chemicals from the ocean and convert them into nutrients.

Giant kelp

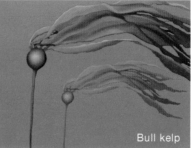
Bull kelp

The waters of the Monterey Bay National Marine Sanctuary off the coast of central California are ideal for kelp forests. The warm waters are pushed offshore by northwesterly winds, to be replaced by the cold, nutrient-rich waters streaming down from Alaska.

The two main types of kelp found in Monterey Bay are giant kelp and bull kelp. Giant kelp is brown with leathery blades, and may grow as large as 100 feet and live as long as seven years. The smaller, sturdy bull kelp has a single stalk with a crown of blades and lives no more than a year.

The kelp canopy

Imagine you are a fish swimming among swaying stalks of kelp nearly 100 feet high. Above you, rays of sunlight seep through the sea's surface. The kelp forest around you is wide and thick—this is called the forest canopy—and contains both giant and bull kelp. The canopy changes with the seasons. In central California's Monterey Bay area, the canopy is thickest in late summer and thins or disappears over the winter months. Other fish and marine life come and go around you. In spring, the kelp begins to grow again, rapidly. It can sometimes grow up to four inches a day.

A community of creatures

Kelp forests are home to hundreds of creatures. Sea anemones, sponges, and corals are found on the floor of the kelp forest. Fish swim and settle among the kelp's stipes and floating blades. Sea otters dive and roll at the surface of the forest, or

Kip Evans

dive to the kelp floor, where they may find treats like sea urchins, clams, crabs, and sea stars. Sometimes the otters wrap themselves in strands of kelp where they sleep. Sharks, rays, sea lions, and harbor seals also may spend time hunting for fish among the kelp.

Monterey Bay Aquarium

If one day you qualify for scuba diving, you may actually see a living kelp forest and its inhabitants below the ocean surface. Or if one day you travel to Monterey, the Monterey Bay Aquarium houses a kelp forest just like those in nature in the ocean. The huge exhibit tank is 28 feet tall, 66 feet wide, and holds 330,000 gallons of seawater. A constant supply of seawater is pumped into the tank from the bay. During the day, the water is filtered and clear so that

visitors can view the kelp and various sea creatures. At night, unfiltered ocean water full of food and nutrients streams into the tank. The exhibit is a living laboratory where researchers hope to learn more about the seasonal and chemical changes of the kelp forest community.

Questions:

1. What are the three main parts of a kelp plant and what are their functions?
2. Where are kelp forests found in the world?
3. How does the canopy of the Monterey Bay forest change with the seasons?
4. How is the kelp forest exhibit at the Monterey Bay Aquarium maintained, and what do researchers hope to learn from it?

 **Create a Species**

Each species that lives in an ecosystem has a unique way in which it interacts with its physical and biological environment, otherwise known as its *niche*. In order to fit into its niche, a species must have certain adaptations to help it survive. For example, a porcupine has sharp quills in order to ward off predators from attacking it. Other examples of adaptations are when species have camouflage to hide from predators or prey. Species do not have just one adaptation to fit into an ecosystem, rather they have several adaptations that allow the organism to find shelter, food, hide from predators, find a mate and many other things that enhance a species' chance of survival.

What you will do

1. Create a species that is perfectly adapted to its environment. This species should be made up.
2. Design an environment and the characteristics of the ecosystem where your species will live. Use the table at the right to guide you in designing your ecosystem.
3. Now, design your species. Include the adaptations that allow the species to live in its environment successfully. List the adaptations in the bottom rows of the table.
4. Draw your species.
5. Name your species and label it on your drawing. Now take a look at the species that your classmates designed, and see the variety of ideas that other students came up with.

Applying your knowledge

a. Why will each of the adaptations you designed for your species help it better survive in its environment.
b. Think of two adaptations that humans have that better allow them to survive in their environment. Name and describe these 2 adaptations below.

Ecosystem feature	What is your ecosystem like?
Climate • average temperature of the time of year • precipitation details • altitude, latitude • proximity to water (fresh or salt water)	
Vegetation • amount • color - can be unrealistic! • height • plant type: flower, tree, cactus etc. • leaf type: needles. etc	
Food source • Type of food in environment species may eat • How does it get its food? • Omnivore, herbivore, or a carnivore?	
Predators • What are the predators in the ecosystem that he/she must hide from? • Are there predators? • How many predators?	
Feature species must adapt to	**Characteristic of organism to adapt to features you designed above**
Climate	
Vegetation	
Food source	
Predators	

Chapter 15 Assessment

Vocabulary

Select the correct term to complete the sentences.

producer	photosynthesis	food web
competition	consumer	energy pyramid
decomposer	predator	carnivore
omnivore	herbivore	symbiosis
ecosystem	prey	pollutant
food chain		

Section 15.1

1. A _____ is a living thing that can take the Sun's energy and store it as food.

2. A consumer that eats only animals is called a _____.

3. A(n) _____ is made up of a group of living things and their physical surroundings.

4. A consumer that eats both plants and animals is called a(n) _____.

5. A _____ is a living thing that consumes wastes and dead things to get energy.

6. _____ happens when a plant uses the Sun's energy to turn water and carbon dioxide into useful molecules such as sugars and starches.

7. A _____ must feed on other living things to get food and energy.

8. A _____ is a consumer that eats only plants.

Section 15.2

9. Another way to represent a food chain is through a(n) _____, which shows how energy is lost as you move through the levels.

10. An ecosystem often has several food chains that overlap, which is called a _____.

11. A(n) _____ shows how each member of an ecosystem community gets its food.

Section 15.3

12. A hawk captures and eats a mouse. In this case, the hawk would be called a _____ and the mouse is its _____.

13. _____ is an interaction where two species live together for a long time and at least one of them benefits.

14. _____ happens when members of an ecosystem depend on the same limited supply of food.

15. Sulfur dioxide is a chemical that is a good example of a _____, because when it is present in the air in large amounts, it can make breathing difficult.

Concepts

Section 15.1

1. Arrange this list of organization levels so it goes from the largest category to the smallest category.

    population, community, biosphere, ecosystem, individual organisms

2. Which of the following would be considered an ecosystem? (You may choose more than one.)

    a. tropical rainforest
    b. school gymnasium
    c. desert
    d. Sun
    e. rotting log and surroundings
    f. bean plant
    g. rock

Section 15.2

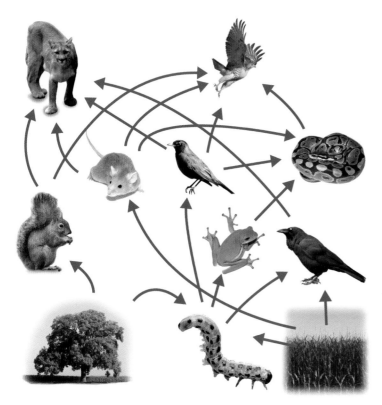

3. In the food web above, name the 2 producers, the 3 herbivores, the 4 carnivores, and the 2 omnivores.

4. Find a food chain within the food web above that has 5 levels. Diagram the food chain.

5. Why is photosynthesis such an important process in an ecosystem? (hint: what would happen to an ecosystem like the one pictured above if there were no producers?)

Section 15.3

6. In the food web above, is the interaction between the snake and the mouse called competition, predator/prey, or symbiosis?

Math and Writing Skills

Section 15.1

1. Study the diagram called "Living and nonliving parts of an ecosystem" in section 15.1. Write a paragraph that describes what this diagram tells you about matter and energy in an ecosystem. Be specific!

Section 15.2

2. Review the energy pyramid pictured in section 15.2. Why is the hawk at the top of the pyramid, and the grass and grasshoppers are at the bottom? Use the word energy in your answer.

Section 15.3

3. Study the table below. Name the lake that has poor water quality and explain the reason for your answer.

Water Quality Test Results

Lake	pH	nitrate level	dissolved oxygen
Citizen Lake	7.5	low	high
Lake Armstrong	4.5	high	low

Chapter Project—Ecosystem Research

Choose one of the following ecosytems. Research which plants and animals live in that ecosystem. Construct a food chain that has at least five levels. Find a photo or draw a picture of each member of the food chain, and show how the members are connected. Be creative! Display your food chain on a large poster, in a diorama, or a mobile. Ecosystems to choose from: desert, tropical rainforest, prairie, or alpine.

Chapter 16
Biomes

In Chapter 6, you learned about seasons, wind, ocean currents, and weather patterns. All of these elements work together to produce different climates in different parts of the world. In this chapter, you will learn about climates and climate regions called *biomes*. Earth has six main biomes that have particular plants and animals. These biomes are deserts, grasslands, temperate deciduous forests, rainforests, taiga, and tundras. In which biome do you live? What types of plants and animals live where you live?

Key Questions

1. *How do plants and animals survive in the desert?*

2. *In which biome would you find a moose?*

3. *What is your biome like?*

16.1 Climates and Biomes

Imagine someone gave you an airplane ticket to travel to Africa to see Serengeti National Park in Tanzania. If you like adventures, you might say "Great! When do I leave?" Then, you would want to pack your suitcase. But, what would you take? What is the climate like in Africa?

Climate

Factors that affect climate
You learned about climates in Chapter 6. A *climate* is defined as the type of weather patterns that a place has, on average, over a long period time. If you wanted to know about the climate in a place you were about to visit, you might ask questions like "How hot and how cold does it usually get? Does it rain a lot? How often is the temperature below freezing?" Climate depends on many factors, including latitude, precipitation, elevation, topography, and distance from large bodies of water.

Weather patterns
Weather is a term that describes the condition of the atmosphere in terms of temperature, wind, and atmospheric pressure. Changes in these conditions cause *weather patterns*. The Sun is the major source of energy for weather and weather patterns.

The entire Serengeti region which is in Tanzania and Kenya is home to thousands of predator species and about 1.6 million herbivores. The Serengeti has elephants, gazelles, zebras, and buffalos.

MY JOURNAL

Packing for an adventure in the Serengeti

1. On a world atlas, find the Serengeti. Describe where it is located.

2. Make a prediction about the kind of weather the Serengeti will have next week.

3. Then, research the seasonal weather in this area on the Internet or in the library. Were you correct in your prediction?

4. Using what you learned, make a list of things you would need to pack in your suitcase to visit the Serengeti.

Characteristics of biomes

What is a biome? Scientists divide the planet into climate regions called **biomes**. Earth has six main biomes: deserts, grasslands, temperate deciduous forests, rainforests, taiga, and tundras. These biomes generally differ in their latitude, weather and relative humidity, amount of sunlight, and topography. Each biome has a unique set of plants and animals that thrive in its climate.

Latitude and humidity *Relative humidity* is a measure of how much water vapor an air mass contains (see full definition in Chapter 6). Humidity is related to plant and animal diversity. From the poles to the equator, humidity and the diversity of plants and animals increases.

Sunlight at the equator vs high latitudes Earth is hottest near the equator where the Sun is closest to being directly overhead year round. At the north and south poles, temperatures are much colder. This effect is related to the fact that light travels in straight parallel lines. To demonstrate what is happening, imagine shining a flashlight on a sheet of paper (Figure 16.1). The light makes a bright, small spot. By tilting the paper, you can make the light spot bigger and less intense.

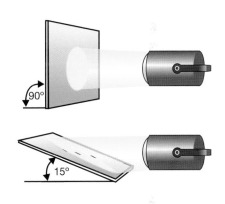

Figure 16.1: *A flashlight shining on a piece of paper represents solar radiation reaching Earth. If you tilt the paper, the spot of light spreads out and becomes less intense.*

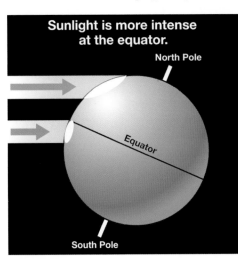

At the equator, sunlight is direct and intense. Earth's north and south poles are tilted away from or toward the Sun depending on the time of year (review Chapter 6). The locations of the poles relative to the Sun and Earth's spherical surface mean that sunlight reaching these areas is spread out and less intense. As a result, the average yearly temperature at the equator is 27 °C (80 °F), while at the North Pole it is -18 °C (0 °F). Generally, as latitude (or distance from the equator) increases, the amount of incoming solar radiation decreases.

Other factors besides latitude can affect climates

Temperatures in inland regions

Have you ever wondered why cities near the ocean don't get as hot in the summer or as cold in the winter as inland cities at the same latitude? Portland, Oregon, and Minneapolis, Minnesota, are two cities near the same latitude (Figure 16.2). Look at Table 16.1 below to see how the average daily temperature ranges for these cities compare.

Table 16.1: Average daily temperature ranges for Portland and Minneapolis.

| Month | Average daily temperature range | |
	Portland	Minneapolis
January	1 – 7 °C, (34 – 45 °F)	-16 – -6 °C (3 – 21 °F)
July	14 – 27 °C (57 – 80 °F)	17 – 29 °C (63 – 84 °F)

Water helps regulate temperature

The differences in temperature between the two cities have to do with water, which is an effective moderator of temperature. Water warms up and cools down slowly. Land warms up and cools down quickly. Therefore, regions near water—like Portland—do not have extremely hot or cold weather. Similarly, wet areas like marshes and swamps don't experience the temperature extremes found in desert regions.

Latitude versus altitude

Latitude is an important factor in defining a biome. However, *altitude* is also a factor. The range of biomes that exist on Earth from the equator to the poles also exists if one goes from the bottom of a mountain to the top of a mountain (Figure 16.3).

Hotter in the summer and colder in the winter than Portland.

Portland

Minneapolis

Figure 16.2: *Portland and Minneapolis are near the same latitude.*

SOLVE IT!

Questions about Table 16.1:

1. It is January 3rd and -10 °C outside. Where am I?

2. It is July 4th and 20 °C. Can you figure out from the table where I am? Why or why not?

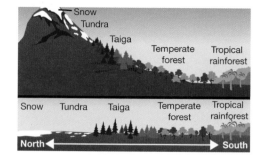

Figure 16.3: *Latitude versus altitude for the Northern Hemisphere.*

Earth's biomes

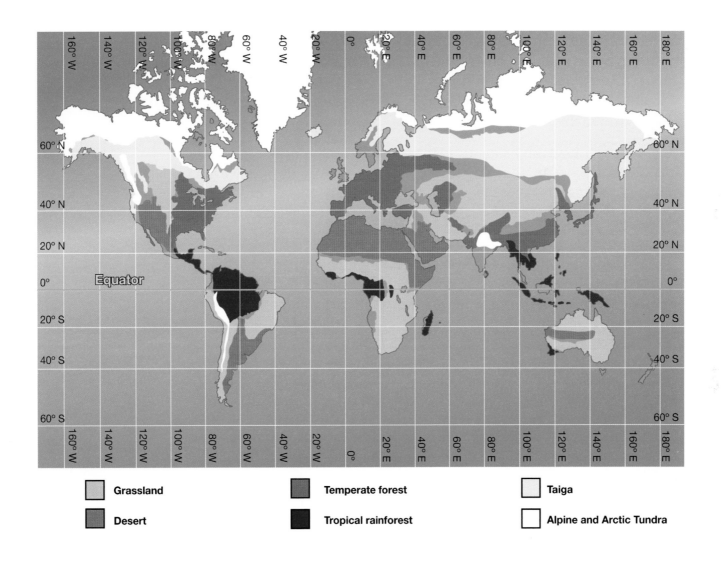

Grassland

Desert

Temperate forest

Tropical rainforest

Taiga

Alpine and Arctic Tundra

Plants and animals in biomes

Jackrabbit

Photo by George Harrison, USFWS

Communities A biome is characterized by its plant and animal communities. The plants and animals in a community interact with each other and survive in a shared environment. The plants and animals in the environment have adaptations that allow them to obtain enough resources (such as food, water, or sunlight) to survive in the environment.

Adaptations For example, how might an animal survive in a hot desert? Jackrabbits have an adaptation to keep cool—enormous ears with many blood vessels near the surface (Figure 16.4). Blood running through the vessels speeds up heat transfer from the jackrabbit's body to the air so it stays cooler.

Figure 16.4: *The large ears of a jackrabbit help this desert animal to cool down.*

Ecosystems Biomes are large geographic areas. Within a biome, there are many interrelated ecosystems. An *ecosystem* is made up of the plants and animals that live there, plus nonliving things like soil, air, water, sunlight, and nutrients. The living and nonliving parts of an ecosystem work together, and each organism plays an important ecological role. On a baseball team, for example, important roles include coach, pitcher, catcher, outfielders, and infielders. Similarly, organisms play roles in their ecosystem.

MY JOURNAL

Biodiversity

Answer the following questions.

1. What does the term *diversity* mean?

2. What does the term *biodiversity* mean?

3. Does this statement surprise you? Why or why not?

The biodiversity of the desert is greater than for other biomes with the exception of the tropical rainforest.

4. Why is biodiversity in an ecosystem important?

How many roles? The number and types of organisms that an ecosystem can support depends on the resources available (food sources) and on environmental factors, such as the amount of available sunlight, water, and the temperature. For plants, another important factor is soil composition. The roles within a biome ecosystem depend on the quantity and type of resources. Each ecosystem of a particular biome type has organisms that play similar roles. For example, both a rainforest in South America and a rainforest in Australia have predators, herbivores, and decomposers suited to surviving in the rainforest environment.

16.1 Section Review

1. What is the main source of energy for weather?

2. Are climate and weather the same thing? If not, explain how these terms are different. (Hint: For more information, review Chapter 6.)

3. Write your own definitions of the terms *ecosystem* and *biome*. What is the difference between these terms?

4. The latitude and relative humidity of a region are used to define a biome. Why is humidity an important factor?

5. What happens to the intensity of solar radiation and Earth's average yearly temperature as you move from the equator to the South Pole or North Pole?

6. A jackrabbit has large ears that help it cool down in its desert biome.

   a. Would this adaptation (the large ears) be a useful adaptation to have in a cold weather environment? Why or why not?

   b. Make a prediction: What kinds of adaptations might be useful for a rabbit to have if it lives in Alaska (tundra biome)?

7. A photograph of an Arctic hare is shown in Figure 16.5. This animal lives in cold environments.

   a. What adaptations do you see that this animal has?

   b. How does the appearance of this animal compare to the jackrabbit in Figure 16.4?

8. The main grass in a grassland in North America is prairie grass. The main grass in a South American grassland is pampas grass. Would you expect the ecological role of these grasses in these two locations to be the same or different? Explain your answer.

What's your climate?

1. From the reading, list the factors that affect the climate of an area.

2. Use these factors to describe the climate where you live.

Arctic hare

Photo courtesy of U.S. Fish and Wildlife Service

Figure 16.5: *An Arctic hare.*

16.2 Deserts and Grasslands

In this section, you will learn about two interesting biomes, deserts and grasslands.

Deserts

Desert regions A **desert** is a climate region that averages less than 35 centimeters of rainfall per year. Most deserts are found between the latitudes of 30° N and 30° S. Because of the lack of cloud cover, deserts receive more than twice as much incoming solar radiation as humid regions. They also emit almost twice as much radiation at night. As a result, deserts have large variations in daily high and low temperatures.

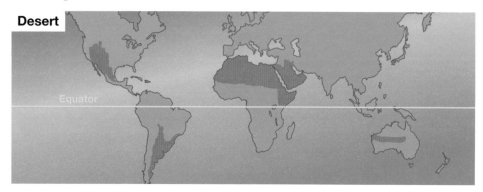

Sahara desert

Australian desert

How deserts form You may wonder why there is so little rain in the desert. The answer depends on which desert you are talking about. The Sahara and Australian deserts are caused by regions of high atmospheric pressure found near 30° latitude lines (Figure 16.6). High pressure prevents air near the ground from rising and cooling. As a result, not much condensation takes place. When the condensation rate is lower than the evaporation rate, skies are usually clear and very little precipitation falls.

Figure 16.6: *The Sahara and Australian deserts are caused by regions of high atmospheric pressure found near 30° latitude lines.*

Rainshadow deserts
Other deserts, such as one found in eastern Washington state, are caused by the "rainshadow effect." Prevailing westerly winds blow moisture-filled air from the Pacific Ocean over the Washington coast. This air rises as it travels up the western slope of the Cascade mountain range and cools, causing condensation and lots of rain. By the time the air blows over the mountains to the eastern side, there is very little moisture left (Figure 16.7). Olympia, Washington, on the western side of the Cascades, receives an average of 201 centimeters of rain per year. This region has fertile, nutrient-rich land for growing trees. Yakima, on the eastern side, receives only 32 centimeters of rain per year and is a "rainshadow desert" (Figure 16.8).

Fog deserts
A third type of desert is known as a "fog desert." Fog deserts are found on the west coasts of continents located between 20° and 30° latitude. Here the prevailing winds are easterly, so moisture-filled air does not blow in from the ocean. Cold water currents run along many of these coastlines. The cold water causes air to condense as fog over the ocean. The fog drifting over land causes a small amount of precipitation (rain). Fog deserts included the Baja desert of California and the Atacama desert in South America.

Desert life
It might seem that few plants and animals could survive harsh desert conditions, but actually many different kinds of organisms have adapted to desert life. In fact, only the tropical rainforest biome contains a greater number of plant and animal species than the desert biome.

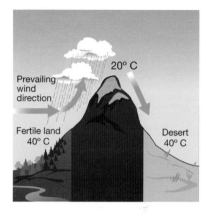

Figure 16.7: *This graphic illustrates how the rainshadow effect works.*

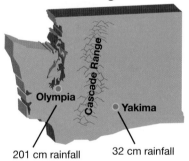

Figure 16.8: *Due to the rainshadow effect Olympia, Washington receives an average of 201 centimeters of rain per year. Yakima receives only 32 centimeters of rainfall each year.*

Atacama Desert, South America
A fog desert

Grasslands

Grasslands are found on every continent except Antarctica. There are two types of grasslands: tropical grasslands, known as *savannas*, and *temperate grasslands*.

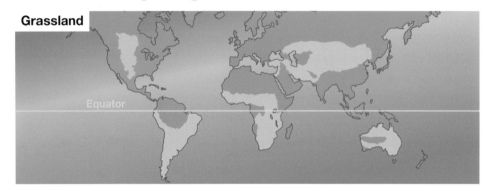

Grassland

Equator

Savannas   Savannas are found in parts of the tropics where there is not enough rainfall throughout the year to create a rainforest. Savannas are characterized by two seasons: rainy and dry. During the rainy season, which lasts for six to eight months, 50 to 127 centimeters of rain falls. This season is followed by a drought, which in many areas culminates with wildfires. The fires and the poor soil conditions prevent the growth of most trees. In fact, in some areas, trees grow only on termite mounds (Figure 16.9). The isolated trees found in savannas have cork-like bark or an outer coating that can withstand some fire damage.

A termite mound

Figure 16.9: *In savannas, trees sometimes grow in the soil of termite mounds.*

Adaptations to survive fires   Many large mammals of the savanna, including the wildebeest pictured at the right, have long legs that enable them to outrun fires. Smaller mammals burrow under the ground and stay there until the fire has passed over them. Most birds fly away from the fire, but several species, including the Fork-tailed Drongos, actually fly toward the fires so that they can feast on the hordes of insects trying to escape the heat.

Wildebeest

Temperate grasslands

Temperate grasslands grow in the middle latitude regions and receive most of their precipitation in late spring and early summer. Most temperate grasslands are found in the interior of continents, far from large bodies of water. The average yearly rainfall is between 51 and 89 centimeters. Summer temperatures can reach over 38 °C, while in the winter they can plummet below -40 °C. The soil is rich in nutrients, and much of this biome has been cleared for farmland. Trees are uncommon except along river valleys.

Grasslands have many names

Around the world, grasslands go by different names (Figure 16.10). In central Asia a grassland is called a *steppe*. A grassland is called a *savanna* or *veld* in southern Africa. In North America, a grassland is called a *prairie*. In South America, it is called a *pampa*. And in Australia, a grassland is called an *outback*.

Location	Name used for grasslands
Central Asia	steppe
Southern Africa	savanna or veld
North America	prairie
South America	pampa
Australia	outback

Figure 16.10: *Grasslands have different names in different parts of the world.*

Temperate grasslands

Prairie   Savanna   Steppe

Photo courtesy National Park Service

Photo courtesy of U.S. Geological Survey

16.2 Section Review

1. What is the maximum amount of average annual rainfall an area can have before it is no longer considered a desert biome?

2. What causes a desert to form?

3. In certain places you can be on one side of a mountain in a lush forest, but if you go to the other side of the mountain you are in a desert. What is this phenomenon called and what causes it?

4. What are the two types of grasslands? Describe both.

5. The graphs in Figure 16.11 show the average monthly precipitation for three areas throughout a year. Which graph most likely represents a desert biome? Explain your answer.

6. Few trees live on savannas. Explain why and explain how termites help trees survive in this biome.

7. Identify which biome characteristics below apply to deserts and which apply to grasslands.

   a. Found on every continent besides Antarctica

   b. Receive more than twice as much incoming solar radiation as more humid regions

   c. Very hot during the day and very cool at night

   d. Mostly found between 30° north and 30° south latitude

   e. Has a rainy season and a dry season

   f. Another word for this biome is a prairie, plain, or savanna

   g. Wildfire is one of the main ecological concerns of this biome

8. Challenge question: Savannas are extremely prone to wildfires. However, animals can still survive there. Research a mammal (other than a wildebeest) that lives in a savanna and propose an explanation of how it can survive there. Use your classroom and library resources to help you.

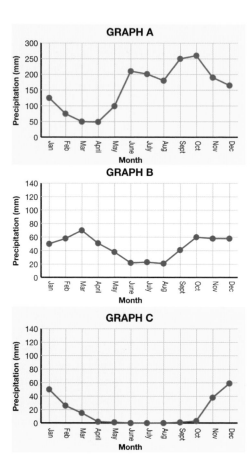

Figure 16.11: *Use these graphs to answer question 5.*

16.3 Temperate Forests and Rainforests

In this section, you will learn about two more biomes, temperate forests and rainforests.

Temperate deciduous forests

A biome with seasons

Temperate deciduous forests are found in middle-latitude regions, where there are four distinct seasons. The winter temperatures in some places dip as low as -30 °C, and in the summer they can be as warm as 30 °C. There are between four and six frost-free months each year. Average yearly rainfall is 75 to 150 centimeters, enough to support the growth of broad-leafed, deciduous trees like oak, beech, maple, basswood, cottonwood, and willow. The word *deciduous* means these trees lose their leaves the end of the growing season (Figure 16.12).

VOCABULARY

temperate deciduous forests - climate regions in the mid-latitudes that have four seasons.

Broad-leafed trees

Spring (beginning of growing season)

Fall (end of growing season)

Figure 16.12: *Broad-leafed deciduous trees lose their leaves in the fall, the end of the growing season.*

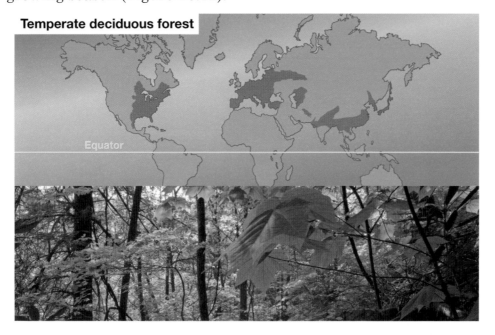

Temperate deciduous forest

Equator

Tropical rainforests

Tropical rainforests   **Tropical rainforests** are found near the equator—between the latitudes of 23.5° N and 23.5° S. They have an average rainfall of at least 200 centimeters per year. This large amount of precipitation occurs in the area where the northern and southern hemisphere trade winds meet. The intense Sun and warm ocean water cause this converging air to rise. As the air rises, it cools, condensing into clouds and rain. This cycle happens over and over, causing a period of thundershowers in the warmest part of the afternoon almost every day. Because the tropical rainforests are near the equator, the temperature varies little year round, averaging about 20 to 25 °C.

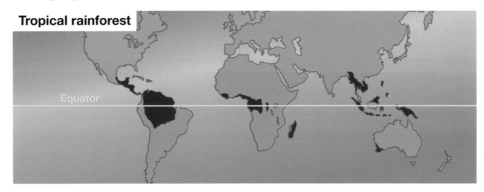

Rainforest life   Although tropical rainforests cover less than 6 percent of Earth's land, these biomes have extremely high biodiversity. Half of all of the animal and plant species in the world are found there. There can be as many as 100 different species of plants per hectare (2.47 acres). The most abundant type of plants are tall trees that form a dense canopy. Many foods we enjoy, including Brazil nuts, bananas, pineapple, cocoa, coffee, vanilla and cinnamon flavorings, and coconut originate in tropical rainforests (Figure 16.13).

Figure 16.13: *Many foods we enjoy, including Brazil nuts, bananas, pineapple, cocoa, coffee, vanilla and cinnamon flavorings, and coconut originate in tropical rainforests.*

Tropical rainforest

Figure 16.14: *Recall from Chapter 6 that "greenhouse gases" describe certain gases in Earth's atmosphere. Like the glass in a greenhouse, greenhouse gases can slow down Earth's natural heat-loss processes. These gases are useful because they keep Earth warm.*

Trees and global climate

According to NASA data, an area of tropical rainforest the size of North Carolina is destroyed every year. Land is cleared for crops, grazing, lumber, or firewood. When clear-cutting occurs in this type of biome, the thin topsoil soon washes away, exposing thick clay that is almost useless for agriculture. This clay absorbs the Sun's energy and then emits infrared radiation, which is absorbed by greenhouse gases. This process warms the atmosphere.

Trees prevent some of this warming. Leaves appear green because they reflect green visible light. Light at this wavelength is not as readily absorbed by greenhouse gases as infrared radiation (Figure 16.14). In a forested area, more of the Sun's energy is reflected directly back to space without first being absorbed by greenhouse gases. In this way, trees keep Earth cooler.

Temperate rainforests

Like temperate deciduous forests, temperate rainforests are found in the middle-latitude regions (Figure 16.15). For example, temperate rainforests are found in coastal areas of the Pacific Northwest. Because these rainforests are in temperate areas, they may have temperate deciduous forest plants like oak trees. Like a tropical rainforest though, temperate rainforests experience a lot of rain (about 250 centimeters per year). Temperate rainforests are cool and periodically covered in fog which provides more moisture for the plants.

Temperate rainforest
Photo courtesy National Park Service

Figure 16.15: *Temperate rainforests are found in the middle-latitude regions.*

16.3 Section Review

1. How many seasons do temperate regions have? What are they?

2. The term *deciduous* describes broad-leafed trees.

   a. What does this term mean?

   b. Why might deciduous trees be suited for a biome with seasons?

3. Figure 16.16 shows three graphs, each with the average monthly precipitation for a given area throughout the year. Which graph most likely represents a temperate deciduous forest biome? Explain why you chose the graph you did.

4. Fill in the blanks to make this description of a tropical rainforest accurate.
   Tropical rainforests cover less than _____% of Earth's land, but _____ of all animal and plant species are found there.

5. How are temperate rainforests and tropical rainforests similar? How are they different?

6. How do tropical rainforests keep our planet cooler?

7. Describe one way that you benefit from tropical rainforests.

8. Research Question: Rainforests in Australia can be compared to rainforests in South America in terms of climate and the variety of animals that live there. The Australian rainforest has kangaroos, wallabies, and bandicoots. The South American rainforest has sloths, deer, monkeys, rodents, and wild, large cats. Research the ecological roles of these and other animals in this biome. Perform your research using your school library resources, the Internet, videos, or CD-ROMs that describe biomes.

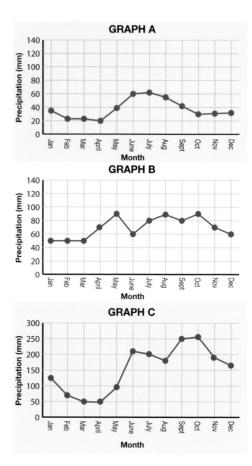

Figure 16.16: *Use these graphs to answer question 3.*

16.4 Taigas and Tundras

In this section, you will learn about the largest and coldest biomes on Earth. The taiga is the largest land biome and the tundra is the coldest.

The taiga

The largest land biome

The **taiga**, otherwise known as a boreal or coniferous forest, is the largest land biome. The taiga can be found between the latitudes of 50° and 70° N in North America and Eurasia, including Canada and Russia. The average temperature in the taiga is below freezing for at least six months of the year. This makes it difficult for animals to stay year-round. Some do stay put, some hibernate, and some migrate (Figure 16.17). Annual precipitation averages 40 to 100 centimeters. Much of this falls during the short growing season (approximately 130 days). Summer temperatures rarely reach above 21°C.

taiga - the largest climate region, found in the higher latitudes; also known as a boreal or coniferous forest.

Lynx
Photo by Erwin and Peggy Bauer, USFWS

Moose
Photo courtesy U.S. Fish and Wildlife Service

Pine Grosbeak
Photo by James C. Leupold, USFWS

Figure 16.17: *Taiga animals. Which of these animals might migrate during the freezing months?*

Taiga life   Evergreen trees with needle-like leaves are the most common type of vegetation found in the taiga, which is the Russian word for forest (Figure 16.18). These include pine, fir, and spruce trees. All of these trees are cone-shaped, which helps them shed snow so its weight doesn't break their branches. The needle shape of the leaves helps prevent moisture loss in the winter. This is important because trees can't take in water from frozen soil. The fact that they don't lose their needles in the fall means that they don't have to waste time in the early spring growing new ones, and can get started on photosynthesis as soon as it is warm enough. The roots of these trees are shallow and spread out wide. This makes it possible for them to take in surface water from melting snow and ice even though much of the ground underneath them is still frozen.

Snow keeps things warm!   Did you know that snow is a great insulator? In the taiga biome, a thick layer of snow (often several meters deep) falls before the coldest part of the winter. The air spaces between snow crystals prevent the ground underneath from losing more and more heat as the winter progresses (Figure 16.19).

Surviving the winter in the taiga   While air temperatures may be well below 0 °C for weeks on end, the ground temperature will remain right around freezing. Mice and other small mammals make tunnels in the snow that link their burrows and food stashes. The temperature in the burrows remains fairly constant, even when the outside air temperature plummets.

Figure 16.18: *Evergreen trees with needle-like leaves are the most common type of vegetation found in the taiga.*

Figure 16.19: *The air spaces between snow crystals prevent the*

Tundra

Tundra

Tundra is the coldest biome on Earth. The word tundra comes from a Finnish word for treeless land. There are two types of tundra—Arctic tundra, found in a band around the Arctic Ocean, and alpine tundra, found high in mid-latitude mountains.

ground from losing more and more heat as the winter progresses.

tundra - a climate region located in high latitudes; known as the coldest land biome.

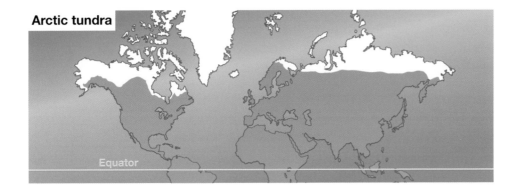

Arctic tundra

Arctic tundra has a growing season of only 50 to 60 days. The average winter temperature is -34 °C. Summer temperatures rarely exceed 12 °C. As a result of these cold temperatures, the ground is permanently frozen from 25 centimeters to about 100 centimeters below the surface. This frozen ground is called *permafrost* (Figure 16.20). There is a thin layer of soil above the permafrost that does thaw in summertime, but it is not deep enough to support the growth of trees. Lichens, mosses, grasses, and a few woody shrubs are the most common plants in the Arctic tundra.

Photo by H.C. Stone, NOAA

Figure 16.20: *This individual is standing in a deep hole cut into permafrost.*

Permafrost stores carbon dioxide

Permafrost has a very important function on our planet: It stores carbon dioxide. Here's how the process works. Usually, when plants die, they decompose into soil. This process releases carbon dioxide into the air. However, when an Arctic tundra plant dies, the cold temperatures prevent it from rapidly decaying into soil. Instead, at least part of its structure remains intact until it is frozen in the permafrost. In fact, remains of plants 1,000 years old have been found in the permafrost. Since the plant structures don't completely decay, carbon that would have been released into the atmosphere as carbon dioxide stays in the ground. For this reason, permafrost is called a "carbon sink" (Figure 16.21).

Alpine tundra

Alpine tundra occurs in middle-latitude regions, but at very high altitudes. Alpine tundra biomes occur in the Andes Mountains in South America, in the Rocky Mountains in North America, and in the Himalayan Mountains. Cold temperatures, windy conditions, and thin soil create an environment where only plants similar to those in the Arctic regions can survive. In rocky alpine regions, lichens and mosses are the dominant plants, but in alpine meadows, grasses and small woody shrubs can be found.

Alpine Meadow

What is a "carbon sink"?

Permafrost is known as a "carbon sink." A sink is an area where more carbon is stored than is released into the atmosphere. Some scientists are concerned that if Earth warms up several degrees, the permafrost will begin to melt. If this happens, the frozen plants would decompose and release carbon dioxide into the air. The permafrost would no longer serve as a "sink." It would become a source of carbon dioxide (a greenhouse gas) in the atmosphere.

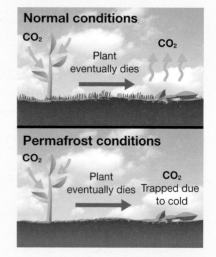

Figure 16.21: *Permafrost is a carbon sink.*

16.4 Section Review

1. Why is it difficult for animals to live in a taiga biome year-round?

2. If you have ever cared for a houseplant, you know that plants need water. Describe how evergreen trees have adapted to obtain enough water to survive in the taiga.

3. Snow is a cold substance, but it can keep the ground from losing heat. How does it do that?

4. The latitude for tundra was not given in the text. What do you think the tundra latitude range would be? Check your answer by researching this information on the Internet.

5. From the list of countries or regions below, list which ones fall in the taiga biome.

   a. Antarctica   b. Australia
   c. Canada   d. Russia
   e. United States   f. Brazil

6. What characteristics would you expect Arctic tundra plants to have?

7. Figure 16.22 shows an Arctic fox in the summer and then in the winter on the tundra. From these photographs, state one way that this animal is adapted to live in this biome.

8. Permafrost is known as a "carbon sink."

   a. What is a carbon sink?

   b. Why is permafrost considered a carbon sink?

   c. How will global warming affect tundra biomes?

Arctic fox

Photo by Brian Anderson, U.S. Fish and Wildlife Service

Photo by Keith Morehouse, U.S. Fish and Wildlife Service

Figure 16.22: *The Arctic fox in the summer (top) and in the winter (bottom).*

Ecological Impact of Forest Fires

What comes to mind when you hear the words "forest fire"? Do you see a fire burning completely out of control? Most of us do imagine raging fires burning vast acres of woods. Unwanted and uncontrollable fires are called wildfires. While it is true that wildfires are not good, it is also true that not all fires in the forest are bad. Some natural fires are healthy for a forest's plants, trees, and animals. Curiously, smaller and lower-intensity fires serve an important purpose: preventing huge, destructive wildfires.

Humans: friends or foes?

A forest is an ecosystem, or natural grouping of plants, animals, and organisms that live together and share an environment. Scientists study how fire affects the animals, trees, and other plants in the forest ecosystem.

How do forest fires start? In one of two ways, typically: lightning or human interference. The human causes include arson, sparks from brush-clearing equipment, campfires, and smoking.

Efforts to prevent fires have affected the makeup of our national forestland. As a result, human interference has caused larger, more damaging fires. It's hard to imagine that the results of fire prevention can be so harmful, but when there is a lack of fire, debris accumulates on the forest floor creating fuel. That debris includes pine needles, cones, twigs, branches, plants, and small trees. Too much debris feeds a wildfire, increasing its size and temperature. Fires are no longer confined to the ground and travel up small trees. The burning foliage adds even more fuel. When this happens, trees are killed as a result of the fire's intensity. The forest and soil are ruined and rendered unable to support new plant growth.

Fires threaten not only plant and animal species but also human life. People are moving into rural areas along forest borders. So now when a wildfire occurs, houses also are at risk. The 2003 Cedar fire in Southern California was the largest in state history. A huge amount of fuel, blowing winds, and drought combined to create intense fires that burned over 280,000 acres, destroyed 2,232 homes, and killed 14 people.

Scientists are learning that some fires benefit the forest ecosystem. Long before human involvement, fires in the wilderness were allowed to burn naturally. Fires cleared the forest floor of dangerous debris. New plants and trees grew, the soil become richer, and food was available for animals. The ecosystems took part in a natural cycle of destruction and regrowth.

One big fire lab: Yellowstone

Yellowstone National Park has an average of 24 fires each year caused by lightning. Over the past 30 years, there have been more than 300 fires sparked by lightning, and they were allowed to burn naturally. When low intensity fires do happen naturally, they help the forest remain healthy.

When there is a fire at Yellowstone, park workers monitor the situation closely. If it is caused by a human, the fire is extinguished immediately. In 1972, the park decided to let most natural fires burn as long as they posed no danger to humans. A great deal has been learned since then. For instance, in 1988 Yellowstone had its driest summer ever, but did not have a record number of fires. While 36 percent of the park was burned by fire, scientists learned even more afterward. Pinecone seeds, plants, and wildflowers grew in the nutrient-rich soil. Birds used the remaining trees to build nests, and insects returned, too. The forest was alive with many plants and animals!

Some trees require fire

There are many trees that can withstand fire or adapt to it. Although lodgepole pines are not resistant to fire, they need fire to open their cones glued shut with resin. Heat melts the resin, opening the cones to release seeds into the soil.

Fire is also important for maintaining the health of redwood trees. These giant trees have bark that is 2 to 4 feet thick. The bark insulates the tree from heat. After a fire, rich soil is formed and Sequoia seeds sprout new plants. Fires thin out the forest, letting in sunlight to help the seedlings grow.

A healthy and vibrant forest ecosystem benefits from fire, which clears debris, allows new plants to grow, provides food for animals, kills diseases, and creates rich soil. Wildfires will always be part of the cycle of life in the forest.

Questions:
1. Why is a fire policy that stops all fires not a good policy?
2. How is fire beneficial to a forest?
3. Describe several fire-resistant or fire-adapted trees.

CHAPTER ACTIVITY Biome Expedition

Each individual biome is a region of Earth that has a unique set of plants and animals that thrive in its particular climate. In this chapter you have studied the desert, tundra, taiga, temperate deciduous forest, tropical rainforest, and grassland. Each biome is equipped with a unique set characteristics and harsh conditions, which you have studied. For instance, the desert is extraordinarily dry, and creatures that live there must have special adaptations to deal with a lack of water.

Could you survive for three days with one suitcase worth of equipment and no shelter? You must plan carefully because it is likely that you would need different equipment to survive in the tundra than to survive in the tropical rainforest. Your challenge is to survive in one of these biomes for three days and two nights. The most important thing you can do to survive is to pack the proper equipment. Good luck on your expedition!

What you will do

You will be working in groups for this activity

1. Your teacher will assign the biome and the season for which you are packing.
2. Make a list of the most difficult obstacles you are going to face during the 3 days and 2 nights you will be in the biome. Remember you have no food or shelter provided for you, but for this exercise, imagine your biome expedition suitcase is big enough to fit any equipment you want to bring.
3. Based on the list of harsh conditions in the biome, discuss with your group what equipment you absolutely need to bring on the expedition.
4. Choose the five most important pieces of equipment to bring with you in order to survive in the biome for a few days.

5. Now, you and your group mates will share the contents of your biome expedition suitcase with your class. Do not tell your classmates why you are bringing each item, simply tell them what you are bringing.
6. When you are done with your presentation, allow your classmate to guess for which biome and season you packed. How did your classmates do? Did they guess correctly?

Reflection

Write a paragraph reflecting on the items you chose for your trip. Are there any items you would exchange or add to your suitcase? Are there any items you would remove?

Chapter 16 Assessment

Vocabulary

Select the correct term to complete the sentences

biome	taiga
deserts	tundra
temperate deciduous forests	tropical rainforests
grasslands	

Sections 16.1, 16.2, and 16.3

1. _____ are characterized by a cover of various grasses, and a dry climate.

2. An area can only be considered a _____ if it receives less than 35 cm of rain a year.

3. A _____ is a large region of Earth that has a unique set of plants and animals that thrive in its climate.

4. _____ are found in middle-latitude regions and have four distinct seasons.

5. Another name for a boreal or coniferous forest is _____.

6. Although _____ cover less than 6 percent of Earth's land, half of all of the animal and plant species in the world live in this biome.

7. Permafrost is found in this extremely cold biome: _____

Concepts

Section 16.1

1. The _____ in a region depends on latitude, precipitation, elevation, topography and the distance from large bodies of water.

2. Explain how latitude, humidity and sunlight play a role in defining a biome.

3. Read the following paragraph and explain the role Earth and the Sun are playing in this phenomenon:
   In the northern hemisphere, we often associate "going south" with "getting warm." Birds, for example, fly south for the winter. States in the American South and Southwest are known as the sunbelt states. But in the southern hemisphere, the opposite is true. Birds fly north for the winter. The warmest part of Australia is the northern section.

4. If you live near a coastline, would you expect your weather to be milder or more extreme than if you lived far away from the coast? Explain your answer.

5. You can expect to find tundra in the high northern latitudes of the northern hemisphere. Where would you expect to find a tundra ecosystem on a mountain?

6. Explain why plants and animals that are unique to a particular continent can play extremely similar roles as other kinds of plants and animals in similar environments elsewhere.

7. A plant that lives in the desert most likely has the following characteristics.
   a. A deep root system to get groundwater deep within the ground.
   b. A shallow, sprawling root system to collect any/all of the rain that falls to the ground.
   c. Thick leaves to help the plant deal with dry conditions.
   d. All of the above

Section 16.2

8. Why do deserts have large variations in daily high and low temperatures?

9. Why does Yakima, Washington have relatively little rainfall each year?

10. How is a temperate grassland like a savanna? How are these two types of grasslands different?

11. What role do termites play in a savanna biome?

Section 16.3

12. How many seasons are there in temperate deciduous forests?

13. If you were to visit a tropical rainforest, what could you expect to happen each afternoon? Why?

14. Why doesn't the temperature of a tropical rainforest change very much?

15. Why is so much area of the tropical rainforest destroyed each year?

16. Where are temperate rainforests found?

Section 16.4

17. Contrast a deciduous (broad-leaf) tree of a temperate deciduous forest with an evergreen tree in a taiga.

18. List the adaptations that evergreen trees have to help them survive the extreme conditions of the winter in the taiga.

19. In the chapter you learned that snow can keep the ground warm. Explain how this cold-weather stuff keeps things warm!

20. _____ is ground that is permanently frozen from 25 cm to about 100 cm below the surface in the tundra.

21. Arctic tundra has a growing season of _____

    a. 6 months

    b. 50-60 days

    c. 20-30 days

    d. 4 months

22. What is the difference between alpine and arctic tundra?

23. Describe the difference in the length of days during the summer compared to the winter in the arctic tundra. What accounts for this difference?

Math and Writing Skills

Section 16.1

1. Explain why the average yearly temperature at the North Pole is -18°C while the average yearly temperature at the equator is 27°C.

2. Study the following map showing population density and the Earth's biomes map from the chapter (Section 16.1).

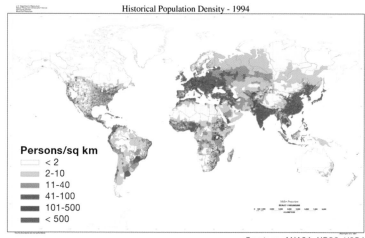

Courtesy of NASA, NRCS, USDA

    a. Which biomes have the most densely populated areas according to the maps?

    b. Which biomes have the least densely populated areas according to the maps?

c. Propose an explanation as to why different biomes or world areas have such vastly different population densities.

d. Did any of the data surprise you? Why or why not?

3. Answer these questions using the Earth's biome map:

a. What biome is located at 60°N and 100°E?

b. What biome is located at 0° and 60°W?

c. What biome is located at 40°N and 80°W?

d. Give the latitude and longitude for a grassland biome on the map.

e. Give the latitude and longitude for a desert biome on the map.

Section 16.2

4. Pick one of the types of grasslands listed in Figure 16.10 and research it using the Internet or your library.

a. What is the main type of vegetation in this grassland?

b. What kinds of animals live in this grassland?

c. List one or more adaptations that animals have to live in this biome?

Section 16.3

5. Writing from a point of view:

a. People that inhabit the tropical rainforest are destroying it at an extremely fast rate. Write a paragraph that justifies why this is being done.

b. Cutting down the rain forest has ecological consequences. What are these consequences? Write a paragraph that explains why the tropical rainforest should not be cut down.

6. Explain the connection between tropical rainforests, and greenhouse gases and global warming?

Section 16.4

7. Use this table to answer the questions below.

Biome	Temperature range	
	Low temp (°C)	High Temp (°C)
Tropical rainforest	20	25
Tundra	-34	12

a. Which biome has the biggest range of temperature?

b. Which biome gets the warmest?

c. Which biome gets the coldest?

d. Using the data above, construct a bar graph that shows the average high temperatures and the average low temperatures for the rainforest compared to the tundra.

8. Antarctica is a special place on Earth. It is the coldest place and gets little or no rainfall making it a very cold desert! Research Antarctica and describe this unique biome in terms of its rainfall, temperature, and plant and animal life.

Chapter Project—People and Places

People live in biomes along with plants and animals. Pick a biome that interests you. Find out about the types of people that have lived in this biome long before cars, electricity, and the Internet. It is possible that ancestors of these people still live in this biome! Answer these questions:

1. How did these people survive in this biome?

2. What did these people do to find food?

3. What kinds of shelters did these people build to protect themselves?

4. What kinds of customs did these people have?

Glossary

A glossary is an alphabetical list of important words found in the sections in this book. Use this glossary just as you would use a dictionary: to find out the meaning of unfamiliar words. This glossary gives the meaning that applies to the words as they are used in the sections of this book. As with any subject, science has its own vocabulary. The study of science is more meaningful if you know the language of science.

A

active volcano – a volcano that is erupting or that has erupted recently.

atom – a particle of matter.

B

basalt – a dark-colored rock that is not silica-rich.

bathymetric map – a map that shows the depths of a body of water such as a lake or an ocean.

beach – a sandy zone above the foreshore in a shallow marine environment.

biomes – major climate regions with particular plant and animal communities. Earth has six important biomes.

body waves – sesmic waves that travel through the interior of Earth.

braided stream – a stream that has many channels that criss-cross each other.

buoyant force – an upward lifting force that acts on an object when it pushes aside a fluid.

C

caldera – the bowl-shaped vent of a volcano after it has erupted.

carnivore – a consumer that eats only animals.

channel – the path that a river or stream follows.

chemical weathering – weathering of rock that involves chemical reactions.

cinder cone – a volcano that has low-silica magma with high levels of dissolved gas; these volcanoes produce "fire fountain" eruptions.

climate – the long-term record of temperature, precipitation, and wind for a region.

coast – the boundary between land and a body of water like the ocean.

competition – happens when members of an ecosystem depend on the same limited supply of food.

composite volcano – a tall, explosive, cone-shaped volcano formed by layers of silica-rich lava and ash.

conduction – transfer of heat by direct contact of atoms and molecules.

consumer – a living thing that eats other living things for food and energy.

continental drift – the idea that continents move around on Earth's surface.

continental plates – thick, less-dense lithospheric plates that are made of granite and form the continents.

continental shelf – the ocean bottom that extends from a coast; where the continental shelf ends, the ocean become distinctly deeper.

contour lines – curved lines on a topographic (or bathymetric) map that indicate all the points where the elevation is the same.

control variable – a variable that is held constant in an experiment.

convection – transfer of heat through the motion of liquids and gases.

convection cells – large wind patterns in Earth's atmosphere caused by convection.

convergent boundary – a lithospheric plate boundary where two plates come together.

core – the center of Earth; it is divided into the inner core and the outer core.

crest – the high point of a wave.

cross bedding – when a graded bedding pattern in a sedimentary rock is cut off and covered with another graded bedding pattern running in another direction.

crust – the outermost surface of Earth.

D

data – pieces of information collected to test a hypothesis.

decomposer – a living thing that breaks down waste and dead things.

deep ocean currents – density- and temperature-driven currents that move slowly within the ocean; also called thermohaline currents.

density – the mass of an object divided by the object's volume.

dependent variable – a variable that is affected by the change to the independent variable. The dependent variable is sometimes called the responding variable.

desert – a climate region that averages less than 35 centimeters of rainfall per year.

direction of younging – the order in which sedimentary rock layers are formed–from larger to finer particles.

disturbance – a movement that begins in one location and sets things in motion farther away.

divergent boundary – a lithospheric plate boundary where two plates move apart.

dormant volcano – a volcano that is not erupting now, but that may erupt in the future.

E

earthquake – the movement of Earth's crust resulting from the building up of stored energy between two stuck lithospheric plates.

ecosystem – a group of living things and their physical surroundings.

element – a substance composed of only one kind of atom.

elevation – the height of an object measured from a reference level.

emissions – tiny particles and gases released into the air.

energy – a measure of a system's ability to change.

energy pyramid – diagram that shows how energy moves from one feeding level to the next in a food chain.

epicenter – a point on Earth's surface right above the focus of an earthquake.

equator – an imaginary line around the middle of Earth between the north and south poles.

evaporation – occurs when a liquid changes to a gas.

experiment – an activity performed to support or refute a hypothesis.

extinct volcano – a volcano that no longer erupts and is in the process of eroding.

F

fault – a region on Earth's surface that is split into two pieces.

flooding – an event that occurs when water overwhelms normally dry land.

floodplain – flat land near a river that tends to flood and that is usually located some distance form the source of the river.

fluid – matter that can flow, usually a liquid or a gas.

focus – the point below Earth's surface where a rock breaks and causes an earthquake.

food chain – shows how each member of an ecosystem community gets its food.

food web – a group of overlapping food chains in an ecosystem.

fossil – a part of a dead animal or plant that has been preserved for a long time.

fossil fuels – substances found in Earth's crust that were formed over millions of years from the remains of dead organisms.

frost wedging – physical weathering that results from freezing water.

G

geologic cycle – a set of processes that keep rocky material moving from place to place on Earth.

geology – the study of rocks and rock formations.

graded bedding – the order of rocks from large to small that settle on a lake or pond bottom when water flow slows down.

gram – the basic unit of mass in the SI Units measuring system; one-thousandth of a liter.

granite – a light-colored igneous rock with large, visible quartz and feldspar crystals made from silica-rich magma.

graph – a picture that shows how two variables are related.

grasslands – climate regions with too little rainfall to support a forest. Grasslands have grasses as the main vegetation.

gyre – a circular motion, such as a circular ocean current.

H

heat – a form of energy caused by the motion of atoms and molecules.

herbivore – a consumer that eats only plants.

hot spot – the top of an established mantle plume.

hurricane – wind that blows at speeds greater than 119 kilometers (74 miles) per hour. Hurricanes start as tropical storms and form over oceans.

hypothesis – a possible answer to a scientific question based on observations.

I

igneous rocks – rocks that are formed from magma or lava.

independent variable – a variable that is changed in an experiment. The independent variable is sometimes called the manipulated variable.

inference – a statement based on experiences.

intertidal zone – the zone of a marine environment below the beach and between the high and low tide lines; also called the foreshore.

K

kinetic energy – energy of motion.

L

lahars – a mudflow that results from a volcanic eruption.

landslide – a large mass of soil or rock that slides down a volcano or mountain. Landslides can be caused by volcanic events, earthquakes, or other factors.

latitude – east-west lines that are north or south of the equator.

lava – magma after it leaves the vent of a volcano.

lava bombs – blobs of glowing lava thrown from an explosive eruption.

lava lake – a lake that contains lava that has formed in a caldera.

legend – a special area on a map that lists the symbols that are used.

liquefaction – when sediment shakes so much during an earthquake that it acts like a liquid.

liter – the basic unit of volume in the SI Units measuring system.

lithosphere – a layer of Earth that includes the crust and a thin part of the upper mantle.

lithospheric plates – large pieces of Earth's lithosphere that move over the aesthenosphere.

longitude – vertical lines that are east or west of the prime meridian. north-south lines that are east or west of the prime meridian.

longshore drift – the flow of sand along a coast.

M

magma – underground melted rock.

magma chamber – a location inside a volcano where magma collects before it leaves the volcano. a location where magma collects inside Earth.

mantle – the warm, flowing, solid layer of Earth between the crust and the core.

mantle plume – heated lower mantle rock that rises toward the lithosphere because it is less dense than surrounding mantle rock.

map – a representational drawing of a location.

marine – a term that describes things that are part of or from the ocean.

mass – the amount of matter that an object has.

matter – the substance of all objects; all matter is made of atoms and has mass.

meanders – S-shaped curves in a river.

measurement – a number that includes a unit.

Mercalli Intensity scale – a scale that rates the damage suffered by buildings, the ground, and people during an earthquake.

metamorphic rock – a rock formed from another kind of rock due to heat and pressure.

meteorologist – an individual who uses scientific principles to forecast the weather.

meter – the basic distance unit for the SI Units system of measurement.

mid-ocean ridges – long chains of undersea mountains.

molecule – a group of atoms.

Moment Magnitude scale – a scale that rates the total energy released by earthquakes.

N

natural hazard – an event in nature that can cause extensive damage to land and property, and that threatens human lives.

natural resource – a feature of Earth that benefits people.

nonrenewable resource – a natural resource that is not replaced as it is used.

O

oceanic plates – thin, dense lithospheric plates that are made of basalt and form the ocean floor.

omnivore – a consumer that eats both plants and animals.

P

Pangaea – an ancient, huge landmass composed of earlier forms of today's continents; an ancient supercontinent.

petroleum – another name for the natural resource called oil.

photosynthesis – the process plants use to make food from sunlight, water, and carbon dioxide.

physical weathering – physical forces that break rocks down into smaller pieces.

plate tectonics – a theory explaining how the pieces of Earth's surface (the plates) move.

pollutant – a variable that causes harm to an organism.

pollution – a change to the environment that is harmful to humans or other living things.

power plant – a place where electricity is generated.

predators – animals that feed on other animals.

prey – animals that are killed for food by a predator.

prime meridian – an imaginary line through Greenwich, England that is perpendicular to the equator.

producer – a living thing that can make its own food.

P-waves – sesmic waves that move with a forward-and-back motion; these waves are faster than S-waves.

pyroclastic flow – a destructive cloud of volcanic material that moves quickly down the side of a volcano after an explosive eruption.

R

radiation – heat transfer that involves energy waves and no direct contact or movement by atoms.

radioactive decay – refers to how unstable atoms lose energy and matter over time.

relative dating – a method of putting events in the order in which they happened.

renewable resource – a natural resource that can be replaced.

resource conservation – protecting, preserving, and managing Earth's natural resources.

resurgent dome – a mound in the vent of an erupted volcano.

revolution – the motion of Earth moving around the Sun; one revolution is called a year.

Richter scale – a scale that rates earthquakes according to the size of the seismic waves.

Ring of Fire – a region of Earth's plate boundaries where oceanic crust is subducting under other plates.

river – a large body of water that flows into an ocean or lake.

rotation – the motion of Earth spinning on its axis; one rotation is called a day.

S

science – a process for answering questions.

scientific law – a statement that describes an observed phenomenon; it is supported by evidence collected from many observations and experiments.

scientific method – a series of steps including observation, forming a question, stating a hypothesis, collecting data, and reaching a conclusion.

scientific theory – a statement that explains a complex idea; it is supported by evidence collected from many experiments.

sea level – the average level of the ocean; the halfway point between high tide and low tide.

sea-floor spreading – a hypothesis that new sea floor is created at mid-ocean ridges and that in the process the continents are pushed apart from each other.

sediment – small pieces and grains of weathered rock; also, small pieces of material from living things.

sedimentary rocks – rocks that are made of sediments.

seismic waves – vibrations that travel through Earth and are caused by events like earthquakes or human-made blasts.

seismograph – an instrument that measures and records seismic waves.

seismologist – a scientist who detects and interprets seismic waves.

shield volcano – a flat and wide volcano that has low-silica magma with low or high levels of dissolved gas.

silica – an ingredient in magma and lava that makes them thick and sticky; quartz is a mineral made of silica.

slumping – an event that occurs when soil particles become surrounded by water so that the ground slides or "slumps." Slumping is a form of mass wasting which is the falling of rock and soil due to the influence of gravity.

solar energy – energy from the Sun.

stream – a small river.

subduction – a process that involves a lithospheric plate sinking into the mantle.

surface ocean currents – wind-driven currents that move at the ocean surface, often for very long distances.

surface waves – body waves that reach and travel along Earth's surface.

S-waves – seismic waves that move with a side-to-side motion and are slower than P-waves.

symbiosis – an interaction where two species live together for a long time and at least one of the species benefits.

system – a group of objects and the factors that affect the objects.

T

taiga – the largest climate region, found in the higher latitudes; also known as a boreal or coniferous forest.

temperate deciduous forests – climate regions in the mid-latitudes that have seasons.

temperature – a measure of the average speed of a sample containing lots of atoms.

thermal – small heat-driven air current.

tidal flat – a flat, muddy area in the intertidal zone.

topographic map – maps that use contour lines to show elevation.

transform fault boundary – a lithospheric plate boundary where two plates slide by each other.

trench – a valley in the ocean created where one lithospheric plate subducts under another.

tropical rainforests – climate regions found near the equator that have a lot of rainfall and high biodiversity.

trough – the low point of a wave.

tsunami – a huge ocean wave caused by underwater earthquakes, volcanic eruptions, or slumping.

tundra – a climate region located in high latitudes; known as the coldest land biome.

U

unit – a specific quantity that is counted to make a measurement.

V

variable – a factor that affects an object; examples include mass, temperature, speed, and time.

volcanic ash – fine particles of cooled magma.

volcanic island – a volcano that forms away from a plate boundary on an oceanic plate.

volcanic island chain – a series of volcanoes formed by a hot spot as a lithospheric plate moves over the hot spot.

volcanic neck – solid remains of magma that filled the conduit of an extinct volcano. The neck is exposed as the volcano erodes.

volcano – an erupting vent through which molten rock reaches Earth's surface, or a mountain built from the products of an eruption.

volume – a measurement of how much space is occupied by an object.

W

water cycle – a set of processes energized by the Sun that keep water moving from place to place on Earth.

water vapor – water in gas form.

wavelength – the distance between two wave crests, or the distance between two wave troughs.

weather – the condition of the atmosphere as it is affected by wind, water, temperature, and atmospheric pressure.

weathering – the process of breaking down rock.

weight – a measure of mass and the force of gravity on an object.

wildfire – an unwanted fire that burns in a forest or other natural area.

wind – air that flows, often because of heating and cooling of air or unequal air pressure.

Index

The index gives the page numbers where you can find a word, definition, information about a topic or a large category. You can use the index when you are studying and need to find information quickly. The index is a good place to look up a vocabulary word to get more information about the meaning of a word.

374

Index

377

These pages provide you with the standards that are taught in this book and are required learning for the state of California.

STANDARD SET 1. Plate Tectonics and Earth's Structure | Completed

1. Plate tectonics accounts for important features of Earth's surface and major geologic events. As a basis for understanding this concept:

1.a. Students know evidence of plate tectonics is derived from the fit of the continents; the location of earthquakes, volcanoes, and midocean ridges; and the distribution of fossils, rock types, and ancient climatic zones.	☐
1.b. Students know Earth is composed of several layers: a cold, brittle lithosphere; a hot, convecting mantle; and a dense, metallic core.	☐
1.c. Students know lithospheric plates the size of continents and oceans move at rates of centimeters per year in response to movements in the mantle.	☐
1.d. Students know that earthquakes are sudden motions along breaks in the crust called faults and that volcanoes and fissures are locations where magma reaches the surface.	☐
1.e. Students know major geologic events, such as earthquakes, volcanic eruptions, and mountain building, result from plate motions.	☐
1.f. Students know how to explain major features of California geology (including mountains, faults, volcanoes) in terms of plate tectonics.	☐
1.g. Students know how to determine the epicenter of an earthquake and know that the effects of an earthquake on any region vary, depending on the size of the earthquake, the distance of the region from the epicenter, the local geology, and the type of construction in the region.	☐

STANDARD SET 2. Shaping Earth's Surface

2. Topography is reshaped by the weathering of rock and soil and by the transportation and deposition of sediment. As a basis for understanding this concept:

2.a. Students know water running downhill is the dominant process in shaping the landscape, including California's landscape.	☐
2.b. Students know rivers and streams are dynamic systems that erode, transport sediment, change course, and flood their banks in natural and recurring patterns.	☐
2.c. Students know beaches are dynamic systems in which the sand is supplied by rivers and moved along the coast by the action of waves.	☐
2.d. Students know earthquakes, volcanic eruptions, landslides, and floods change human and wildlife habitats.	☐

California Standards

STANDARD SET 3. Heat (Thermal Energy) (Physical Science)		Completed
3. Heat moves in a predictable flow from warmer objects to cooler objects until all the objects are at the same temperature. As a basis for understanding this concept:	3.a. Students know energy can be carried from one place to another by heat flow or by waves, including water, light and sound waves, or by moving objects.	☐
	3.b. Students know that when fuel is consumed, most of the energy released becomes heat energy.	☐
	3.c. Students know heat flows in solids by conduction (which involves no flow of matter) and in fluids by conduction and by convection (which involves flow of matter).	☐
	3.d. Students know heat energy is also transferred between objects by radiation (radiation can travel through space).	☐

STANDARD SET 4. Energy in the Earth System		
4. Many phenomena on Earth's surface are affected by the transfer of energy through radiation and convection currents. As a basis for understanding this concept:	4.a. Students know the sun is the major source of energy for phenomena on Earth's surface; it powers winds, ocean currents, and the water cycle.	☐
	4.b. Students know solar energy reaches Earth through radiation, mostly in the form of visible light.	☐
	4.c. Students know heat from Earth's interior reaches the surface primarily through convection.	☐
	4.d. Students know convection currents distribute heat in the atmosphere and oceans.	☐
	4.e. Students know differences in pressure, heat, air movement, and humidity result in changes of weather.	☐

STANDARD SET 5. Ecology (Life Sciences)		Completed
5. *Organisms in ecosystems exchange energy and nutrients among themselves and with the environment. As a basis for understanding this concept:*	5.a. Students know energy entering ecosystems as sunlight is transferred by producers into chemical energy through photosynthesis and then from organism to organism through food webs.	☐
	5.b. Students know matter is transferred over time from one organism to others in the food web and between organisms and the physical environment.	☐
	5.c. Students know populations of organisms can be categorized by the functions they serve in an ecosystem.	☐
	5.d. Students know different kinds of organisms may play similar ecological roles in similar biomes.	☐
	5.e. Students know the number and types of organisms an ecosystem can support depends on the resources available and on abiotic factors, such as quantities of light and water, a range of temperatures, and soil composition.	☐

STANDARD SET 6. Resources		
6. *Sources of energy and materials differ in amounts, distribution, usefulness, and the time required for their formation. As a basis for understanding this concept:*	6.a. Students know the utility of energy sources is determined by factors that are involved in converting these sources to useful forms and the consequences of the conversion process.	☐
	6.b. Students know different natural energy and material resources, including air, soil, rocks, minerals, petroleum, fresh water, wildlife, and forests, and know how to classify them as renewable or nonrenewable.	☐
	6.c. Students know the natural origin of the materials used to make common objects.	
		☐

STANDARD SET 7. Investigation and Experimentation		Completed
7. Scientific progress is made by asking meaningful questions and conducting careful investigations. As a basis for understanding this concept and addressing the content in the other three strands, students should develop their own questions and perform investigations. Students will:	7.a. Develop a hypothesis.	☐
	7.b. Select and use appropriate tools and technology (including calculators, computers, balances, spring scales, microscopes, and binoculars) to perform tests, collect data, and display data.	☐
	7.c. Construct appropriate graphs from data and develop qualitative statements about the relationships between variables.	☐
	7.d. Communicate the steps and results from an investigation in written reports and oral presentations.	☐
	7.e. Recognize whether evidence is consistent with a proposed explanation.	☐
	7.f. Read a topographic map and a geologic map for evidence provided on the maps and construct and interpret a simple scale map.	☐
	7.g. Interpret events by sequence and time from natural phenomena (e.g., the relative ages of rocks and intrusions).	☐
	7.h. Identify changes in natural phenomena over time without manipulating the phenomena (e.g., a tree limb, a grove of trees, a stream, a hillslope)	☐